D1499070

THE HARVEY LECTURES

WILLIAM HARVEY

BORN APRIL 1, 1578–DIED JUNE 3, 1657

THE HARVEY LECTURES

DELIVERED UNDER THE AUSPICES OF

The HARVEY SOCIETY of NEW YORK

1982–1983

BY

M. V. L. BENNETT ET AL. VICTOR NUSSENZWEIG
J. MICHAEL BISHOP MARY JANE OSBORN
EDWARD C. FRANKLIN ALEXANDER RICH
LEROY E. HOOD RUTH SAGER
RUTH S. NUSSENZWEIG DONALD F. STEINER

SERIES 78

1984

ACADEMIC PRESS, INC.

(Harcourt Brace Jovanovich, Publishers)

Orlando   San Diego   New York   London
Toronto   Montreal   Sydney   Tokyo

ACADEMIC PRESS, INC.
Orlando, Florida 32887

United Kingdom Edition published by
ACADEMIC PRESS, INC. (LONDON) LTD.
24/28 Oval Road, London NW1 7DX

Library of Congress Cataloging in Publication Data 7-2726

ISBN 0-12-312078-0

PRINTED IN THE UNITED STATES OF AMERICA

84 85 86 87   9 8 7 6 5 4 3 2 1

CONTENTS

CONSTITUTION OF THE HARVEY SOCIETY vii

BY-LAWS OF THE HARVEY SOCIETY, INC. ix

OFFICERS OF THE HARVEY SOCIETY xv

HARVEY LECTURES 1982–1983

THE HEAVY CHAIN DISEASES 1
Edward C. Franklin, Irvington House Institute, Department of
Medicine, New York University Medical Center, New York,
New York 10016

CONTROL OF INTERCELLULAR COMMUNICATION BY WAY OF GAP
JUNCTIONS 23
M. V. L. Bennett, D. C. Spray, A. L. Harris, R. D. Ginzberg, A.
Campos de Carvalho, and R. L. White, Division of Cellular Neu-
robiology, Department of Neuroscience, Albert Einstein College
of Medicine, Bronx, New York 10461

IMMUNOPROPHYLAXIS OF MALARIA: CHARACTERIZATION OF A
PROTECTIVE SURFACE ANTIGEN 59
Ruth S. Nussenzweig and Victor Nussenzweig, Departments of Microbiology and Pathology, New York University School of Medicine, New York, New York 10016

GENES OF THE MAJOR HISTOCOMPATIBILITY COMPLEX:
A MODEL FOR CELL–CELL COMMUNICATION
Leroy E. Hood,* Division of Biology, California Institute of
Technology, Pasadena, California

*Manuscript not received.

v

BIOGENESIS OF THE OUTER MEMBRANE OF *Salmonella*   87
  Mary Jane Osborn, Department of Microbiology, University of
  Connecticut Health Center, Farmington, Connecticut 06032

LEFT-HANDED Z-DNA   105
  Alexander Rich, Department of Biology, Massachusetts Institute
  of Technology, Cambridge, Massachusetts 02139

VIRUSES, GENES, AND CANCER   137
  J. Michael Bishop, George W. Hooper Foundation and Depart-
  ment of Microbiology and Immunology, University of California
  Medical Center, San Francisco, California 94143

CHROMOSOME MODIFICATION AND CANCER   173
  Ruth Sager, Department of Microbiology and Molecular Genet-
  ics, Harvard Medical School and Dana-Farber Cancer Institute,
  Boston, Massachusetts 02115

THE BIOSYNTHESIS OF INSULIN: GENETIC, EVOLUTIONARY, AND
  PATHOPHYSIOLOGIC ASPECTS   191
  Donald F. Steiner, Department of Biochemistry, The University
  of Chicago, Chicago, Illinois 60637

FORMER OFFICERS OF THE HARVEY SOCIETY   229

CUMULATIVE AUTHOR INDEX   241

ACTIVE MEMBERS   251

THE HARVEY SOCIETY*

A SOCIETY FOR THE DIFFUSION OF KNOWLEDGE
OF THE MEDICAL SCIENCES

CONSTITUTION

I

This Society shall be named the Harvey Society.

II

The object of this Society shall be the diffusion of scientific knowledge in selected chapters in anatomy, physiology, pathology, bacteriology, pharmacology, and physiological and pathological chemistry, through the medium of public lectures by men and women who are workers in the subjects presented.

III

The members of the Society shall constitute two classes: Active and Honorary members. Active members shall be workers in the medical or biological sciences, residing in the metropolitan New York area, who have personally contributed to the advancement of these sciences. Active members who leave New York to reside elsewhere may retain their membership. Honorary members shall be those who have delivered lectures before the Society and who are not Active members. Honorary members shall not be eligible to office, nor shall they be entitled to a vote.

Active members shall be elected by ballot. They shall be nominated to the Executive Committee and the names of the nominees shall accompany the notice of the meeting at which the vote for their election will be taken.

IV

The management of the Society shall be vested in an Executive Committee to consist of a President, a Vice-President, a Secretary, a Treasurer, and

---

*The Constitution is reprinted here for historical interest only; its essential features have been included in the Articles of Incorporation and By-Laws.

three other members, these officers to be elected by ballot at each annual meeting of the Society to serve one year.

V

The Annual Meeting of the Society shall be held at a stated date in January of each year at a time and place to be determined by the Executive Committee. Special meetings may be held at such times and places as the Executive Committee may determine. At all meetings ten members shall constitute a quorum.

VI

Changes in the Constitution may be made at any meeting of the Society by a majority vote of those present after previous notification to the members in writing.

THE HARVEY SOCIETY, INC.

A SOCIETY FOR THE DIFFUSION OF KNOWLEDGE
OF THE MEDICAL SCIENCES

BY-LAWS

ARTICLE I

Name and Purposes of the Society

SECTION 1. The name of the Society as recorded in the Constitution at the time of its founding in 1905 was the Harvey Society. In 1955, it was incorporated in the State of New York as The Harvey Society, Inc.

SECTION 2. The purposes for which this Society is formed are those set forth in its original Constitution and modified in its Certificate of Incorporation as from time to time amended. The purposes of the Society shall be to foster the diffusion of scientific knowledge in selected chapters of the biological sciences and related areas of knowledge through the medium of public delivery and printed publication of lectures by men and women who are workers in the subjects presented, and to promote the development of these sciences.

It is not organized for pecuniary profit, and no part of the net earnings, contributions, or other corporate funds of the Society shall inure to the benefit of any private member or individual, and no substantial part of its activities shall be carrying on propaganda, or otherwise attempting, to influence legislation.

ARTICLE II

Offices of the Society

SECTION 1. The main office and place of business of the Society shall be in the City and County of New York. The Board of Directors may designate additional offices.

ARTICLE III

Members

SECTION 1. The members of the Society shall consist of the incorporators, members of the hitherto unincorporated Harvey Society, and persons elected from time to time. The members of the Society shall constitute two classes: Active and Honorary Members. Active members shall be individuals with either the Ph.D. or the M.D. degree or its equivalent, residing or carrying on a major part of their work in the New York metropolitan area at the time of their election, who are personally making original contributions to the literature of the medical or biological sciences. Honorary members shall be those who have delivered a lecture before the Society and who are not Active members. Honorary members shall be exempted from the payment of dues. Active members who have remained in good standing for 35 years or who have reached the age of 65 and have remained in good standing for 25 years shall be designated Life members. They shall retain all the privileges of their class of membership without further payment of dues. Honorary members shall not be eligible to office, nor shall they be entitled to participate by voting in the affairs of the Society. Volumes of The Harvey Lectures will be circulated only to Active and Life members. Honorary members will receive only the volume containing their lecture. New Active members shall be nominated in writing to the Board of Directors by an Active member and seconded by another Active member. They shall be elected at the Annual Meeting of the Society by a vote of the majority of the Active members present at the meeting. Members who leave New York to reside elsewhere may retain their membership. Active members who have given a Harvey Lecture and who have moved out of the New York metropolitan area may, if they wish, become Honorary members. Membership in the Society shall terminate on the death, resignation, or removal of the member.

SECTION 2. Members may be suspended or expelled from the Society by the vote of a majority of the members present at any meeting of members at which a quorum is present, for refusing or failing to comply with the By-Laws, or for other good and sufficient cause.

SECTION 3. Members may resign from the Society by written declaration, which shall take effect upon the filing thereof with the Secretary.

ARTICLE IV

Meetings of the Members of the Society

SECTION 1. The Society shall hold its annual meeting of Active members for the election of officers and directors, and for the transaction of such other business as may come before the meeting in the month of January or

February in each year, at a place within the City of New York, and on a date and at an hour to be specified in the notice of such meeting.

SECTION 2. Special meetings of members shall be called by the Secretary upon the request of the President or Vice-President or of the Board of Directors, or on written request of twenty-five of the Active members.

SECTION 3. Notice of all meetings of Active members shall be mailed or delivered personally to each member not less than ten nor more than sixty days before the meeting. Like notice shall be given with respect to lectures.

SECTION 4. At all meetings of Active members of the Society ten Active members, present in person, shall constitute a quorum, but less than a quorum shall have power to adjourn from time to time until a quorum be present.

ARTICLE V

Board of Directors

SECTION 1. The number of directors constituting The Board of Directors shall be seven: the President, the Vice-President, the Secretary, and the Treasurer of the Society, and the three members of the Council. The number of directors may be increased or reduced by amendments of the By-Laws as hereinafter provided, within the maximum and minimum numbers fixed in the Certificate of Incorporation or any amendment thereto.

SECTION 2. The Board of Directors shall hold an annual meeting shortly before the annual meeting of the Society.

Special meetings of the Board of Directors shall be called at any time by the Secretary upon the request of the President or Vice-President or of one-fourth of the directors then in office.

SECTION 3. Notice of all regular annual meetings of the Board shall be given to each director at least seven days before the meeting and notice of special meetings, at least one day before. Meetings may be held at any place within the City of New York designated in the notice of the meeting.

SECTION 4. The Board of Directors shall have the immediate charge, management, and control of the activities and affairs of the Society, and it shall have full power, in the intervals between the annual meetings of the Active members, to do any and all things in relation to the affairs of the Society.

SECTION 5. Council members shall be elected by the members of the Society at the Annual Meeting. One Council member is elected each year to serve for three years, there being three Council members at all times. Vacancies occurring on the Council for any cause may be filled for the unexpired term by the majority vote of the directors present at any meeting at which a quorum is present. Only Active members of the Society shall be eligible for membership on the Council.

SECTION 6. A majority of the Board as from time to time constituted shall be necessary to constitute a quorum, but less than a quorum shall have power to adjourn from time to time until a quorum be present.

SECTION 7. The Board shall have power to appoint individual or corporate trustees and their successors of any or all of the property of the Society, and to confer upon them such of the powers, duties, or obligations of the directors in relation to the care, custody, or management of such property as may be deemed advisable.

SECTION 8. The directors shall present at the Annual Meeting a report, verified by the President and Treasurer, or by a majority of the directors, showing the whole amount of real and personal property owned by the Society, where located, and where and how invested, the amount and nature of the property acquired during the year immediately preceding the date of the report and the manner of the acquisition; the amount applied, appropriated, or expended during the year immediately preceding such date, and the purposes, objects, or persons to or for which such applications, appropriations, or expenditures have been made; and the names of the persons who have been admitted to membership in the Society during such year, which report shall be filed with the records of the Society and an abstract thereof entered in the minutes of the proceedings of the Annual Meeting.

ARTICLE VI

Committees

SECTION 1. The Board of Directors may appoint from time to time such committees as it deems advisable, and each such committee shall exercise such powers and perform such duties as may be conferred upon it by the Board of Directors subject to its continuing direction and control.

ARTICLE VII

Officers

SECTION 1. The officers of the Society shall consist of a President, a Vice-President, a Secretary, and a Treasurer, and such other officers as the Board of Directors may from time to time determine. All of the officers of the Society shall be members of the Board of Directors.

SECTION 2. The President shall be the chief executive officer of the Society and shall be in charge of the direction of its affairs, acting with the advice of the Board of Directors. The other officers of the Society shall have the powers and perform the duties that usually pertain to their respective offices, or as may from time to time be prescribed by the Board of Directors.

SECTION 3. The officers and the directors shall not receive, directly or indirectly, any salary or other compensation from the Society, unless authorized by the concurring vote of two-thirds of all the directors.

SECTION 4. The officers shall be elected at the Annual Meeting of the Active members. All officers shall hold office until the next Annual Meeting and until their successors are elected or until removed by vote of a majority vote of the directors. Vacancies occurring among the officers for any cause may be filled for the unexpired term by the majority vote of the directors present at any meeting at which a quorum is present. Officers must be Active members of the Society.

ARTICLE VIII

Fiscal Year—Seal

SECTION 1. The fiscal year of the Society shall be the calendar year.

SECTION 2. The seal of the Society shall be circular in form and shall bear the words "The Harvey Society, Inc., New York, New York, Corporate Seal."

ARTICLE IX

Amendments

SECTION 1. These By-Laws may be added to, amended, or repealed, in whole or in part, by the Active members or by the Board of Directors, in each case by a majority vote at any meeting at which a quorum is present, provided that notice of the proposed addition, amendment, or repeal has been given to each member or director, as the case may be, in the notice of such meeting.

OFFICERS OF THE HARVEY SOCIETY

1982–1983

DeWITT S. GOODMAN, *President*
MATTHEW D. SCHARFF, *Vice President*
ALFRED STRACHER, *Treasurer*
EMIL C. GOTSCHLICH, *Secretary*

COUNCIL

1982–1983

KURT HIRSCHHORN   RALPH L. NACHMAN

GERALD WEISSMANN

THE HEAVY CHAIN DISEASES*

EDWARD C. FRANKLIN

Irvington House Institute
Department of Medicine
New York University Medical Center
New York, New York

I T is difficult for me to express how deeply I appreciate having the opportunity of reading Ed's lecture. Both Ed and I have been long-time members of the Harvey Society and we know how much care is taken in the planning of the program and selection of the speakers. We are grateful for the honor you have bestowed on him.

The most pleasant task Ed has asked me to perform is to acknowledge the role of his collaborators. These are Dr. Blas Frangione, a partner in the design, execution, and interpretation of much of the work done over the past 15 years. Next, he asked me to mention myself. He says that I have a knack of providing the right morphology at the right time. Dr. Joel Buxbaum, a former fellow, has over the last 10 years contributed to studies on biosynthesis and more recently gene cloning and DNA sequencing. His efforts have always complemented Ed's. Many thanks are due to Ed's technician, Frances Prelli. Fran has been Ed's right hand for over 20 years. Rumor has it that once, when he turned his back, she even discovered one of the heavy chain diseases. In addition, we owe thanks to some more transient collaborators and fellows, including Drs. Shelley Cooper, Carlota Wolfenstein-Todel, Jay Adlersberg, Alice Alexander, Eve Flechner, Denis Barritault, Bernie Recht, and Fernando Goni.

*Dr. Edward C. Franklin was one of the Harvey Lecturers of the year 1981–1982, but because of illness his lecture was read on November 19, 1981 by his wife, Dr. Dorothea Zucker-Franklin, with Dr. E. C. Franklin in attendance. Dr. E. C. Franklin died February 20, 1982, and the Society mourns the passing of this member, who also served as treasurer for a period of 4 years. Because of Dr. Franklin's demise it was not possible to include the lecture in the Series 77 volume and it is included in this volume. We are grateful to Dr. Dorothea Zucker-Franklin for the preparation of the manuscript, and she has thought it most fitting to publish it nearly verbatim as it was originally presented.

1

While preparing for this Harvey Lecture, Ed browsed through previous Harvey Lectures on the same or related subjects to trace the growth of the field. The field of immunochemistry, at least for the Harvey Society (Table I), started in 1933 with the lecture by Michael Heidelberger, exactly 50 years ago. It established immunochemistry as a quantitative science. Work on immunoglobulins, as well-defined proteins, was first mentioned in 1939, when Arne Tiselius illustrated the versatility of electrophoresis in the analysis of serum proteins. His lecture anticipated many of the concepts that we accept as absolute truths today. He showed one of the first electrophoretic patterns of a monoclonal serum protein in the plasma from a patient with multiple myeloma, mentioned the pioneering work with Elvin Kabat a few years earlier, which had demonstrated that antibodies were γ-globulins, and he also predicted that many species of animals would have multiple γ-globulin types. In 1961, Jan Waldenström, discussing multiple myeloma and macroglobulinemia, made the brilliant prediction that organ-specific antibodies would be found in monoclonal proteins.

In 1964, we heard the lecture by Henry Kunkel, Ed's scientific mentor and subsequent role model. This lecture proved to be prophetic in a number of ways. First of all, Henry emphatically supported the concept that myeloma proteins represented homogeneous antibodies produced by individual clones of cells. He introduced the concept of idiotypes and illustrated how the discovery of subclasses of immunoglobulins was aided by the use of Bence Jones and myeloma proteins. His final prediction that ''the biochemical analysis of the antibody problem is at hand'' was soon fulfilled as evidenced by the Harvey Society lectures of Rodney Porter in 1970 and Gerald Edelman in 1973. Porter emphasized the structure of the antibody combining site, while Edelman, through his complete structural analysis of a single myeloma protein, carried this one step further and introduced the domain concept, attributing separate functions to different regions of the molecule. He anticipated many of the mechanisms whereby antibody diversity could be generated.

In 1973, Matthew Scharff turned his attention to murine immunoglobulin mutants which occurred with an inordinately high frequency in cultured mouse plasmacytomas. In 1975, Nils Jerne proposed the concept of the control of antibody synthesis by means of a network of idiotypes and antiidiotypes.

TABLE I

HARVEY LECTURES DEALING WITH IMMUNOGLOBULIN STRUCTURE AND FUNCTION

Date	Lecture
1933	Michael Heidelberger: Founder of immunochemistry
1939	Arne Tiselius: Development and potential use of electrophoresis; defined γ-globulins
1961	Jan Waldenström: Proposed that myeloma proteins are monoclonal antibodies
1964	Henry G. Kunkel: Concept of the monoclonality of antibodies; deduced the concept of idiotypes and used myeloma proteins to study the immunoglobulin structure
1970	Rodney Porter: Defined the structure of the antibody combining site
1973	Gerald Edelman: Completed structural analysis of myeloma protein; domain concept
1973	Matthew Scharff: Defined murine immunoglobulin variants
1975	Niels Jerne: Proposed the existence of a network of idiotypes and antiidiotypes controlling antibody synthesis
1980	S. Tonegawa: Defined the organization of immunoglobulin genes; exons, introns, gene rearrangements and splicing

Last year marked the beginning of a new era in the study of immunoglobulins, when Susumu Tonegawa presented his novel and far-reaching concepts of the organization of the immunoglobulin genes based on the discovery of exons, introns, gene rearrangements, and the discontinuity of immunoglobulin genes. Chronologically, Tonegawa's Harvey Lecture was a year premature, since it actually provided proof for many of the postulates that had been developed in Ed's laboratory by studying human immunoglobulin mutants over a period of 15 years. Tonight, we will try to close this gap by showing that many of the conclusions drawn from studies in the Franklin/Frangione laboratory complement, and in some instances anticipated, concepts that are now being proven so elegantly by DNA cloning. In addition, this presentation is intended to show that protein chemistry still has an important role to play in molecular biology.

Let us look at this work somewhat chronologically. In the 1960s, when the immunochemical characterization of proteins in serum and urine had its heyday, the analysis of pathological sera was started, not only to see whether immunoglobulins had antibody activity, but also to characterize classes, subclasses, and allotypes of these proteins. Perhaps it was thought one might even discover some immunoglobulin mutants, a likely occurrence among proteins that were designed to adapt constantly to changes in the environment. This was not believed to be an easy task, because such mutations would be subtle and difficult to detect short of analysis of the primary structure of a large number of myeloma and Bence Jones proteins. In view of this atmosphere, one can imagine the excitement when in the afternoon of December 24, 1962, Ed noticed a strikingly abnormal electrophoretic pattern in the serum and urine of no less a man than a Bellevue Hospital employee. Because of unexplained lymphadenopathy and fever, this patient's serum had been examined 2 months previously, at which time it had appeared unremarkable. In the intervening period, the normal globulin fraction had almost completely disappeared. It had been replaced by a $\gamma–\beta$ spike which was identical in the serum and the urine (Fig. 1). It was helpful that this patient, Mr. CRA, excreted approximately 15 g of protein in his urine per day, assuring an ample supply for future analysis. Within 3 days, the protein had been defined as a molecule with many properties of an Fc fragment, and an abstract was submitted to the FASEB with the

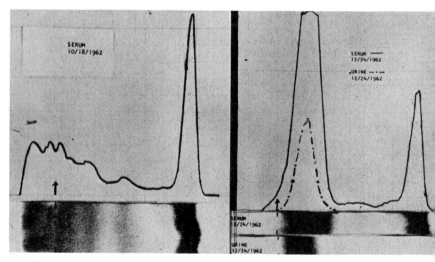

FIG. 1. Electrophoretic pattern of serum and urine of the first patient diagnosed to have heavy chain disease. On the left is the normal pattern October 18, 1962; on the right, the abnormal "spike" shown in serum and urine 2 months later.

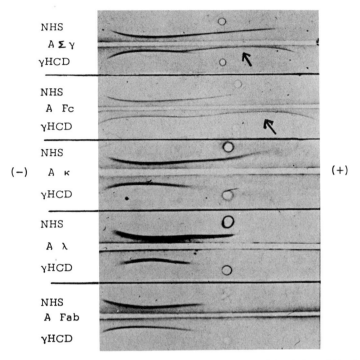

Fɪɢ. 2. Immunoelectrophoretic patterns illustrating missing light chain and identical Fc fragment in serum and urine. NHS, normal human serum; γ HCD, γ heavy chain disease.

noncommittal title, "An Unusual Micro-gamma-globulin in the Serum and Urine of a Patient" (Franklin *et al.*, 1964). Now, 18 years later, there have been approximately 80 instances of γ heavy chain disease (HCD) reported. This diagnosis cannot be made pathologically, and is dependent on the detection of an identical protein in the serum and urine having the antigenic properties of the Fc fragment and missing a light chain (Fig. 2). Incidentally, the term *heavy chain disease* was coined by Dr. Elliot Osserman when, on the basis of our patient's clinical features and laboratory analyses, he identified four additional cases by studying sera and urines stored in his freezer. Ed is grateful to Elliot Osserman for having been more courageous, and willing to step out on a limb by calling this anomaly "γ heavy chain disease" (Osserman *et al.*, 1963).

TABLE II

CLINICAL AND LABORATORY FEATURES OF γ HEAVY CHAIN DISEASE

Age: predominantly middle aged
Lymphadenopathy, hepatosplenomegaly, often waxing and waning
Palatal edema in about one-third of the patients
No characteristic pathological features
Heavy chain disease protein in the serum and urine

Being more conservative, Ed had planned to call this new biochemical entity "Fc fragment disease," and from what has been learned since, that would have been a misnomer.

The clinical aspects of the disease (Table II) consist of lymphadenopathy, hepatosplenomegaly, often waxing and waning, frequently palatal edema, and many other features of a lymphoproliferative disorder. The laboratory diagnosis is illustrated in Fig. 2.

By comparing the turnover of this protein with that of normal γ-globulins, it became apparent that it is a synthetic product. Antigenic and superficial biochemical analyses showed a striking resemblance, yet certain subtle differences in structure from the Fc fragment of normal IgG. At any rate, this observation led in 1964 to the proposal of a six-chain model of IgG: two light chains, two heavy chains corresponding to the monomeric segment of the carboxy terminal end of the heavy chain, namely the Fc fragment, and two additional chains corresponding to the amino terminal of the H chain. Obviously, in retrospect this was an oversimplification, but it was on the right track toward recognition of some of the unique structural features of the immunoglobulin molecules.

Turning back to the clinical aspects of the heavy chain diseases, it did not take very long until two other kinds of heavy chain diseases were identified.

In 1968, Seligman and his collaborators discovered α chain disease (Table III). The α is the heavy chain of another class of immunoglobulins, namely IgA. α heavy chain disease presents as a lymphoproliferative disorder, almost always involving the intestinal tract. It has been recognized clinically for a number of years as Mediterranean lymphoma. α chain disease is by far the most common type of heavy chain disease. Patients are predominantly found in the lower socioeconomic

TABLE III

α Chain Disease

Lower socioeconomic groups in Mediterranean region
"Mediterranean lymphoma" with malabsorption
Plasma cell infiltrate in small intestine
Pathology varies from benign lymphoid infiltrate to sarcoma
Occasionally spontaneous or antibiotic induced remissions
Diagnosis made primarily on the basis of characteristic protein in the serum

groups in the Mediterranean region. They are rarely identified in Northern Europe or the United States. One of the most interesting features is the observation that spontaneous or antibiotic induced remissions are not uncommon.

In 1970, μ chain disease was discovered (Table IV), the μ chain being the heavy chain of IgM. μ chain disease is the rarest of these disease entities, less than 20 cases having been reported. It is usually associated with chronic lymphocytic leukemia. It has a number of unusual features, among them the presence of vacuolated plasma cells which are almost pathognomonic (Fig. 3). Unlike the other heavy chain diseases, in μ chain disease the production of light chains usually persists, and they are synthesized in the same cell as the H chains. When the plasma cells were stained with rhodamine-conjugated antiserum to μ chain, they stained red. When they were stained with fluorescein-conjugated antiserum to κ chains, they stained green. When these antisera were used sequentially, a yellow color resulted indicating that both the μ and the κ chains are present in the same cell (Zucker-Franklin *et al.*, 1971). Apparently, the light chains do not form disulfide bridges

TABLE IV

Clinical Features of μ Chain Disease

Rare: < 20 cases reported
Usually associated with chronic lymphocytic leukemia or other lymphomas
Mainly visceral involvement
Light chains, κ type in approximately ¾
Vacuolated plasma cells, almost pathognomonic

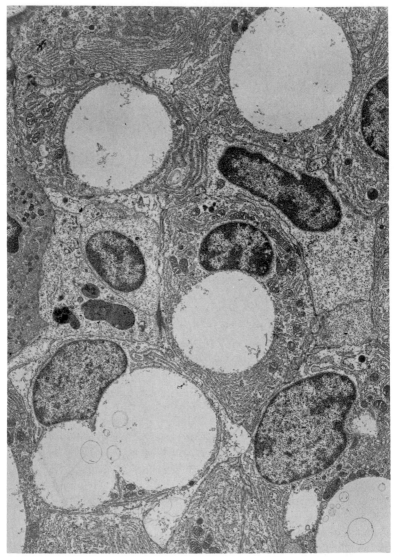

FIG. 3. Electron photomicrograph of bone marrow of a patient with μ chain disease. Note that almost all the plasma cells are vacuolated. (Reproduced from Zucker-Franklin and Franklin, 1971.) ×4500.

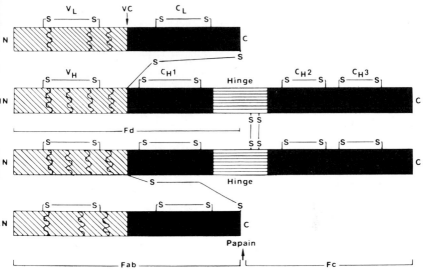

Fɪɢ. 4. Structure of the immunoglobulin molecule (see text).

with the incomplete μ chains and can be detected in the serum and urine as free light chains or light chain dimers (Frangione *et al.*, 1976).

Before discussing the biochemical abnormalities of the heavy chain disease proteins, it may be useful to provide a schematic view of the structure of an Ig molecule (Fig. 4).

All Igs are made up of two types of polypeptide chains: two light and two heavy chains; both are divided into variable and constant regions. The region between the constant and variable region of the light as well as of the heavy chains is called the VC region. Each of the chains consists of structurally and functionally defined domains of approximately 110 residues, and the chains are usually linked by one or more disulfide bridges. Genetic and evolutionary studies have shown a great deal of structural homology between the domains of the Ig polypeptide chains and point to a common evolutionary origin. In the middle of the γ and α heavy chains there is a region known as the "hinge," whereas the μ and the ε chains have an extra domain. The hinge has little homology in amino acid sequence with any other part of the molecule. Typically it is rich in cysteine and proline and forms the disulfide bridges holding the two heavy chains together. Functionally, the hinge provides the flexibility necessary to permit antibody to react with antigen and to coordinate the function of the Fc fragment and the Fab arms. The hinge is of particular interest for our discussion tonight.

Three aspects of this region of the molecule bear keeping in mind: First of all, the hinge does not have homology with the rest of the molecule, second, it is controlled by a separate gene segment, and third, it can be duplicated or triplicated repeatedly, which will become obvious when we discuss some of the normal or pathological Ig subclasses.

Let us turn our attention now to the chemical structure of the γ heavy chain disease protein. For them to be of interest, it had to be first established that they are synthetic products and not the result of degradation. Four lines of evidence support a synthetic origin. First, their turnover is normal. In the initial patient, CRA, the turnover of ^{125}I-labeled IgG was consistent with a normal catabolic rate even at the time when the patient was excreting 15 g of protein per day. Second, *in vitro* labeling of heavy chain producing cells, which has been possible for the γ, α, and μ types, demonstrated that the heavy chain disease proteins were synthetic products rather than being derived from the breakdown of an intact immunoglobulin. Third, the amino acid sequence shows internal deletions; and the fourth point of evidence is derived from the translation of mRNA and the nucleotide sequence. The last two points will be discussed later, but we can conclude meanwhile that heavy chain disease proteins mark an unusual disorder of protein synthesis.

Though, as mentioned, it was recognized early on that protein CRA had one or two unusual peptides not derived from the Fc fragment, it remained for the late Jim Prahl to discover in 1967 that the heavy chain disease protein ZUC, kindly provided by Dr. Elliot Osserman, had a blocked amino terminus. Prahl (1967) considered the possibility that this was evidence for an internal deletion. Surprisingly, the internal deletion of protein ZUC, mapped in 1969 and CRA in 1971 seemed to end at exactly the same spot, namely the beginning of the hinge. This was an extremely important observation, for it suggested for the first time that deletions were nonrandom (Franklin *et al.*, 1971). This is what prompted a search for the rules which might regulate the boundaries of the internal deletions. The search has occupied Ed's laboratory for the past 10 years, and we shall lead you on this trip of exploration step by step.

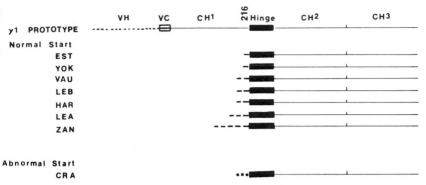

Fig. 5. Illustration of similarities of seven γ1 heavy chain mutants (see text).

Let us turn in more detail to the primary structure of the heavy chain disease proteins. Since this laboratory has concentrated most extensively on the γ heavy chain disease proteins, they will be focused on primarily.

In man, there are four subclasses of γ chains: γ1, γ2, γ3, and γ4. Let us look at γ1 heavy chain (Fig. 5).

At the top you see the prototype of a normal γ1 heavy chain with the VH, VC joining region, CH1, CH2, CH3 domains, and the hinge between CH1 and CH2. Underneath, 8 γ1 heavy chain disease proteins are depicted. As you can see, all of them are shorter than the normal γ1 heavy chain, and all of them have an internal deletion, involving part of the VH, the entire CH1 domain, and ending at the beginning of the hinge. Seven of these mutants have a variable stretch of 1–13 residues indicated by dotted lines and representing the amino terminal end of the VH region, which is followed by the hinge and the intact Fc fragment. Normal synthesis resumes at position 216. Protein CRA, the last mutant in Fig. 5, is unusual in that the amino terminal sequence is atypical of any VH subgroup. Ambiguities in sequence at several positions both in the intact protein as well as in peptic and tryptic peptides of the amino terminus suggest that protein CRA may actually result from the expression of two VH genes. It should be noted that, regardless of variabilities among the deleted proteins at the amino terminus, they have one feature in common: namely, the constancy of the sequence at the end of the deletion at the glutamic acid residue 216.

Figure 6 shows the salient features of the two γ2 heavy chain disease

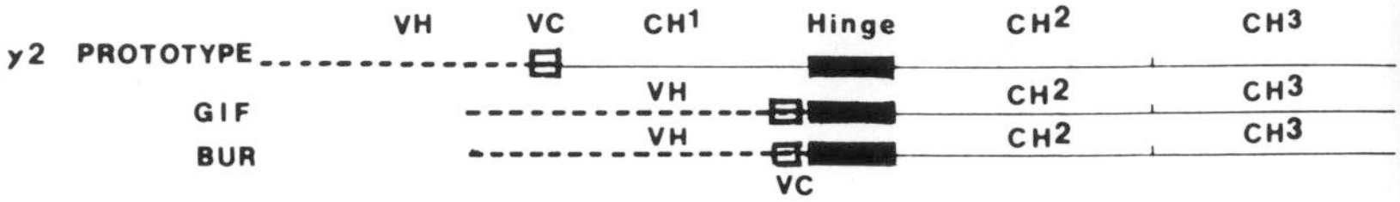

FIG. 6. γ2 heavy chain mutants retain VH and VC joining regions. They lack the CH1 domain. Note that deletion ends at the beginning of the hinge.

proteins. They are different from the γ1 proteins in that both have retained the entire VH region and the VC joining region. The deletion only starts after a stretch of sequence typical for the VC joining region. They lack the CH1 domain. Once again, the deletion ends at the beginning of the hinge which has, of course, the γ2 hinge sequence. Thus, even though the extent of the deletion of the VH domain is different for the γ1 and γ2 deletion mutants, the point where the deletion ends is again similar.

Since the γ3 deletion mutants are complex, we will skip them for a moment and dispose quickly of the only example of a γ4 heavy chain disease protein (Fig. 7).

This is unusual in that it does not fit the established pattern. Rather than having a deletion ending at the boundary of the hinge, there is no hinge at all. A normal sequence begins with methionine at residue 252. To explain this feature, one would have to postulate that a unique mechanism is operative in this instance. Two possibilities that come readily to mind are the use of an internal codon for methionine or an unusual splice site.

So far, we have considered the structure of the γ1, γ2, and γ4 heavy chain disease proteins. Let us now look at the γ3s. It is perhaps of interest that even though in normal serum the γ3 subclass makes up less than 10% of the total IgG fraction, γ3 heavy chain disease proteins occur with an inordinately high frequency. In order to appreciate the γ3 heavy chain disease proteins, the structure and evolution of the hinge for γ chain subclasses should be understood. Comparison of the four

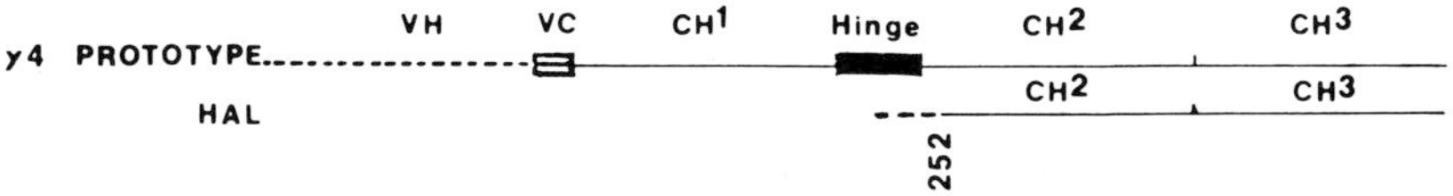

FIG. 7. Note that γ4 heavy chain disease lacks the hinge region. Normal sequence begins with methionine at residue 252.

subclasses of γ chains reveals striking homologies, suggesting a sufficient number of differences to permit their characterization by analysis of ^{14}C-labeled peptides separated by high-voltage electrophoresis after partial reduction and alkylation and peptic tryptic digestion. This technique, known as chemical typing, yields characteristic patterns of radioactive bands for all classes and subclasses of Igs, and has also proven useful as a screening method for deletion mutants.

Figure 8 shows the radioactive carboxymethylcysteine-containing

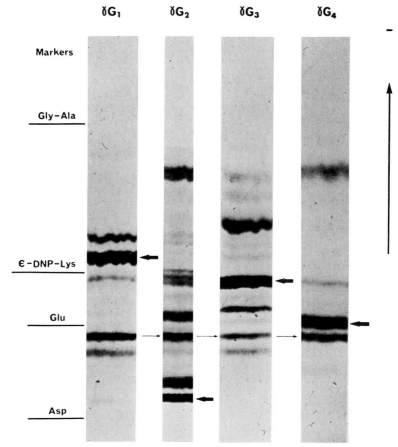

FIG. 8. Radioactive carboxymethylcysteine containing peptides show that pattern for each subclass is different. Arrows indicate hinge region. Electrophoresis, pH.3.5.

FIG. 9. γ3 heavy chain hinge.

peptides. It is evident that the pattern for each subclass is different. The hinge region of the different subclasses is indicated by an arrow.

Another interesting feature, which became apparent only about 5 years ago, is that the γ3 heavy chain is approximately 10,000 daltons heavier than the heavy chain of the other γ subclasses and that it is exceedingly rich in prolines and cysteines (Adlersberg *et al.,* 1975).

In 1977, it was established that this was due to quadruplication of a 15-residue segment (Fig. 9). There were three exact duplications of 15 residues, following 17 residues which had a striking homology yet were different in sequence. It was fascinating to find that this 62-residue stretch contained 11 cysteine and 21 proline residues (Michaelsen *et al.,* 1977).

We are now prepared to examine the γ3 heavy chain disease proteins (Fig. 10). At the top, the prototype of the γ3 heavy chains is shown. Underneath the structure of five γ3 heavy chain disease proteins that have been studied since 1969 is shown. In all of them, the deletion ends at one of the duplicated segments of the hinge. In the first and second mutants, the deletion ends at the beginning of the fourth segment of the hinge. In two proteins, SPA and CHI, the hinge region is complete including all the duplications, but much of the VH, all of the VC, and CH1 regions are deleted. The last mutant protein WIS starts as a normal H chain, then there is a deletion of the rest of the VH domain, with the exception of VC joining region which is attached to the hinge. We shall return to the structure of protein WIS later.

To fully appreciate the conclusions drawn from these chemical data,

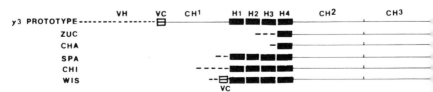

FIG. 10. γ3 heavy chain disease proteins.

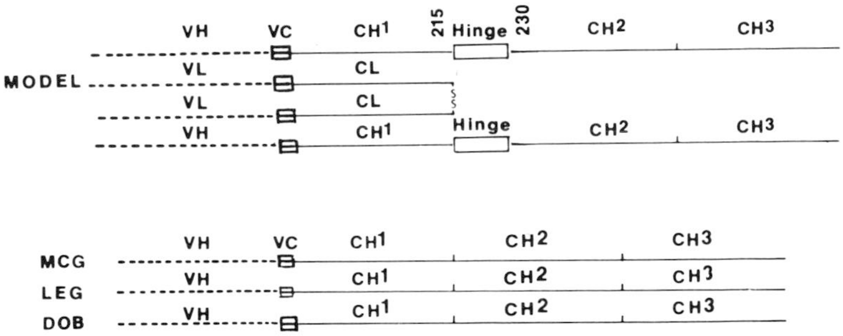

Fig. 11. Myeloma proteins with hinge deletion.

we must also examine a group of proteins which have an isolated deletion of the hinge from residue 215–230 (Fig. 11). These are not strictly heavy chain disease proteins because the cells continue to produce light chains which are not covalently bound to H chains. In these myeloma proteins the light chains are disulfide bridged to each other, but the heavy chains are not linked by disulfide bridges because they lack available cysteines. As can be seen, they do not have a hinge. Consequently these proteins dissociate into L chain dimers and single heavy chains in nonreducing buffers and can be easily recognized by this property. The defect in these proteins complements the abnormality of the typical γ heavy chain disease proteins since it delineates exactly the amino and carboxy terminal boundary of the hinge region. Together then, these observations clearly supported the concept that the hinge is under the control of a separate gene segment (Frangione *et al.*, 1979).

As an aside, it should be mentioned that the amino acid sequence of the remainder of the Fc fragment has been determined for only a very limited number of proteins. Among different γ chain subclasses, only two or three amino acid substitutions have been detected to date, suggesting that the remainder of the heavy chain is rather resistant to mutational events. Indeed, some of the substitutions proved to be related to allotypes.

At any rate, by now it had become clear, largely on the basis of the results obtained by studying the primary structure of the heavy chain disease proteins, that the hinge and each domain might be coded for by separate gene segments. Furthermore, it was postulated that each of the quadruplicated units of the hinge of the γ3 peptides could be under the control of separate exons. Indeed, cloning experiments with murine γ1 (Honjo *et al.*, 1979), γ2a (Yamawaki-Kataoka *et al.*, 1981), γ2b (Yamawaki-Kataoka *et al.*, 1980), and α genes (Early *et al.*, 1979), as well as for the human γ4 subclasses (Ellison *et al.*, 1981), have confirmed that the hinge is coded for by a separate gene fragment. What is not yet known is whether each of the reduplicated units of the γ3 hinge is coded for by a separate exon.

Curiously, patients with γ and α chain disease never produce light chains. This finding is difficult to explain since it is unlikely that such patients have two structural mutations, one involving the light chain gene and the other affecting the H chain gene. We would like to propose that light chain synthesis is a regulatory event, perhaps under the control of the CH1 domain. Deletion of the CH1 domain would result in failure of light chain synthesis.

Over the years, many proteins have been sequenced from patients who looked as though they had γ heavy chain disease but whose proteins probably represented degradation products since they began after the hinge region. Therefore, it was assumed that these proteins had undergone posttranslational modification. Needless to say, these did not help to elucidate mechanisms of genetic control of immunoglobulin expression. However, during the past 2 years some new information has actually been derived from one of these proteins (OMM). The findings on patient OMM were atypical since the serum had both a fragment of the γ3 heavy chain and an intact IgG$_3$ λ myeloma protein (Adlersberg *et al.*, 1978). The heavy chain disease protein appeared to be a product of proteolysis since it began with the sequence of Gly-Asp inside the γ3 hinge, which is known to be susceptible to proteolysis. The cells of this patient were put in long-term culture in the hope that this would permit an analysis of the synthetic and degradative history of the protein. It was fortunate that the cells which survived in culture represented the variant clone which produced only the mutant protein. Thus, the molecule could be studied at various stages of its biosynthesis. Furthermore, it became possible to compare the complete nucleotide sequence of the cloned cDNA with the products synthesized at different stages of culture (Buxbaum *et al.*, 1978).

At the bottom of Fig. 11 is shown the sequence of the normal γ3 hinge. Above it, the serum protein, which patient OMM had in his serum, started seven residues away from the beginning of the hinge. On the other hand, when the intracellular protein was studied following homogenization of the cells and analysis of the specific immunoprecipitated product of pooled long-term culture supernatants, a molecule was found which, after treatment with pronase, yielded the peptide PCA-Val. This thus indicated that the synthesized molecule had a blocked amino terminus and that proteolysis must have occurred in the serum after the protein had been secreted. Going one step further back, we identified the mRNA coding for the deleted heavy chain disease protein among the 15–16 S species of mRNA. When the product translated in the wheat germ cell-free system was analyzed by PAGE, the translation product was 2000 daltons larger than that of the native protein when incorporation of carbohydrate was prevented. Subsequently, the typical hydrophobic leader sequence was searched for with the help of radioactive amino acid incorporation. [^{35}S]Met was identified at the amino terminus, tritiated leucine was incorporated at positions 4, 8, 9, 10, and 18, and phenylalanine at positions 6 and 7. The distribution of these residues is typical of the hydrophobic leader sequence of other secreted proteins. Thus, there was little doubt that the molecule was synthesized with the hydrophobic leader sequence, that it had a blocked amino terminus, followed by an indeterminate number of amino acids, and that the serum protein was the product of proteolysis.

Finally, we shall describe the results obtained when cDNA transcribed from the mRNA of mutant OMM was cloned and its nucleotide sequence determined (Fig. 12). A glance at the sequence allows the following conclusions: There is a 19-residue leader peptide underlined starting with methionine at −19, and with the leucines and phenylalanines precisely in the same positions as had been found in the wheat germ translation product of the mRNA.

After 15 residues, most of which were quite typical of the VH1 sequence, there appeared, as anticipated, not the sequence Gly-Asp which was the amino terminal residue of the molecule in the serum, but instead Glu-Leu-Lys, which represents the beginning of the normal hinge.

This was followed by the quadruplicated hinge, followed by CH2 and CH3 domains, which were strikingly similar but not identical to the γ3 heavy chain. The amino acid sequence deduced from the OMM mRNA agrees with the published γ3 protein sequence with the exception of a few residues (Alexander *et al.*, 1982).

Sequence of a heavy-chain cDNA/protein. Nucleotide codons, single-letter/three-letter amino acids, and residue numbers are shown. Boxed residues denote allotypic/variant positions.

```
......CCUGGACCUCCUGCUGCAAGAAC
```

Leader
```
                        Gln
            AUG AAA  CAM  CUG UGG UUC CUU CUC CUG GUG GCA GCU CUC UCC
            Met Lys  His  Leu Trp Phe Phe Leu Leu Val Ala Ala Leu Ser
            -19                                           -3  -2  -1
```

V Region
```
CAG GUG CAC CAG GAG CAG CUG CCA GGA CUG UCG GGC CCA GGA CUG
Gln Val His Gln Glu Gln Leu Pro Gly Leu Ser Gly Pro Gly Leu
 1   2   3
```

Hinge
```
          15 | 216 217 218 219  220 221 222 223 224 225 226 227 228
     ...CCU CCA | GAG CUC CCA AAA GGU GAC ACA CAC UGC CCA CCA UGC CCA CGG
        Pro Pro | Glu Leu Pro Lys Gly Asp Thr His Cys Pro Pro Cys Pro Arg
```

```
                                                                CH2
UGC CCA GAG CCC AAA UCU UCU GAC ACA CCU CCG CCG CCG UGC CCA | GCA CCU GAA CUC CUG GGA GGA UCA GUC UUC CUC UUC
Cys Pro Glu Pro Lys Ser Ser Asp Thr Pro Pro Pro Pro Cys Pro | Ala Pro Glu Leu Leu Gly Gly Ser Val Phe Leu Phe
229 230                                                       231                                          243
```

```
CCC CCA AAA CCC AAG GAU ACC CUU AUG AUC UCC CGG ACC CCU GAG GUC ACA UGC GUG GUG GUG GAC GUG AGC CAC GAA GAC CCN GUC
Pro Pro Lys Pro Lys Asp Thr Leu Met Ile Ser Arg Thr Pro Glu Val Thr Cys Val Val Val Asp Val Ser His Glu Asp Pro Val
244                                                                                                           273
```

```
                                                                      Tyr
CAG UUC AAG UGG UAC GUG GAC GGC GUG GAG GUG CAU AAU GCC AAG ACA AAG CCG CGG GAG GAG CAG UAC |Asn| AGC ACG UAC CGU GUG GUC
Gln Phe Lys Trp Tyr Val Asp Gly Val Glu Val His Asn Ala Lys Thr Lys Pro Arg Glu Glu Gln  Gln|Tyr| Ser Thr Tyr Arg Val Val
274                                                                                     296                          303
```

```
AGC GUC ACC GUC CUG CAC CAG GAC UGG CUG AAU GGC AAG GAG UAC AAG UGC AAG GUC UCC AAC AAA GCC CUC CCA GCC CCC AUC GAG
Ser Val Thr Val Leu His Gln Asp Trp Leu Asn Gly Lys Glu Tyr Lys Cys Lys Val Ser Asn Lys Ala Leu Pro Ala Pro Ile Glu
304                                                                                                           333
```

```
                      CH3                              CH3
AAA ACC AUC UCC AAA GCC|Ala|GGG CAG|Gly|CCC CGA GAA CCA CAG GUG UAC ACC CUG CCC CCA UCC CGG GAG GAG AUG ACC AAG AAC CAG GUC AGC CUG ACC UGC CUG GUC AAA GGC UUC
Lys Thr Ile Ser Lys Ala|Lys|Gly Gln|Pro|Pro Arg Glu Pro Gln Val Tyr Thr Leu Pro Pro Ser Arg Glu Glu Met Thr Lys Asn Gln Val Ser Leu Thr Cys Leu Val Lys Gly Phe
334                 339     341 342                                                                                       356                                    372
```

```
                                                                  Asn
UAC CCC AGC GAC AUC GCC GUG GAG UGG GAG AGC AAU GGG CAG|Asn|CCG GAG AAC AAC UAC AAG ACC ACG CCU CCC AUG CUG GAC UCC GAC GGC
Tyr Pro Ser Asp Ile Ala Val Glu Trp Glu Ser Asn Gly Gln|Asn|Pro Glu Asn Asn Tyr Lys Thr Thr Pro Pro Met Leu Asp Ser Asp Gly
373                                             384                                                                   402
```

```
UCC UUC UUC CUC UAC AGC AAG CUC ACC GUG GAC AAG AGC AGG UGG CAG CAG GGG AAC GUC UUC UCA UGC UCC GUG AUG CAU GAG GCU CUG
Ser Phe Phe Leu Tyr Ser Lys Leu Thr Val Asp Lys Ser Arg Trp Gln Gln Gly Asn Val Phe Ser Cys Ser Val Met His Glu Ala Leu
403                                                                                                           432
```

```
                Tyr                                           End of CH3
                                                              CH3
CAC AAC CGC UAC|Tyr|ACG CAG AAG AGC CUC UCC CUG UCU CCG GGU|Lys|AAA UGA  GUGCCAUGGCCGGCCACCCCGCCCAAGCCCCGGCGCUCUCGCGGGGUCGCCGGAGGAUGC   — GC linker
His Asn Arg Tyr|Tyr|Thr Gln Lys Ser Leu Ser Leu Ser Pro Gly|Lys|Lys End
433        436                                                    446
```

```
UUGGCCACUACCCCGUUACAUUACUUCCCAGCGACCACCAUCGGAAAUAAAGCACCCACCACCGCCGGAGUCCCUGGAAAAAAAAAAAA  COMMODITIES...
```

The variant residues marked by boxes around positions around 296, 339, 284, and 436, are identical to residues found in the normal $\gamma 1$ sequence, but not in the normal $\gamma 3$ sequence. This sequence resembles that of the heavy chain of a recently described intact γ-myeloma GOE studied in this laboratory (Recht *et al.*, 1981), which also contains $\gamma 1$ specific residues in three of these four positions, the fourth being undetermined. These data suggested that GOE and OMM proteins may be very closely related, perhaps even allelic forms of $\gamma 3$, or a less likely possibility is that they may represent a new γ subclass. The similarity between the OMM heavy chain and the heavy chain of myeloma protein GOE, suggests that most of the discrepancy between the published $\gamma 3$ sequence and that deduced from the OMM mRNA sequence can be attributed to a naturally occurring genetic polymorphism.

It is of interest that OMM has arginine and GOE histidine at position 435 (Fig. 12), a finding which explains the fact that GOE, unlike the typical $\gamma 3$ molecule, binds to staphylococcal protein A. It should be recalled that of all subclasses of γ chains, the only one which normally does not bind staph protein A is $\gamma 3$. Last, immediately before the stop codon in the mRNA sequence, indicated by END in Fig. 12, there is information for an additional lysine beyond position 446 which is not present in any of the published $\gamma 3$ amino acid sequences. The nucleotide sequences of the human $\gamma 4$ and mouse $\gamma 1$, $\gamma 2a$, and $\gamma 2b$ genes also encode information for a C-terminal lysine not present in the mature proteins. Apparently, the lysine is removed from immunoglobulin H chains of both species postsynthetically.

Finally, one can at least make an attempt to explain the deletion by correlating the structural defects in the protein with current knowledge of gene structure and organization. Figure 13 presents a schematic diagram of the organization of a human H chain gene. The top line depicts the primary transcript, namely, the variable region gene, CH1, hinge, CH2, and CH3 exons separated by loops or intervening sequences. In the mature mRNA, the intervening sequences are removed. In most instances, deletions are nonrandom and generally involve genetic units coding for well-defined domains or the hinge region. They usually end at points involved in RNA splicing or gene rearrangement. In the majority of heavy chain disease molecules which lack most of the VH and CH1 domain, as indicated on the third line, the possibility exists that the deletion of one domain is related to an inability to utilize

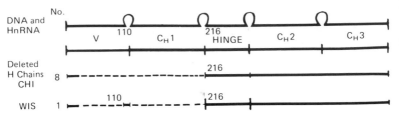

Fig. 13. Presumed structure of H chain genome based on deleted mutants.

the next splice site to correct the error, thus forcing it to skip to the next one. Alternatively, the extent of the deletion may encompass a more extensive region of DNA.

In favor of the former possibility is the result obtained with protein WIS (Fig. 13), where an abortive effort to correct the deletion at the VC junction was uncovered. An apparent attempt to correct the lesion failed. There was no CH1 domain and the protein synthetic machinery had to jump to the next site at the beginning of the hinge. Even though DNA rearrangement and RNA processing usually occur in an orderly and consecutive sequence, it is quite conceivable that alternate sites can be used and that correction will not occur in the first possible instance, either because of conformational or structural variations.

The mechanism accounting for deletions still remains to be defined. In view of the fact that during differentiation of Ig genes there is abundant excision, joining, and rearrangement of pieces of DNA, it seems more than likely that the process occurs at the DNA level. Alternatively, the deletion could occur during mRNA processing, or it is even possible that both these mechanisms pertain. Ed favors the view that the deletion occurs at the DNA level. In support of this is the observation by Dunnick *et al.* (1980) in the IF2 mouse mutant, which has a deletion of the sequence of DNA that codes for the CH1 domain. It was shown that the gap began and ended in the intervening sequences before and after the CH1 domain, respectively. In addition, recent Southern blot analysis of the OMM genome DNA has revealed a pattern which varies from that seen in normally rearranged human γ3 DNA.

An even more difficult question to answer is the reason for the invariable failure of light chain synthesis in the γ and α heavy chain diseases. Preliminary observations derived from hybridization studies of OMM cells have revealed that κ-related genes are absent, but rearranged genes coding for λ chains are expressed. Either these rearranged λ genes are abnormal, which would then constitute a second structural gene abnormality, or the rearrangement is normal, in which case the lack of expression could be attributed to a regulatory aberration.

Despite the fact that in the IF2 mouse mutant the absence of the CH1 domain has not precluded the synthesis of light chain (Adetugbo *et al.*, 1977)—this may be different in man—and for the time being, Ed likes to hold on to the hypothesis that the absence of the CH1 domain is causally related to the absence of light chains.

Obviously, many questions remain to be answered in the future. Among them are, what is the nature and cause of the gene deletion? What is the defect in the proteins that have both light and heavy chain deletions? And above all, what is the correction mechanism that so reproducibly and accurately permits a normal sequence to resume?

In this era of DNA cloning, it is comforting for a clinician and protein chemist to realize that much information can still be obtained by carefully studying materials obtained from patients with the time-honored methods of protein chemistry. Only by using these old fashioned disciplines in parallel with modern methods of molecular biology will we ultimately be able to unravel important biological as well as clinical problems.

REFERENCES*

Adetugbo, K. Milstein, C., and Secher, D. S. (1977). *Nature (London)* **265**, 299–304.
Adlersberg, J., Frangione, B., and Franklin, E. C. (1975). *Proc. Natl. Acad. Sci. U.S.A.* **72**, 723–727.
Adlersberg, J., Grann, V., Zucker-Franklin, D., Frangione, B., and Franklin, E. C. (1978). *Blood* **51**, 85–96.
Alexander, A., Steinmetz, M., Barritault, D., Frangione, B., Franklin, E. C., Hood, L., and Buxbaum, J. (1982). *Proc. Natl. Acad. Sci. U.S.A.* **79**, 3260–3264.
Buxbaum, J., Alexander, A., and Olivier, O. (1978). *Clin. Exp. Immunol.* **32**, 489–497.
Dunnick, W., Rabbitts, T. H., and Milstein, C. (1980). *Nature (London)* **286**, 669 675.
Early, P. W., Davis, M. M., Kaback, D. B., Davison, N., and Hood, L. (1979). *Proc. Natl. Acad. Sci. U.S.A.* **76**, 857–861.
Edelman, G. (1973) *Harvey Lect.* **68**, 149–184.
Ellison, J., Buxbaum J., and Hood, L. (1981). *DNA* **1**, 11–18.
Frangione, B., and Franklin, E. C. (1979). *Nature (London)* **281**, 600–602.

*Dr. Franklin's death on February 20, 1982 precluded inclusion of a more complete bibliography.

Frangione, B., Franklin, E. C., and Prelli, F. (1976). *Scand. J. Immunol.* **5**, 623–627.

Franklin, E. C., and Frangione, B. (1971). *Proc. Natl. Acad. Sci. U.S.A.* **68**, 187–191.

Franklin, E. C., Lowenstein, J., Bigelow, B., and Meltzer, M. (1964). *Am. J. Med.* **37**, 332–350.

Heidelberger, M. (1933). *Harvey Lect.* **28**, 184–201.

Honjo, T., Obata, M., Yamawaki-Kataoka, Y., Kataoka, T., Kawakmi, T., Takahashi, N., and Mano, Y. (1979). *Cell* **18**, 559–568.

Jerne, N. (1975). *Harvey Lect.* **70**, 93–110.

Kunkel, H. G. (1964). *Harvey Lect.* **59**, 219–242.

Michaelsen, T., Frangione, B., and Franklin, E. C. (1977). *J. Biol. Chem.* **252**, 883–889.

Osserman, E. F., and Takatsuki, K. (1963). *Medicine* **42**, 357–384.

Porter, R. (1970). *Harvey Lect.* **65**, 157–174.

Prahl, J. (1967). *Nature (London)* **215**, 1386–1387.

Recht, B., Frangione, B., Franklin, E. C., and Van Logham, E. (1981). *J. Immunol.* **127**, 917–923.

Scharff, M. (1973). *Harvey Lect.* **69**, 125–142.

Seligmann, M., Danon, F., Hurez, D., Mihaesco, E., and Preudhomme, J. L. (1968). *Science* **162**, 1396–1397.

Tiselius, A. (1939). *Harvey Lect.* **35**, 37–70.

Tonegawa, S. (1980). *Harvey Lect.* **75**, 61–83.

Waldenström, J. (1961). *Harvey Lect.* **56**, 211–231.

Yamawaki-Kataoka, Y., Kataoka, T., Takahashi, N., Obata, M., and Honjo, T. (1980). *Nature (London)* **283**, 786–789.

Yamawaki-Kataoka, Y., Miyata, T., and Honjo, T. (1981). *Nucleic Acids Res.* **9**, 1365–1381.

Zucker-Franklin, D., and Franklin, E. C. (1971). *Blood* **37**, 257–271.

CONTROL OF INTERCELLULAR COMMUNICATION BY WAY OF GAP JUNCTIONS*,[1]

M. V. L. BENNETT, D. C. SPRAY, A. L. HARRIS,[2] R. D. GINZBERG, A. CAMPOS DE CARVALHO,[3] AND R. L. WHITE

Division of Cellular Neurobiology
Department of Neuroscience
Albert Einstein College of Medicine
Bronx, New York

INTERCELLULAR communication means the transmission of a message between cells. As far as neurons are concerned the transmission can be chemically or electrically mediated, modes that were proposed by DuBois Raymond in the last century. A common form of electrical communication occurs at gap junctions which, between neurons, comprise electrotonic synapses, ''electrotonic'' because transmission at these synapses is similar to electrotonic spread along a core conductor. Other excitable cells, such as those in cardiac and smooth muscle, also communicate electrically through gap junctions. We will not review here the extensive data indicating both inductively and deductively that gap junctions couple cells (cf. Bennett, 1977; Bennett and Goodenough, 1978).

Gap junctions are characterized morphologically in thin section by close apposition of cells with a space between them, the gap, which is

---

*Lecture delivered September 16, 1982.

[1]Harry Grundfest who died in October, 1983, would no doubt have argued persuasively against the disruption presented here of the old dichotomy between chemically and electrically excitable membrane. As his time's foremost exponent of a general and comparative approach to electrobiology, he would also have welcomed the characterization of many different kinds of channel, and ultimately he would have recodified the kinds of behavior we discuss. Our paper is dedicated to him with respect and affection.

[2]Present address: Department of Biology, Stanford University, Stanford, California.

[3]Present address: Instituto Biologia, Universidade do Estado do Rio de Janeiro, Rio de Janeiro, Brazil.

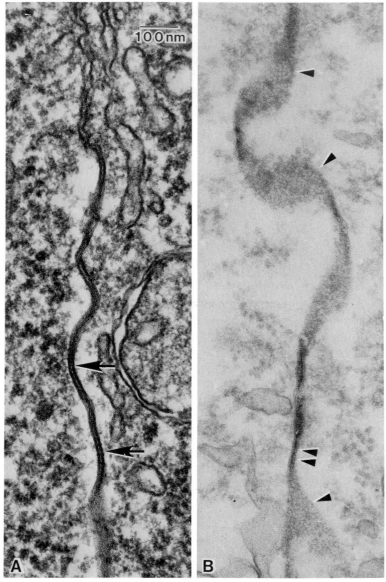

FIG. 1. Gap junctions in thin sections of squid blastomeres. (A) After membrane staining with en bloc uranyl acetate, junctions appear as close appositions with periodic bridges crossing gap (arrows). The membranes are separated at the top of the figure. (B) With La(OH)₃ treatment during fixation and only lead staining of sections, the junctions show close apposition and a stain filled gap in sections perpendicular to the membranes

permeable to the extracellular space marker La(OH)$_3$ (Fig. 1). In freeze fracture the junctions are comprised of an aggregate of intramembrane particles with pits on the complementary face (Fig. 2A).

In many tissues, gap junctions are found between cells that do not generate action potentials. Examples are liver, glands, and various other epithelia. In these instances gap junctions probably mediate chemical communication, because the pathway provided for flow of ions and electrotonic coupling also permits passage of the molecules up to a diameter of about 1.2 nm and molecular weight of about 1000 (Fig. 3). This size range includes molecules of intermediary metabolism and intracellular messengers such as cAMP. A considerable body of data indicates that chemical communication via gap junctions operates in development, but as yet identification of the messages and direct demonstration of their transmission via gap junctions have not been obtained (cf. Bennett *et al.*, 1981).

Most gap junctions originally described appeared to be electrically linear, with a few rectifying electrotonic synapses as exceptions (Furshpan and Potter, 1959; Auerbach and Bennett, 1969). The electrical linearity and nonselective permeability suggested that the junctions were simple ultramicroscopic aqueous channels connecting cells as in the diagram of Fig. 2B. We shall show here that this picture is oversimplified in that gap junctions have a number of mechanisms whereby they can be gated, that is, opened or shut. Also, gap junctions are not all the same, and a fairly wide range of properties is observed.

I. Electrotonic Synapses in Integration

We will make a small aside at this point. Even where gap junctions act as simple linear channels connecting cells, they can function quite well as integrative synapses, and excitatory transmission mediated electrically can be difficult to distinguish from that mediated chemically (cf. Bennett, 1977). Temporal and spatial summation of graded excitatory transmission that is electrically mediated is easily demonstrated experi-

---

(double arrowhead). A nonjunctional region lies just above. In regions sectioned tangentially the bridging structures appear as polygonal aggregates negatively stained by La(OH)$_3$ in the gap (single arrowheads). Methods in Ginzberg *et al.* (1984). A and B at same magnification.

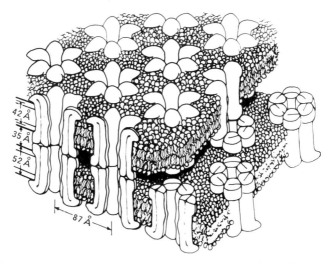

Fig. 2. Gap junctions in freeze fracture and imagination. (A) A freeze fracture replica from killifish blastomeres. The gap junction is recognizable as an aggregate of P face particles above and E face pits below. (B) A model of a gap junction. Two hemichannels, one in each membrane, meet in the center of the intercellular gap to form the complete channel. Each hemichannel is composed of a hexamer of subunits. Phospholipids are indicated with small round polar head groups and hydrophobic tails. (From Makowski *et al.*, 1977.)

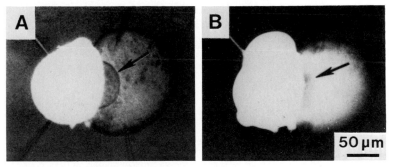

Fig. 3. Passage of the small molecule, Lucifer Yellow, between electrotonically coupled blastomeres of the killifish. (A) Mixed transmitted and fluorescent micrograph of two coupled cells, each penetrated by two microelectrodes. An almost semicircular profile of the space between the cells can be seen (arrow). (B) Fluorescent micrograph. The tracer spread to the right cell from the injected cell on the left. [The left cell changed its shape somewhat compared to (A).] The space between cells shows less fluorescence than the right cell's cytoplasm indicating that dye spread did not occur by way of extracellular space. (From Bennett *et al.*, 1978a.)

mentally, and is known at a number of sites. To be sure, electrotonic synapses are often found at loci where precise synchronization or rapid and reliable transmission occur, and ordinary integration is not the normal mode of operation. A prominent feature of chemical transmission is change in potency as a result of prior activation, as in postactivation facilitation or depression wherein a postsynaptic response gets bigger or smaller following a response in the same pathway. We know of no changes in junctional conductance at electrical synapses as a result of activity in the same pathway, but in terms of impulse transmission one can see relatively long-lasting facilitation associated with afterpotentials or changes in the impulse generating membranes of the cells (e.g., Bennett and Pappas, 1983). Furthermore, interaction with chemically transmitting synapses can alter nonjunctional conductances and thereby alter the degree of coupling. It was first shown that inhibitory synapses can short-circuit electrotonic transmission and lead to virtually complete uncoupling in terms of electrotonic spread between cell bodies (Spira and Bennett, 1972; Spira *et al.*, 1980). Appropriate circuitry to mediate a similar effect occurs in the mammalian inferior olive (Llinas *et al.*, 1974). In another instance chemical synapses that decrease nonjunctional conductance increase coupling (Carew and Kandel, 1976). In a final example the sign of coupling can be in effect reversed by the action of inhibitory interneurons, themselves apparently coupled (Spira *et al.*, 1976).

II. pH Gating of Junctional Conductance

In 1978 an important observation was made by Turin and Warner, namely that lowering cytoplasmic pH, pH_i, decreased junctional conductance, g_j. We were able to reproduce this phenomenon and, by use of cell pairs rather than intact blastulas, could quantitate the result (Spray *et al.*, 1981a). A simple procedure for lowering pH_1 is to bathe the cells in CO_2 equilibrated saline or in a weak acid such as acetate. CO_2 or undissociated acid diffuses across the cell membrane where it releases H ions in the cell interior, decreasing g_j (Fig. 4). Other agents releasing H ions through action of intracellular esterases can also be used (Spray *et al.*, 1984b), and acid can be injected. (Because the cell membrane has limited permeability to H ions themselves, bathing in strong acids or impermeant buffers has negligible effect on junctional conductance.) When pH_i is measured with a pH microelectrode, g_j is seen to fall as acidity increases, and to rise as pH_i recovers on rinsing in normal saline (Fig. 4). The response is fast and reversible. If one plots g_j vs pH_i one obtains a simple sigmoidal curve (Fig. 5A). The conductance for increasing acidity falls along the same line as the conductance for decreasing acidity. There is no hysteresis in the g_j–pH_i relation, although rates of change can be quite different. One inference from these data is that H ions act directly on the junctional channels rather than through a cytoplasmic intermediate. The smooth curves in Fig. 5A are plots of the Hill equation and constitute titration curves. The half maximal value of conductance determines the apparent K_m as about 50 nM or the pK_H as about 7.3. The two curves are for Hill coefficients of 4 and 5, which are the relations that would obtain if 4 or 5 H ions acted at each site with a high degree of cooperativity. More ions could be involved if there were a lesser degree of cooperativity. The cell "rests" at a pH_i where the junctional conductance is near maximal, but where change by only a few tenths of a pH unit can markedly decrease g_j.

The effectiveness of increasing cytoplasmic acidity in closing gap junctions has now been demonstrated in a number of neural and non-neural tissues of vertebrates and invertebrates. Minor differences in K_ms and Hill coefficients occur (cf. Spray *et al.*, 1984a). For example in

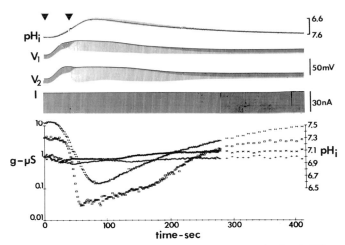

FIG. 4. Effect of CO_2 on electrotonic coupling between a pair of axolotl blastomeres. Current pulses (I) were alternately passed in cell 1 and cell 2 (V_1 and V_2), producing approximately equal voltage deflections in the polarized cell and somewhat smaller potentials in the other cell. Application of saline equilibrated with 100% CO_2 in the superfusate (between arrowheads at the top of figure) decreased cytoplasmic pH (uppermost trace, increased H activity upward) and decreased the spread of current from cell to cell (seen as a decrease in the potential produced in each cell by current injected into the other). Washing the cells with CO_2-free saline at normal pH restored the pH_i and electrotonic coupling over a similar but slower time course. Junctional and nonjunctional conductances calculated from these data are plotted along the same time scale in the bottom portion of the figure. Response time for the pH electrode to measure a change of 1 pH unit was < 10 seconds; measurements were made at intervals of 2 seconds. The nonjunctional conductances of the two cells ($+$, $\times$) decreased and then slowly recovered. Junctional membrane conductance (g_j, rectangular symbols) was initially about 5 μS and began to decrease as pH_i (H symbol, right ordinate) reached about 7.4. The junctional conductance reached a minimum value of about 0.02 μS at the minimum of pH_1 and then recovered toward the initial value as pH_i recovered. (From Spray et al., 1981a.)

crayfish septate axon the pK_H for g_j is about 6.7 and the Hill coefficient is about 2.7 (Campos de Carvalho et al., 1984). Rat cardiac muscle has a similar sensitivity (unpublished). Junctions in adult lens and between toad rods may be even less sensitive (Schuetze and Goodenough, 1982; but see Rae et al., 1982; L. Griff and L. Pinto, personal communication), although pH_i and g_j have not been measured in these cases. The pH action on g_j is widespread, but quite possibly not universal. Our early resistance to the idea of pH insensitivity softened somewhat when we

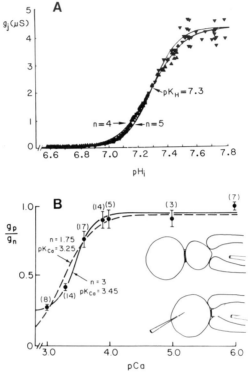

Fig. 5. Sensitivity of g_j to H and Ca ions. (A) The conductance data of Fig. 4 are plotted as a function of pH$_i$. Triangles with apices down represent initial values and values during cytoplasmic acidification. Triangles with apexes up are values during recovery. The points fall along Hill curves with pK_H = 7.3 and n between 4 and 5. There is no evidence of hysteresis between falling and rising pH$_i$. The data are consistent with H ions acting directly on a channel macromolecule. (From Spray *et al.*, 1981a.) (B) From cell pairs in which one cytoplasmic aspect of the junctions was perfused with a solution buffered to pH 7.6 and various pCa levels. The ordinate g_p/g_n is a normalized measure of junctional conductance; standard errors and number of experiments are indicated. The curves are Hill plots fit by eye, assuming that the minimum value of g_p/g_n was either zero or just below that at pCa 3.0 (1 mM). Junctional conductance is very insensitive to Ca as compared to H ions. The inset shows how one cell of a coupled pair was sucked into the perfusion pipet and broken to expose its junctions to the perfusate. The electrode in the intact cell allowed the measurement of g_p/g_n when its potential was compared to that in the pipet and in the bath. (From Spray *et al.*, 1982a.)

found chemical treatments that blocked H ion dependence, as will be discussed further below.

Data had previously been obtained implicating cytoplasmic Ca as decreasing junctional conductance, most convincingly by Rose and Loewenstein (1975). The question then arose whether H ions acted by releasing Ca from intracellular stores. Experiments with Ca-sensitive electrodes (Rink *et al.*, 1980) and with aequorin (Bennett *et al.*, 1978a) indicated that Ca was little increased during cytoplasmic acidification adequate to shut down gap junctions.

The converse question remained whether Ca acted via H ions. To investigate this problem we developed a perfused preparation in which one of a pair of cells was sucked into the pipet and broken exposing its internal aspect to the perfusate buffered to particular H and Ca concentrations (Fig. 5B, inset, Spray *et al.*, 1982a). We found that at low Ca, equivalent to or somewhat above normal cytosolic values, the H concentrations required to decrease the conductance of the perfused membrane were the same as those determined by intracellular pH measurements to decrease g_j in intact cells. Thus the technique was validated. When the junctions were perfused with Ca ions at pH 7.6, we found that a much higher concentration of Ca was required to produce an effect. As indicated by conductance of the perfused patch, g_j did not begin to fall until Ca was in the range of tenths of a millimole and even at millimolar concentrations it was not clear that the junctions were completely shut down (Fig. 5B). Thus, these junctions are much less sensitive to Ca than to H. The sensitivity to Ca may be only slightly greater in *Chironomus* (40–80 μM, Oliveira-Castro and Loewenstein, 1971). A greater sensitivity was reported in cardiac muscle (Dahl and Isenberg, 1980) but pH was not measured and may have been changed by the treatment with DNP, a weak acid as well as an uncoupler of oxidative metabolism. We observe that Ca levels adequate to cause irreversible contracture of ventricular myocytes do not uncouple pairs of cells (unpublished).

It is unlikely that cytoplasmic Ca would rise high enough to affect gap junctions under normal conditions (at least in these cell types). It would, however, reach the required high levels on disruption of the surface membrane, letting in Ca from the external medium, and a well-known method of uncoupling cells is mechanical injury. We believe that H is a more attractive candidate than Ca for physiological control of

TABLE I

SENSITIVITY OF GATING MECHANISMS

	pH sensitivity	V sensitivity
pH gating	High (vertebrate blastomeres) Medium (crayfish, vert. heart) Low (adult lens?)	High (*Chironomus*) Medium (squid blastomeres) Low (crayfish septate axon)
	V sensitivity	pH sensitivity
V gating	High (amphibian blastomeres) Medium (teleost blastomeres) Low (rat heart)	None in pH 6–8 range

junctional conductance, and significant shifts in H ion concentration are known under some physiological conditions as well as pathological ones like acidosis secondary to anoxia. We admit we do not know of any instance where "normal" decreases of pH uncouple cells.

The first conclusion of this article is in the upper left block of entries in Table I. Gap junctions are closed by decreasing pH_i in a number of tissues, with various degrees of sensitivity. Provisionally, we will call this pH gating. It is reasonable to suggest that H and Ca act on the same gating mechanism, and the most appropriate name will depend on determining the most common way in which the mechanism is activated.

III. VOLTAGE GATING

As stated above, gap junctions were generally found to behave linearly in electrical terms consistent with simple aqueous channels connecting the cell cytoplasms. It then came as something of a surprise to find that junctions between amphibian blastomeres were strongly voltage dependent as illustrated in Fig. 6A (cf. Spray *et al.*, 1981b; Harris *et al.*, 1981). In this experiment current pulses (I) were applied in one of a coupled cell pair. During the smallest current (A_1) the cells were coupled throughout the pulse. During the larger currents (A_3–A_4) the cells were coupled at the beginning of the pulse, but then the voltage rose rapidly in the first cell while dropping in the second; later in the pulse the cells were very poorly coupled. By simple examination it is

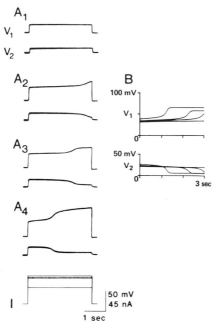

Fig. 6. Comparison of current clamp responses and calculations from voltage clamp data. (A_1–A_4) Currents (I, superimposed traces at the bottom) were applied to cell 1 of a coupled pair. For the smallest current (A_1), the potentials in cell 1 (V_1) and cell 2 (V_2) remained nearly constant. Near the end of a larger current (A_2) the input resistance of cell 1 increased and the electrotonic coupling to cell 2 decreased. With still larger currents (A_{3-4}), the uncoupling occurred earlier. (B) Calculations from opening and closing rates determined by voltage clamp. Comparable currents to those in A were applied to a pair of model cells with junctional conductance for small V_j and nonjunctional conductances chosen to give the same coupling coefficients. The agreement with records in (A) is good, except for the upward trend for large currents in (A). This drift was probably due to decrease in nonjunctional conductance, which was assumed constant for the calculations. (From Harris *et al.*, 1983.)

clear that a decrease in junctional conductance could account for the observations; by reducing current flow between cells the voltage drop in the second cell is reduced, and more current must flow through the nonjunctional membrane of the first cell and the voltage across it must increase. The mechanism was confirmed in other experiments by showing linearity of nonjunctional membrane. The effect is also symmetrical with transjunctional voltage, V_j; current passed in either cell of either sign produces the same kind of response.

This change in junctional conductance was a natural candidate for study by voltage clamping in the hope that determining rates at specific voltages might give insight as to mechanisms. The use of two isopotential cells allows accurate measurement of junctional properties, since all the junctions are at the same potential and can be treated as a single element, as is also true of each nonjunctional conductance. Because two cells were involved it was necessary to use two clamps, one for each cell. Consider two cells clamped to a common potential near their resting potential (Fig. 7). When the second cell is stepped from that potential to a new voltage, the additional current supplied by the clamp on the first cell to hold its voltage constant equals the transjunctional current, I_j (since the voltage in this cell and hence current across its nonjunctional membrane remains fixed). The junctional conductance then is simply I_j divided by the voltage step in the second cell, which is V_j. One immediately sees the time course of the conductance changes.

Clamping shows that for small voltages g_j remains constant, but for

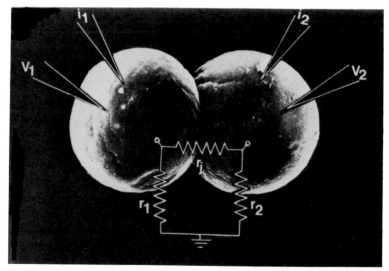

FIG. 7. Scanning electron micrograph of a pair of killifish blastomeres with diagrams of microelectrodes and the equivalent circuit for determining junctional conductance. (From Spray *et al.*, 1982b.)

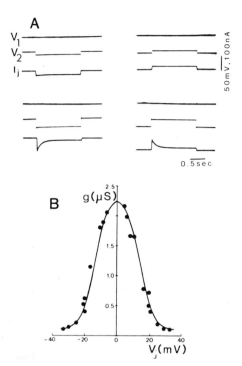

FIG. 8. Voltage clamp records of junctional current and the steady-state g_j-V_j relation for a coupled pair of amphibian blastomeres. Cell 1 was clamped at its resting potential (V_1); cell 2 was stepped to various values (V_2) and the clamp current to cell 1 gave junctional current (I_j). (A) For small steps of either sign, current remained constant during the pulse. For larger steps the current decayed exponentially to a lower steady-state value. (B) Steady-state values of g_j are plotted as a function of V_j from data like those in (A) Steady-state g_j decreased steeply for increasing V_j of either sign, the half-maximum values occurring at about ± 15 mV. The points for each polarity of V_j are well fit by a Boltzmann relation (smooth curve). (From Spray *et al.*, 1981b.)

larger voltages g_j decreases over time (Fig. 8A). The decreases are symmetrical for opposite voltages and are greater and more rapid for progressively larger pulses. Also they are exponential in time course, which is consistent with a first-order process. We suppose that there are many channels which are open at zero V_j. When V_j is stepped, a channel remains open until it closes very rapidly compared to the time course of decrease in total current. The smooth exponential decay results, because each channel closes independently of the others, and the probability of closing remains constant at a constant voltage. Channels will have a probability of reopening, but with a fixed voltage determining opening and closing rates an exponential decay (or relaxation) to a steady state conductance still occurs. Although not the only mechanism resulting in an exponential decay, this is a simple one that can in principle be directly demonstrated by patch clamp techniques which have shown similar processes in other membrane channels.

We determined the steady state g_j as a function of V_j. For V_j of either polarity the conductance falls off steeply (Fig. 8B). (It ultimately reaches a small residual component of about 5 percent which may represent voltage insensitive channels or incomplete closure of channels). The solid curve is what would occur if the distribution of open and closed channels followed the Boltzmann relation. This relation is obtained if the energy difference between open and closed states is a linear function of transmembrane voltage. The reasonableness of this view as a first approximation for conformational changes of membrane macromolecules is generally accepted (e.g., Neher and Stevens, 1977). A model for the gating mechanism involves a conformational shift of the channel macromolecule that changes its dipole moment in the direction of the applied field as diagramed in Fig. 9. Some may be bothered by our pushing two negative charges together in the closed position, which we will not defend vigorously, because we have no structural data. The necessary energy, however, could be provided by the applied voltage, and when the voltage is turned off the channels do return to the open position, so that some restoring force must be present.

Because of the basic symmetry of the gap junctional structure, both morphologically and in its response to transjunctional voltage, we diagramed one gate in each membrane. Other schemes are possible, but this one is attractive because the channels are insensitive to the voltage between inside and outside of the cells (Spray et al., 1981b) as distinct from transjunctional potential, and the placement is as far from the extracellular space as possible. Other junctions are sensitive to inside–outside potential as discussed below, and the gates of these junctions may be differently situated. Further evidence for, and implications of, series gating are given in a subsequent section.

From the voltage clamp data on steady-state conductance and time constants of relaxation to these values we computed opening and clos-

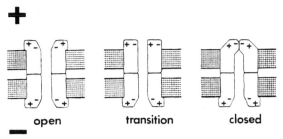

FIG. 9. Model for gating of the gap junction channel between amphibian blastomeres. Each channel is composed of two oppositely oriented hemichannels, each containing a gating structure sensitive to local voltage within the channel. The action of a large voltage of appropriate polarity on dipoles of the hemichannel affects the energy of the molecule such that it is more stable in the conformation that closes the channel. The orientation of the dipole in the transition state is arbitrarily drawn normal to the field. (From Harris *et al.*, 1981.)

ing rates, which proved to be exponentially related to voltage (Harris *et al.*, 1981). By conventional theory one obtains an exponential relation if the energy difference between the open or closed state and an intermediate transition state is linearly related to voltage. These results are consistent with the gap junction channels behaving in a simple all-or-none, open-or-closed fashion, and the conductances have very similar properties to those of conventional excitable membranes. However, changes in g_j are much slower with time constants of hundreds of milliseconds.

Following on the memorable work of Hodgkin and Huxley (1952) it is customary to see if one's voltage clamp data can account for the current clamp results. In this procedure one assumes that the rates of opening and closing are instantaneous functions of voltage unaffected by previous history (really, one is testing this assumption). Figure 6 compares responses to rectangular pulses of increasing amplitude in a real pair of cells (A), and responses calculated from voltage clamp data (B). The fit is reasonable. The tilt in the plateaus in the actual data can be explained as a slow change in the nonjunctional membrane, which was assumed to have constant properties for the calculations.

The degree of voltage sensitivity of g_j varies in different cells. In amphibian blastomeres the sensitivity is comparable to that of the Na channel. In killifish (*Fundulus*) blastomeres the sensitivity is distinctly less (Spray *et al.*, 1984a). In rat cardiac myocytes there is no measurable voltage sensitivity over a range of ± 100 mV (Spray *et al.*, 1984a, Table I, lower left). In amphibian gating the sensitivity is great enough to suggest a switching function. In teleosts the low sensitivity does not carry a clear implication of function; its presence remains unexplained. The absence of voltage sensitivity in cardiac myocytes may mean the conformational change is impossible or that it does not involve a dipole moment change.

IV. VOLTAGE GATING AS A CONTROL MECHANISM

Granted now that we can explain the current clamp results in amphibians, it is reasonable to ask what the gating mechanism does for the animal. These responses have the appearance of action potentials and one might expect that there was a threshold for their initiation. For appropriate levels of current there is in fact a threshold and bistability of coupling, that is, over a particular range the cells can be stably well coupled or stably poorly coupled. One way to observe bistability is by applying a gradually rising and then falling ramp of current (Fig. 10). For low levels of current the cells are coupled. At some value the cells suddenly uncouple. The uncoupling is regenerative in the following way. At threshold current an increase in voltage in cell 1 decreases g_j which decreases the junctional current and the voltage in cell 2. Current through the nonjunctional membrane of cell 1 increases, increasing the voltage in cell 1. Thus, V_j is increased, which further decreases the g_j, and so on around again. The description is analogous to that for any other regenerative response. The cells remain uncoupled as current continues to increase. As current then decreases the cells remain coupled to well below the level at which the cells were previously coupled, because V_j is large enough to keep g_j low. Eventually V_j becomes small and the cells abruptly recouple. This recoupling is also regenerative. Thus, at intermediate levels of current the state of coupling depends on previous history. The cells are well coupled if current has been increased from a low level; the cells are poorly coupled if the current has been decreased from a high level. The bistability of coupling also follows from voltage clamp data (Harris *et al.*, 1983). Calculations of steady-state voltages as a function of current (equivalent to a very slowly rising and falling ramp) shows an intermediate region where

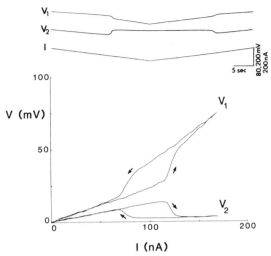

Fig. 10. Effects of a slow ramp of applied current on coupling. A slowly rising and falling current (about 30 seconds in each direction) was applied to cell 1 in order to obtain a quasi steady-state V–I relation. In the upper portion of the figure are the applied current (I) and the resulting voltages in the two cells (V_1 and V_2). In the lower portion of the figure, V_1 and V_2 are plotted as a function of I. As the current increased (arrows indicate direction), the cells rapidly uncoupled at a current level of about 120 nA and remained uncoupled as the ramp continued upward. As the ramp of current decreased from its peak, the cells remained coupled until the current reached a level of about 80 nA, then rapidly recoupled. The observed hysteresis and bistability in the V–I relation follow from the voltage dependence of the junctional conductance and reflect the regenerative nature of the uncoupling and recoupling events. (From Harris *et al.*, 1983.)

cells are either coupled or uncoupled depending on whether current is increasing or decreasing.

Bistability as illustrated occurs only over a range of steadily applied current (between about 80 and 120 nA in Fig. 10). Embryos do not normally develop with microelectrodes in them, so for this phenomenon to have a real function one would need to find another source of current. If one were to make a leak in one of the cells, there would be steady state currents flowing across the junctions driven by the potential difference between the cells. A sufficiently large leak would shift the range of bistability along the current axis to the point where coupling would be bistable in the absence of applied current. Then current of one sign could uncouple the cells, and current of the opposite sign could recouple

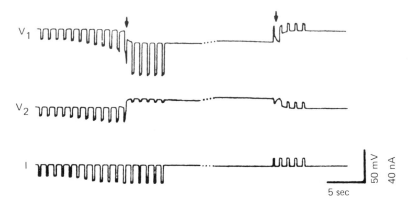

FIG. 11. Bistability of coupling without steadily applied current. Small hyperpolarizing current pulses (I) of increasing amplitude were delivered to cell 1 (V_1); the smaller
pulses show that it was well coupled to cell 2 (V_2). Partial uncoupling occurred during the
pulses as they increased in amplitude. At the termination of one pulse (first arrow) there
was a sudden transition where the cells assumed new steady-state potentials, cell 1
hyperpolarized, and cell 2 depolarized from their previous potentials. At this point they
had shifted to a poorly coupled state (in the absence of externally applied constant
current), as indicated by the stable difference in the resting potentials and by the decreased
coupling during the current pulses following the first arrow. At the second arrow, depolarizing current pulses were applied to cell 1. The first pulse increased junctional
conductance to some extent, but the cells largely uncoupled following the pulse. The
second pulse initiated recoupling, which persisted, indicated by the effects of brief pulses
and by restoration of the original membrane potentials. The dotted line indicates a gap of
100 seconds. (From Harris *et al.*, 1983.)

them. Bistability without application of maintained current is quite easily demonstrated (Fig. 11).

Precise criteria for the presence of bistability can be defined that
involve the two nonjunctional conductances, the junctional conductance, and its voltage sensitivity (Harris *et al.*, 1983). There exist rather
broad optima for efficacy of intercellular signaling, which the properties
of embryonic cells appear to satisfy. Moreover, bistability can be seen
in situ (Spitzer, 1982). However, the real question is whether it serves a
control function. Blackshaw and Warner (1976) have seen sufficiently
large voltage gradients in embryos between lateral ectoderm and presumptive neural tube. There is evidence that this voltage gradient is not
essential for development (Messenger and Warner, 1979), but it has not
been determined whether voltage dependent uncoupling does or does
not occur. The gradient plus voltage dependence could lead to develop-

ment of a sharp boundary of reduced communication between populations of cells that were originally smoothly and continuously coupled. A role of electrical control of communication is unlikely to be universal in embryos, for in other species voltage sensitivity is reduced or absent, and coupling may be so close that transjunctional voltages are kept small.

In proposing a role for voltage dependence of junctional conductance in intercellular communication, one should distinguish between chemical and electrical messages. In amphibian blastomeres electrical uncoupling drastically reduces dye coupling, a rather nice demonstration of the identity of pathways for electrical and dye coupling (Spray *et al.*, 1979). Steady state coupling coefficients for electrical coupling and dye spread can be quite different, although given that channel closure is all or none, permeability is directly proportional to junctional conductance. Another point is that electrical signals may actually be important. Jaffe (1981) has pioneered and championed the idea of currents iontophoretically changing the concentration of substances and affecting development in this manner. Relatively modest potential gradients can move membrane macromolecules along the cell (e.g., McLaughlin and Poo, 1981). Also, it would be rash to conclude that there are no important membrane molecules that are affected by transmembrane potential other than electrically excitable channels. Thus, all this electrophysiology may yet have some developmental significance.

V. Independence of pH and Voltage Gating

Since the amphibian junctions can be closed by either transjunctional voltage or cytoplasmic acidity, one may ask whether there is any relation between the two mechanisms. Two lines of evidence indicate that they are independent. First, when conductance is decreased by cytoplasmic acidification, the voltage dependence of the remaining conductance remains the same (Fig. 12). Thus, if the pH gate is open, the voltage gate continues to operate in the same way; there is no change in its voltage sensitivity as might be expected if it were gradually binding increased numbers of H ions before it finally underwent the conformational change of closure. Second, various agents can block pH sensitivity (or at least shift it out of the range usually tested) without affecting voltage sensitivity. Weak glutaraldehyde (about 10 μM), EEDQ (0.2 mM, Fig. 13, see also Carvalho and Ramon, 1982), and

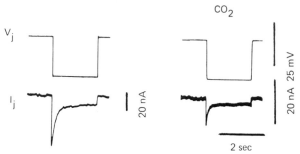

FIG. 12. Independence of pH and voltage gates in pairs of amphibian blastomeres. Junctional currents recorded from a pair of coupled cells during a rectangular step in V_j had an initial peak with an exponential decline to a steady-state value. During exposure to CO_2 (right), peak and steady-state values were reduced to about 25% of their initial (left) and recovery values. The ratio of steady-state to peak conductance and the time course of decrease in conductance were similar in the two conditions, suggesting that the two gates are independent.

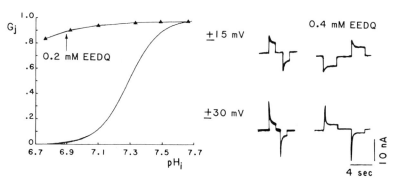

FIG. 13. EEDQ reduces pH dependence of g_j in vertebrate blastomeres but does not affect g_j magnitude or voltage dependence. On the left the normal g_j–pH_i relation (lower line) is plotted with the pH sensitivity after 0.2 mM EEDQ exposure (data from killifish). On the right data are shown from amphibian blastomeres. Currents due to applying rectangular V_js of +15 and +30 mV before and after 0.4 mM EEDQ had similar steady state values of g_j and time constants of decay, showing that voltage dependence was little changed. (From Spray et al., 1984a.)

retinoic acid (0.4 mM) block or reduce pH sensitivity of g_j in vertebrate blastomeres and do not alter its voltage sensitivity in amphibian blastomeres (Spray *et al.*, 1984a). The modes of action of these agents should be different; EEDQ and glutaraldehyde covalently react with amino acid side chains, whereas retinoic acid is lipid soluble and presumably does not covalently bond.

VI. INTERACTION OF pH AND VOLTAGE GATING

While vertebrate gap junctions can have separate voltage and pH gates (or more accurately gating mechanisms), two invertebrate gap junctions are known to have a gating mechanism in which pH and voltage interact. Early squid blastomeres are very closely coupled, and apparently their junctions are V_j insensitive over a range of at least ± 20 mV. The cells are uncoupled by cytoplasmic acidification with a sensitivity probably like that of crayfish septate axon, although not yet quantified. However, when g_j is reduced by cytoplasmic acidification, g_j becomes voltage sensitive and can be increased by transjunctional voltages. The effect can be rather symmetrical wherein either hyperpolarization or depolarization of either cell increases g_j (Fig. 14, voltage clamp data). In other cases the effect is quite asymmetrical and the junctions rectify, hyperpolarization of one cell and depolarization of the other cell increasing g_j substantially while the opposite polarizations have very little effect (Fig. 15, current clamp data). The asymmetry probably results from asymmetrical acidification, because if one injects acid into one cell of a pair, response asymmetry is always observed such that depolarization of the injected cell and hyperpolarization of the other cell increase junctional conductance. The dependence of polarity on side of injection requires two gates in series in order that the acid can preferentially affect the gate on the injected side.

We explain voltage sensitivity found after cytoplasmic acidification as resulting from a dipole moment shift associated with channel closure. Then transjunctional voltage alters the open–closed distribution produced at a given level of acidification. Since acid injected on one side should act on the nearer gate, we know the polarity of voltage sensitivity; transjunctional voltage positive on the channel side tends to open it. In vertebrate blastomeres the data do not determine which gate is closed by a given polarity of voltage.

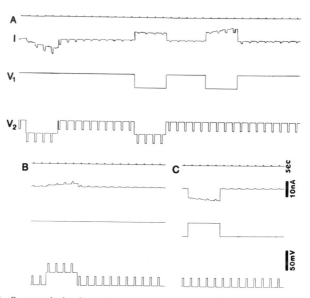

FIG. 14. Symmetrical voltage dependence of g_j in squid blastomeres after cytoplasmic acidification, a dual voltage clamp experiment. Brief test voltage pulses in cell 2 were superimposed on long pulses in either cell 1 or 2. The current trace shows currents in cell 1. (A) When cell 2 was hyperpolarized (first long pulse) the junctional current associated with the long pulse and the currents associated with the brief test pulses increased during the pulse, indicating increase in g_j. When cell 1 was hyperpolarized (third long pulse), the brief pulses show that g_j increased. The current during the long pulse is the sum of junctional and nonjunctional currents; the gradual rise represents change in g_j as indicated by the brief pulses. After the long pulses, g_j declined to its initial value over several seconds. When both cells were hyperpolarized, a smaller increase in g_j, about twofold, was seen (second long pulse). Since V_j was zero, g_j exhibited some dependence on V_{i-o}. (B, C) Depolarizing either cell caused a smaller increase in g_j than equal hyperpolarization of the other cell, again indicating that g_j is not simply dependent on transjunctional voltage. (From Spray et al., 1984a.)

The presence of two gates in series allows for a channel to have four states, both gates open, either gate open and the other closed, and both gates closed (Fig. 16A). In squid blastomeres the voltage-dependent opening presumably represents opening of channels closed on only one side, since the same voltage should tend to close the series gate. If both gates were closed, voltage of a given sign would tend to open only one of the gates while keeping the other closed. Often during cytoplasmic acidification that uncouples cells, the junctions transiently exhibit voltage sensitivity during uncoupling and then become voltage insensitive, and then again transiently exhibit voltage sensitivity during wash out of the acid and recovery of coupling. The voltage-insensitive state may result from doubly closed channels.

By our hypothesis voltage increases g_j by opening channels singly closed on one side, but the same voltage should also close open channels by closing the gate on the other side. Thus, competing processes

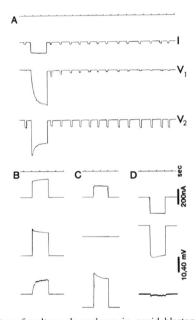

FIG. 15. Asymmetry of voltage dependence in squid blastomeres, a current clamp experiment. Upper trace, marks 1/second; second trace, current; third and fourth traces, voltages in cell 1 and 2, respectively. (A) A hyperpolarizing current in cell 2 caused V_2 to rise to an early peak, then decay somewhat. The decay was probably due to membrane breakdown, as the input conductance measured by the short pulses was decreased immediately after the long pulse. During the pulse V_1 rose slowly to more than 20 mV indicating an increase in g_j. This increase, measured by the brief test pulses, decayed after the hyperpolarization with a time constant of several seconds. (B) A depolarizing current in cell 1 changed V_1 by an amount comparable to the hyperpolarization of cell 2 in (A). However, V_2 increased to only about 10 mV, although the input conductance of cell 2 was less. Thus, the change in g_j was smaller than in (A), although V_j was about the same. (C, D) Polarization in the two cells to produce comparable transjunctional voltages of the opposite sign had little effect on g_j as indicated by the small degree of coupling. In each record the polarized cell is recorded from at the lower gain.

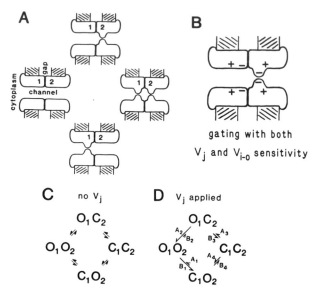

Fig. 16. Diagrams of voltage dependent gating. (A) The four states allowed by having two gates in series. (B) Series gates whose operation causes dipole moment shifts in both V_j and V_{i-o} directions; the gate on the left is open, that on the right is closed. (C) the four states of (A) in the absence of applied potential. Equality of arrows is meant to imply equilibrium, not equality of rates for each reaction. (D) With an applied V_j the rates are altered unequally so as to give a component of counterclockwise cycling around the reaction scheme.

should be present. The conductance increases are in fact a small fraction of the initial conductance at normal pH_i, although they may be many-fold over the reduced g_j produced by cytoplasmic acidification.

Because of instability of the preparation, probably due to drift in pH_i, we do not have voltage clamp measurements over a wide range of potentials. These will in any case be complicated by the presence of series gates. We can say that time constants are slow and that the steady state g_j–V_j relation is concave upward for voltages up to at least 50 mV.

VII. INSIDE–OUTSIDE AND TRANSJUNCTIONAL VOLTAGE GATING

A membrane channel is a two-terminal device; it is affected by the transmembrane potential, i.e., the potential between the inside and outside of the cell. A gap junction is essentially a three-terminal device.

There is a terminal in each cell and one in the extracellular space of the intercellular cleft. Thus, a gap junction might be affected by the potentials between each cell interior and the intercellular cleft as well as by the transjunctional potential. The cleft should be at or close to the bath potential, because $La(OH)_3$ can get into the space (Fig. 1B), and the leakage out between closely coupled cells is very small. (The small leakage follows for closely coupled cells because a leak would limit coupling to a value of $1/(1+n)$ where n is the ratio of leakage conductance to one-half of g_j.) Furthermore, many polar dyes pass freely between cells but do not penetrate from the exterior, implying a private pathway or channel (e.g., Bennett *et al.*, 1978a). Thus, conformational changes can (in principle) be affected by transjunctional voltage and by voltage between the cell interior and the exterior, V_{i-o}. Moreover, a sensor for V_{i-o} may lie within the channel, where V_{i-o} is intermediate between the potentials in the cells. However, by keeping $V_j = 0$ one can investigate dependence on V_{i-o} without this complication.

In squid blastomeres g_j is affected not only by V_j but also by inside–outside voltage V_{i-o}. In Fig. 14A (the second pulse) g_j was increased by a factor of two when both cells were hyperpolarized equally so that V_j was zero. This increase is in contrast to the approximately five-fold increase when either cell was hyperpolarized. Other experiments showed that g_j is decreased when both cells are equally depolarized. The sensitivity to V_{i-o} in squid is less than that to V_j, but its presence explains why the increase in g_j when one cell is depolarized is smaller than when the other cell is hyperpolarized, even though the V_js are the same.

In terms of molecular structure it seems quite reasonable that the conformational change of channel opening involves components in both transjunctional and inside–outside directions. In Fig. 16B the gating mechanism is shown nearer the middle of the channel rather than at the cytoplasmic ends as shown in Fig. 9. One reason for the changed arrangement is to place the gate where it would be more likely to exhibit sensitivity to voltage between channel and intercellular cleft. The dipole, indicated by $+$ and $-$ signs, shifts with respect to both V_j and V_{i-o} when moving between open and closed positions. We are inclined to call this gating mechanism a pH gate, because it is not very voltage sensitive. What it does physiologically is unclear. The voltage sensitivity may well have no physiological role, but only follow from the conformational dipole moment shifts associated with pH gating.

In *Chironomus* salivary gland junctional conductance is strongly dependent on V_{i-o} with hyperpolarization increasing g_j as in squid (Obaid *et al.*, 1983). The effects of voltage on the *Chironomus* cells fit the same kind of dual gating scheme we have proposed for amphibian blastomeres with distribution between open and closed states exponentially dependent on V_{i-o} instead of V_j. This model does not entirely explain the data, for its predictions fail dramatically when transjunctional voltages are applied, in a way that indicates to us that there is a component of V_j sensitivity. (The initial measurements of Obaid *et al.*, 1983, were made by polarizing both cells uniformly and testing with V_j pulses too brief to alter g_j.)

It is unclear how dual V_j and V_{i-o} sensitivity operates. It is not enough to add into the energy equation a term for V_j because with large V_j one should then be able to drive the system to one extreme or the other. Another complication is that a change in V_j also changes at least one V_{i-o} and both, if the V_{i-o} sensors are located at some distance along the channel at which there is a voltage drop from the cytoplasmic value of potential (as would be true of Fig. 16B). The extent to which these possibilities can be disentangled by electrical measurements is unclear.

Although *Chironomus* is quite V_{i-o} sensitive, the same gating mechanisms is affected by pH_i. Acidifying the cytoplasm simply shifts the g_j–V_{i-o} relation along the voltage axis, the gates requiring a more inside negative potential to remain open. A similar shift is obtained by treatments expected to raise intracellular Ca, and the shift is in the opposite direction when intracellular Ca should be lowered. Thus, the *Chironomus* gate may be homologous to the pH gate in squid, but with sufficient voltage sensitivity that this feature may be of physiological significance. In this case nomenclature could become ambiguous. Nonetheless, in the upper right quadrant of Table I we have entered the *Chironomus*, squid, and crayfish gating mechanisms as pH gates that exhibit high-, medium-, and low-voltage sensitivity, respectively. The pH gate of vertebrate blastomeres also appears to have little V sensitivity.

The relative sensitivity to V_{i-o} and V_j varies among junctions in different species. V_{i-o} sensitivity is high in *Chironomus*, moderate in squid, and absent in amphibian blastomeres; V_j sensitivity increases going from *Chironomus* to squid to amphibian blastomeres. (To be sure, we have no reason to suspect that the amphibian gating mechanism is homologous to the invertebrate ones, and have drawn it in different parts of the channel.) To complete Table I we note that the voltage sensitive gate in vertebrates exhibits no pH sensitivity in the range from 6 to 8.

VIII. IMPLICATIONS OF SERIES GATES

Although the asymmetric effect of unicellular acidification provides the best evidence for two gates in series, we had previously formulated the scheme of Fig. 9. As well as symmetry and absence of effect of V_{i-o}, the series gates accounted for the effects of sudden reversal of V_j as illustrated in Fig. 17. In this double-voltage clamp procedure, one cell was given a hyperpolarizing prepulse long enough for g_j to reach its steady-state value and then clamped to 36 mV depolarization. Junctional currents during the depolarizing pulse are shown superimposed in Fig. 17A for hyperpolarizations of 19 and 34 mV and for no prepulse. Following the prepulses the currents did not have a simple exponential time course; instead they rose from their initial value, became larger than the control exponential decay, and then fell back to the same steady-state value.

We modeled these data in two ways, both involving two oppositely oriented series gates that behave in the way indicated by effects of a single polarity of V_j. First, we assumed that each gate responded to the entire V_j independently of whether the series gate was closed (i.e., that the gates operated independently) and that the fraction of open channels was the product of the fractions of each gate that was open. This scheme gave the curves illustrated in Fig. 17C. Second, we assumed that all the voltage drop was across the closed gate and that the V_j sensor in the open series gate saw no voltage until the closed gate opened. Calculations from this scheme of interactive or contingent gating could be made to fit the data very well as shown in Fig. 17B. Not only are these data consistent with two gates in series, but they suggest that the voltage sensor detects local voltage drop in the junctional channel.

There is an interesting extension of this argument. When a channel is closed by one series gate, there is no voltage drop across the other gate, and therefore this open gate can close spontaneously as it occasionally does in the absence of applied voltage. Once it closes the voltage drop across the other gate is reduced and it can open. Then the initially open

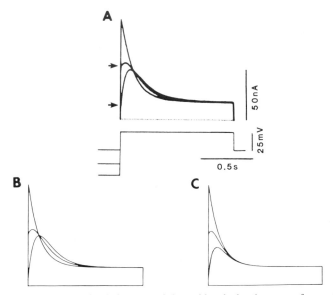

FIG. 17. Comparison of polarity reversal data with calculated currents for contingent and independent gating. (A) The junctional currents (upper trace) during the test pulses are photographically superimposed to allow comparison of the currents flowing when V_j was stepped to the test voltage from zero voltage and from prepulses of the opposite polarity. The initial currents at the onset of the test voltage are indicated by arrows. The prepulses and test voltage are diagrammed on the lower trace. (B) Time courses calculated from the contingent or interactive gating model, which assumes that the gate closed by the prepulse must open before the gate in series with it senses the test pulse. (C) Time courses calculated from the independent gating model, which assumes that each gate responds to V_j independently of the other. The currents in (B) and (C) were calculated for the test voltage and prepulse voltages that produced the junctional currents shown in (A). The form of the data is best reproduced by the contingent gating model. (From Harris *et al.*, 1981.)

gate will rapidly open again followed by reclosure of the initially closed gate. The foregoing chain of events constitutes cycling around the circular reaction scheme of Fig. 16C–D. A more explicit prediction can be made with respect to this figure.

For a V_j tending to drive channels to the C_1O_2 state, transitions on the left are of a gate with the series gate open; these are more voltage sensitive than transitions on the right, which occur with the series gate closed. Larger downward and smaller upward rates occur on the left than on the right, and there is a net movement of gates counterclockwise through the four states.

Viewed alternatively, on the lower left and upper right are transitions of gate 1; the series gate 2 is closed on the upper right and the downward tendency is less than on the lower left where gate 2 is open. Similarly, on the upper left and lower right are transitions of gate 2; the series gate 1 is closed on the right and the downward tendency is less than on the left. Again, counterclockwise cycling is predicted.

Cycling does not violate conservation of energy or microscopic reversibility, for energy is provided by the applied voltage. An analogous scheme for voltage dependent single-membrane channels has been proposed by Finkelstein and Peskin (1984). Cycling of gap junction channels is unlikely to be of great physiological importance. Calculations from parameters for amphibian blastomeres show a relatively small rate, but one that might be detectable in single-channel recordings as a component of the closed and open interval histograms (Bennett and Spray, 1984). Demonstration of cycling would confirm the picture of series gates. What may be more important is the concept that the field distribution can differ around closed and open gates, and a voltage sensor may see quite different voltages depending on whether or not its channel is conducting.

IX. OTHER PHARMACOLOGY

Long chain alcohols as exemplified by octanol block g_j (Fig. 18, see also Johnston et al., 1980). The effect is rapid and reversible. We have not determined whether octanol acts on or through the voltage and pH gating mechanisms or whether a third mechanism is involved. Octanol, like retinoic acid, would not be expected to act on charged groups, but rather to alter the lipid environment of the channels.

Horizontal cells of the vertebrate retina are electrotonically coupled, which mediates center surround interactions. It has now been found that the degree of coupling is affected by dopamine; evidently by increasing cytoplasmic cAMP, g_j is decreased (Piccolino et al., 1984; Teranishi et al., 1984). This is apparently a proper synaptic response and one that admits gap junctions fully to the company of modifiable synapses. The effect is opposite to that produced by cAMP in a number of cultured cell systems where g_j is increased (Flagg-Newton et al., 1981, Kessler, et

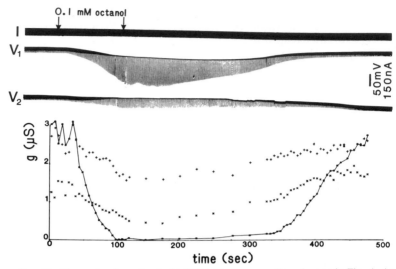

Fig. 18. Uncoupling by octanol of killifish blastomeres. Procedure as in Fig. 4. An octanol solution was applied between arrows. The cells rapidly uncoupled, then recoupled as the octanol was washed away. The graph in the lower part of the figure shows g_j (connected symbols) and nonjunctional conductances (pluses and crosses) computed from input and transfer resistances. The variation in g_j at early times is due to measurement error arising from very close coupling of the cells. (From Spray *et al.*, 1984a.)

al., 1984). In these latter cases the changes are slow enough to be produced by new formation of junctions (see below).

X. Self Recognition

Gap junctions form or go away and these processes are under cellular control. One hypothesis of formation is that hemichannels floating in each membrane meet, recognize, and join up with their partners to form a patent channel. There is no evidence that a hemichannel can be open, and treatment with low Ca solutions, which splits junctions between the apposed membranes in at least one tissue (Hirokawa and Heuser, 1982), closes the hemichannels in fish blastomeres (unpublished). If this picture is correct then self-recognition provides an additional form of chemically controlled gating by gap junction macromolecules. Another form of self-recognition is the interaction of cell adhesion molecules, which presumably does not result in channels (Edelman, 1983).

If gap junctions form in this manner, one might expect to see single-particle junctions in freeze fracture preparations. While gap junctions are recognizable as aggregates of particles, they also exhibit a narrowing of the intercellular cleft. We have observed in squid blastomeres single particles of the same size as those in gap junctional aggregates associated with a narrowing of the cleft as indicated by an elevation in the P face (Fig. 19B). Corresponding E face pits in membrane depressions are also observed (Fig. 19C). Fortuitous cross fractures show

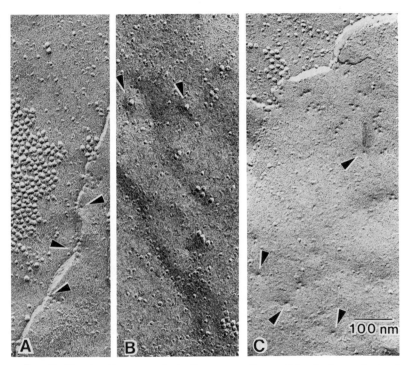

Fɪɢ. 19. Gap junctions comprised of one or a few particles in freeze fractured blastomeres of squid. (A) A fracture crossing from P to E faces (left to right) shows narrowing of the intercellular space where only a few particles or pits are present (arrowheads). A large particle aggregate to the left is unequivocally a gap junction. (B) Single P face particles like those of gap junctional aggregates occur on small elevations of the membrane indicating narrowing of the intercellular cleft (arrowheads). Other aggregates of two to four particles also occur on elevations. (C) E face pits near a P face gap junctional aggregate (upper left) occur in small depressions, again suggesting narrowing of the intercellular cleft (arrowheads). Methods in Ginzberg *et al.* (1984). A–C at same magnification.

narrowing of the intercellular cleft where there are only a few particles or pits typical of gap junctions (Fig. 19A). The aggregation of particles may be a subsequent step that could result simply from reduction in the amount of membrane that would have to be pushed close together into an otherwise unfavorable energetic situation. The commonness of apparent single-particle junctions in squid may result from a high formation rate in this rapidly dividing tissue. With slower formation most single particles might aggregate before being observed, or formation might occur at the edge of a junction where the cleft was already narrowed.

It is beyond the scope of this article to consider formation and removal of junctions. It is certainly possible that junction closure by one or more of the gating mechanisms described here is a necessary precursor or even a signal for slower processes of removal and degradation (e.g., Hanna et al., 1984). However, gap junctions can form between killifish blastomeres at low pH_i where there is no coupling (unpublished).

XI. Relation to Other Channels

This article shows that the gap junction macromolecule is not as inflexible as we thought, but has different control mechanisms, a general and a comparative physiology, and a growing pharmacology. In this respect gap junctions are developing complex personalities, as are ordinary excitable channels. For example, the Na channel, a classical voltage dependent channel, exhibits different voltage sensitivities in different tissues and can be caused to open or close by specific toxins or chemical agents, i.e., it has ligand binding regions (cf. Catterall, 1984). Other voltage-sensitive channels are modulated by intracellular messengers, i.e., chemical transmitters (Tsien and Siegelbaum, 1983). On the other hand, classical chemically activated channels can exhibit some degree of voltage sensitivity (Neher and Stevens 1977), and the old dichotomy of chemically and electrically excitable channels is no longer supportable.

The chemical modification of electrically excitable channels has an obvious role in modulation of cell behavior. Similarly, biological toxins that act on specific aspects of channel function represent a gating mechanism reflecting channel structure, even if it is a perversion of normal function. As a macromolecule will generally change its dipole moment when it undergoes a conformational change, so will a channel classified as chemically sensitive by virtue of its response to low levels of a transmitter generally exhibit a dipole moment change after binding of its ligand. Thus, some voltage sensitivity will be conferred on the process.

XII. Conclusions and Summary

The knowledge of gating mechanisms may help in elucidating how cells control their junctions. Also, by finding a spectrum of treatments that block coupling we may find out more about what gap junctions do. Specificity of block may not be obtainable, but a common effect of agents with different modes of blocking gap junctions would suggest that blocking the junctions was the proximate cause. The pharmacology and the use of group specific reagents may also tell us about the structure of gap junctions and the nature of active sites, work that should interact in a mutually facilitatory way with structural analysis.

The gap junction is a morphological entity with a clear physiological action allowing flow of small molecules between coupled cells. A number of ways of turning off the channels have recently been found. The properties, instead of being fixed, are modifiable; gap junctions have responsiveness that suggests a number of physiological and pathophysiological roles. This responsiveness is also allowing probes of active sites and should help in validating proposed physiological functions. The slow changes of formation and disappearance are as yet of unknown mechanism; exploration of cellular controls of these process may, or may not, follow from our studies of the more rapid gating processes.

Not all gap junctions have the same responsiveness, as revealed by the growing physiology and pharmacology. Homologies of different kinds in different and also the same species seem reasonable, and one anticipates that relatively minor changes in protein structure will account for the manifest differences. There is a long way to go, but one can see some light at the end of the channel.

Acknowledgments

These studies were supported in part by NS-07512, NS-12627, HD-04248 (to MVLB), NS-16524, and NS-19830 (to DCS), a Fogarty Fellowship (to ACC), and a McKnight Foundation Development Award (to DCS).

References

Auerbach, A. A., and Bennett, M. V. L. (1969). *J. Gen. Physiol.* **53,** 211–237.

Bennett, M. V. L. (1977). *Hanb. Physiol.* **1,** 357–416.

Bennett, M. V. L., and Goodenough, D. A. (1978). *Neurosci. Res. Program Bull.* **16,** 373–486.

Bennett, M. V. L., and Pappas, G. D. (1983). *J. Neurosci.* **3,** 748–761.

Bennett, M. V. L., and Spray, D. C. (1984). *Biophys. J.* **45,** 60a.

Bennett, M. V. L., Spira, M. E., and Spray, D. C. (1978a). *Dev. Biol.* **65,** 114–125.

Bennett, M. V. L., Brown, J. E., Harris, A. L., and Spray, D. C. (1978b). *Biol. Bull.* **155,** 428–429.

Bennett, M. V. L., Spray, D. C., and Harris, A. L. (1981). *Am. Zool.* **21,** 413–427.

Blackshaw, S. E., and Warner, A. E. (1976). *J. Physiol. (London)* **255,** 231–247.

Campos de Carvalho, A., Spray, D. C., and Bennett, M. V. L. (1984). *Brain Res.,* in press.

Carew, T. J., and Kandel, E. R. (1976). *Science* **192,** 150–153.

Carvalho, A., and Ramon, F. (1982). *Biophys. J.* **37,** 287a (Abstr.).

Catterall, W. A. (1984). *Science* **223,** 653–661.

Dahl, G., and Isenberg, G. (1980). *J. Membr. Biol.* **53,** 63–75.

Edelman, G. M. (1983). *Science* **219,** 450–457.

Finkelstein, A., and Peskin, C. S. (1984). *Biophys. J.* submitted.

Flagg-Newton, J. L., Dahl, G., and Loewenstein, W. R. (1981). *J. Membr. Biol.* **63,** 105–121.

Furshpan, E. J., and Potter, D. D. (1959). *J. Physiol. (London).* **145,** 289–325.

Ginzberg, R. D., Morales, E., Spray, D. C., and Bennett, M. V. L. (1984). *Cell Tissue Res.* Submitted.

Hanna, R. B., Pappas, G. D., and Bennett, M. V. L. (1984). *Cell Tissue Res.* **235,** 243–249.

Harris, A. L., Spray, D. C., and Bennett, M. V. L. (1981). *J. Gen. Physiol.* **77,** 95–117.

Harris, A. L., Spray, D. C., and Bennett, M. V. L. (1983). *J. Neurosci.* **3,** 79–100.

Hirokawa, N., and Heuser, J. (1982). *Cell* **30,** 395–406.

Hodgkin, A. L., and Huxley, A. F. (1952). *J. Physiol. (London)* **117,** 500–544.

Jaffe, L. F. (1981). *Philos. Trans. R. Soc. London, Ser. B* **295,** 553–566.

Johnston, M. F., Simon, S. A., and Ramon, F. (1980). *Nature (London)* **286,** 498–500.

Kessler, J. A., Spray, D. C., Saez, J. C., and Bennett, M. V. L. (1984). *Proc. Natl. Acad. Sci. U.S.A.,* in press.

Llinas, R., Baker, R., and Sotelo, C. (1974). *J. Neurophysiol.* **37,** 560–571.

McLaughlin S., and Poo, M. (1981). *Biophys. J.* **34,** 85–93.

Makowski, L., Caspar, D. L. D., Phillips, W. C., and Goodenough, D. A. (1977). *J. Cell Biol.* **74,** 629–645.

Messenger, E. A., and Warner, A. E. (1979). *J. Physiol. (London)* **292,** 85–105.

Neher, E., and Stevens, C. F. (1977). *Annu. Rev. Biophys. Bioeng.* **6,** 345–372.

Obaid, A. L., Socolar, S. J., and Rose, B. (1983). *J. Membr. Biol.* **73,** 69–89.

Oliveira-Castro, G. M., and Loewenstein, W. R. (1971). *J. Membr. Biol.* **5,** 51–57.

Piccolino, M., Neyton, J., and Gerschenfeld, H. M. (1984). *J. Neurosci.* in press.

Rae, J., Thompson, R. D., and Eisenberg, R. S. (1982). *Exp. Eye Res.* **35,** 597–609.

Rink, T. J., Tsien, R. Y., and Warner, A. E. (1980). *Nature (London)* **283**, 658–660.

Rose, B., and Loewenstein, W. R. (1975). *Nature (London)* **254**, 250–252.

Schuetze, S. M., and Goodenough, D. A. (1982). *J. Cell Biol.* **92**, 694–705.

Spira, M. E., and Bennett M. V. L. (1972). *Brain Res.* **37**, 294–300.

Spira, M. E., Spray, D. C., and Bennett, M. V. L. (1976). *Science* **194**, 1065–1076.

Spira, M. E., Spray, D. C., and Bennett, M. V. L. (1980). *Brain Res.* **195**, 241–269.

Spitzer, N. C. (1982). *J. Physiol. (London)* **330**, 145–162.

Spray, D. C., Harris, A. L., and Bennett, M. V. L. (1979). *Science* **204**, 432–434.

Spray, D. C., Harris, A. L., and Bennett, M. V. L. (1981a). *Science* **211**, 712–715.

Spray, D. C., Harris, A. L., and Bennett, M. V. L. (1981b). *J. Gen. Physiol.* **77**, 77–93.

Spray, D. C., Stern, J. H., Harris, A. L., and Bennett, M. V. L. (1982a). *Proc. Natl. Acad. Sci. U.S.A.* **79**, 441–445.

Spray, D. C., Harris, A. L., and Bennett, M. V. L. (1982b). *In* "Intracellular pH" (R. Nucitelli and D. Deamer, eds.), pp. 445–461. Liss, New York.

Spray, D. C., White, R. L., Campo de Carvalho, A., Harris, A. L., and Bennett, M. V. L. (1984a). *Biophys. J.* **45**, 219–230.

Spray, D. C., Nerbonne, J., Campos de Carvalho, A., Harris A. L., and Bennett, M. V. L. (1984b). *J. Cell Biol.* **99**, 174–179.

Teranishi, T., Negishi, K., and Sato, S. (1984). *J. Neurosci.* **4**, 1271–1280.

Tsien, R. W., and Siegelbaum, S. A. (1983). *Trends Neurosci.* **6**, 307–310.

Turin, L., and Warner, A. E. (1980). *J. Physiol. (London)* **300**, 489–504.

IMMUNOPROPHYLAXIS OF MALARIA: CHARACTERIZATION OF A PROTECTIVE SURFACE ANTIGEN*

RUTH S. NUSSENZWEIG AND VICTOR NUSSENZWEIG

Departments of Microbiology and Pathology
New York University School of Medicine
New York, New York

CONTRARY to what is believed by many people who live in developed countries, malaria continues to be a disease of exceptionally high incidence. It is number one among the severe parasitic diseases, and although the exact number of individuals affected is unknown, estimates vary from 200 to 400 million.

In certain areas, particularly in tropical Africa, malaria contributes greatly to the very high mortality rates among young children. Although the exact figure is unknown, a frequently quoted estimate from the World Health Organization is that in Africa alone, 1 million children below 5 years of age die of malaria each year. For those individuals who reach adulthood, and who acquire a variable degree of resistance, malaria is still a debilitating disease, and incapacitates those afflicted for long periods. The impact of malaria on the health of communities of less developed countries is enormous. For example, in Ghana it has been recently estimated (Nimo *et al.*, 1981) that about 33 days per year per individual are lost due to malaria, as compared to 5.1 days lost due to hypertension, or 3.8 days lost due to cancer (Table I).

General measures of sanitation, combined with the widespread use of residual insecticides and chemotherapeutic agents, have reduced the incidence of malaria. In fact, in some parts of the world, such as the United States, transmission of malaria has been eliminated. Nevertheless, the disease continues to plague the populations of most tropical and subtropical regions. The distribution of malaria is strikingly illustrated in the poster distributed by the British Department of Health (Fig. 1). Looking at this poster we felt that, considering all the infected

*Lecture delivered October 21, 1982.

TABLE I

Diseases in Ghana, Ranked in Order of Healthy Days
of Life Lost[a]

Rank order	Disease	Days of healthy life lost per person per year
1	Malaria	32.6
8	Accidents	11.9
17	Hypertension	5.1
25	Schistosomiasis	4.4
27	Cancer	3.8

[a] Adapted from Nimo et al. (1981).

mosquitoes produced and processed in our laboratories, a little mosquito dot should also have been placed over the New York area.

The records show that in many countries the beneficial results derived from control measures have proven to be either short-lived, difficult to sustain, or only marginally effective. The persistence of malaria has greatly disappointed health administrators who had forecast its eradication. The reasons for this failure are multiple: the enormity of the task, in view of the broad distribution of the disease, the lack of adequate resources, the appearance of drug-resistant parasites and insecticide-resistant vectors, and the emergence of silvatic mosquitoes, difficult, if not impossible, to exterminate.

This situation gives a sense of urgency to attempts to develop new control measures. In spite of the foreseeable difficulties both in development and delivery, a vaccine may provide a powerful tool for malaria control.

The rationale for development of malaria vaccines is based largely on the life cycle of malaria parasites, represented schematically in Fig. 2.

Sporozoites are present in the salivary glands of mosquitoes. Infection is initiated by the bite of the mosquitoes and injection of sporozoites into the circulation of the host. A few minutes thereafter, as was recently shown by Shin and Vanderberg (1983), some sporozoites have already entered hepatocytes. There they undergo rapid multiplication, so that one sporozoite gives rise to thousands of merozoites upon rupture of the hepatocyte. Free in the circulation, the merozoites invade red blood cells and differentiate in one of two directions: either into

Fig. 1. Distribution of malaria according to a poster distributed by the U.K. Department of Health.

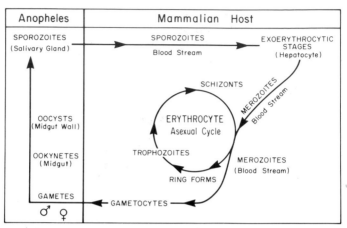

FIG. 2. Schematic representation of the life cycle of the malaria parasite. The possible targets of a vaccine in the mammalian host are those stages of the parasite which are free in the plasma; that is, sporozoites and merozoites. Gametocytes leave the red cell in the gut of mosquitoes, where they can also be attacked by antibodies.

asexual stages, which multiply in red cells, or into gametocytes. After the gametocytes are taken up by mosquitoes, the sexual cycle takes place. Following fertilization, the zygotes penetrate the epithelial cells of the gut of the mosquito and transform into oocysts. This is followed by a series of schizogoniclike divisions and the development of thousands of threadlike sporozoites. The latter become free in the hemocoele, and migrate to the salivary glands where they mature into the infective forms.

The preferential sources of antigens for vaccines correspond to the three extracellular stages which can be targets of the immune response; that is, sporozoites, merozoites, and gametocytes after they leave the erythrocytes in the stomachs of mosquitoes.

In this article we shall discuss only the rationale for the development of a vaccine based on the use of sporozoites which, if successful, would interrupt all parasite development and disease. Studies on vaccination against blood stages or sexual forms are reviewed elsewhere (Cohen, 1982). First, we will summarize the original findings on protective immunity induced by the inoculation of live attenuated parasites in rodents and primates. This will be followed by a discussion of the nature and properties of the protective antigens, and of the recent evidence indicating that they are part of a family of proteins present on the membranes of sporozoites of all the different species of malaria parasites. Finally, we will show that these antigens have a single immunodominant region containing a repetitive epitope.

Immunization with sporozoites was first undertaken by Mulligan and collaborators (1941), using an avian malaria system. They injected birds with ultraviolet-irradiated sporozoites, and obtained a substantial degree of protection against an otherwise lethal malaria infection. They also made the important observation that immunity was stage specific; that is, it conferred protection against challenge with sporozoites, but not with blood stages. Mulligan's findings were ignored for over 20 years, perhaps because they were in direct conflict with the widely accepted dogma that sporozoites could not induce an effective immune response since they were present in blood only transiently, and the dose inoculated during the bite of mosquitoes was small.

Experimental evidence proved that this view was incorrect. Sporozoites are presently known to be highly immunogenic. Intravenous injection of small numbers of these parasites in rodents and monkeys induces a very effective antibody response (Nussenzweig et al., 1967; Chen, 1974; Chen et al., 1976). One of our colleagues at New York University, Dr. Nardin, recently showed that over 90% of adults living in The Gambia, West Africa, in an area of high malaria endemicity, had detectable levels of antisporozoite antibodies (Nardin et al., 1979b).

Two studies by investigators from the Division of Parasitology at New York University paved the way for our studies on sporozoite-induced immunity in mammals. The late Professor Meir Yoeli demonstrated that *Plasmodium berghei,* a rodent malaria parasite, could be used as a bona fide experimental model for human malaria (Yoeli et al., 1966). This was accompanied by studies on the cyclical transmission of this parasite in the laboratory, which made it feasible to obtain large numbers of sporozoite-bearing mosquitoes on a predictable basis (Yoeli et al., 1965.).

Using this experimental model, we dissected salivary glands of *Anopheles stephensi* mosquitoes, obtained sporozoites of *P. berghei,* subjected the sporozoites to γ-radiation, and immunized mice by repeated intravenous inoculation. A large proportion of the vaccinated mice developed protective immunity. As shown in Table II, 84% of the mice

TABLE II

PROTECTION PRODUCED IN MICE
BY MULTIPLE INJECTIONS OF 5×10^3
X-IRRADIATED SPOROZOITES OF *P. berghei*[a]

	Number of animals	Number of deaths
Vaccinated	147	23 (15.6%)
Controls	149	145 (97.3%)

[a] Adapted from Nussenzweig *et al.* (1969a).

survived, and they did not develop parasitemia, while 97.1% of the controls died (Nussenzweig *et al.*, 1967, 1969a). Mice could also be vaccinated by immunization with viable sporozoites if a curative chemophylactic regimen was instituted soon after challenge (Orjih *et al.*, 1982).

We then determined the basic characteristics of sporozoite-induced immunity in rodents. Protection is stage specific: sporozoite-immunized mice, protected against sporozoite challenge, are fully susceptible to inoculation of blood stages of the same parasite strain (Nussenzweig *et al.*, 1969b). The protection, in most instances, is species specific. Immunization with sporozoites of one malaria species does not generally confer protection against infection with sporozoites of other malaria parasites. This has been shown in human (Clyde *et al.*, 1973a, 1975) and monkey (R. W. Gwadz, unpublished observation) malarias. Immunization of mice with *P. berghei* protects them against challenge with sporozoites of some but not all rodent malaria species or subspecies (Nussenzweig *et al.*, 1972b; N. Yoshida and R. S. Nussenzweig, unpublished observations).

The most effective routes of immunization are intravenous innoculation and the bite of infected, irradiated mosquitoes. In vaccinated mice, sporozoites are cleared more rapidly from the peripheral blood than in normal mice (Nussenzweig *et al.*, 1972a). Immunization does not require adjuvants (Nussenzweig *et al.*, 1967; Spitalny and Nussenzweig, 1972; Clyde *et al.*, 1973b; Chen, 1974; Gwadz *et al.*, 1979). Although the protection obtained under these conditions is brief, lasting approximately 3 months, immunity can be boosted by the repeated bite of infected mosquitoes. Using this procedure, we were able to maintain mice resistant to *P. berghei* challenge for more than 1 year. In endemic areas the repeated bites of mosquitoes and periodic injection of malaria sporozoites probably have a similar effect, namely, to increase resistance to infection. Also of interest is the observation that sporozoite-immunized adult female mice transfer their immunity to their litters. The offspring acquire antisporozoite antibodies from their mothers through the milk (Orjih *et al.*, 1981). The congenital transfer of antibodies against *Plasmodium falciparum* sporozoites was also detected in infants in Gambia (Nardin *et al.*, 1981).

Some of the antibodies produced in the course of immunization are directed against the outer sporozoite membrane. Incubation of viable sporozoites with the serum of vaccinated mice results in the appearance of prominent deposits on the surface of the parasite, and a taillike precipitate which increases in size with time of incubation (Fig. 3). This was designated as the circumsporozoite precipitation or CSP reaction (Vanderberg *et al.*, 1969; Cochrane *et al.*, 1976). More important, antisporozoite antibodies have neutralizing activity. Sporozoites incubated with the sera of immunized, protected animals lose their infectivity (Nussenzweig *et al.*, 1969a).

All these findings in rodent malaria were confirmed in other systems. Immunization of monkeys with irradiated sporozoites of *Plasmodium knowlesi* and *Plasmodium cynomolgi* resulted in complete protection of several of these animals (Chen, 1974; Gwadz *et al.*, 1979). A small number of human volunteers has been successfully vaccinated by the repeated bite of *P. falciparum-* and *Plasmodium vivax*-infected, irradiated mosquitoes (Clyde *et al.*, 1973a,b; Rieckmann *et al.*, 1979). Incubation of viable, homologous sporozoites with serum of vaccinated and protected humans and monkeys resulted in CSP reaction. Of interest and relevance for vaccine development was the finding that immunization with one isolate of the parasite induced protection against challenge with sporozoites of different isolates of the same parasite species.

In view of these encouraging results it seemed worthwhile to try to identify the protective antigens. Some observations provided important clues about their nature and anatomical localization. The serum of protected animals bound to the membrane of the parasites, and mediated

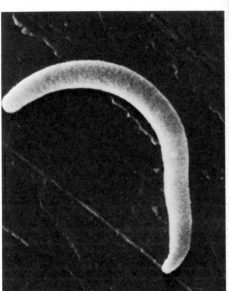
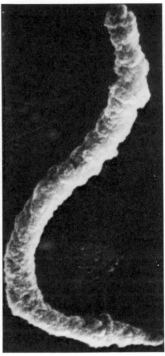

FIG. 3. Scanning electron micrographs showing the alterations of sporozoites follow-ing incubation with serum from animals vaccinated with X-irradiated sporozoites. (Left): sporozoites incubated in normal serum. Note that the surface is smooth. The anterior end of the sporozoite is narrow and can be clearly distinguished from the rounder posterior end. (Right): sporozoites incubated in immune serum. The whole surface of the parasite appears rough, and a taillike precipitate with irregular surface extends a considerable distance posteriorly. This is called the circumsporozoite (CSP) reaction. (Photographed by M. Aikawa.)

the CSP reaction, which had the same characteristics as protective im-munity; that is, it was also stage and species specific, but not strain specific (Vanderberg *et al.*, 1969; Nardin and Nussenzweig, 1978; Nar-din *et al.*, 1979a). Sporozoites incubated in immune serum lost their infectivity. Taken together, these findings suggested that protective immunity was at least in part antibody mediated, and that the protective antigens, and the antigens involved in the CSP reaction, were identical.

For these reasons, we focused our attention on the membrane of the parasite. Viable *P. berghei* sporozoites were labeled by lactoperoxidase-catalyzed radioiodination. The extracts of the radiolabeled membranes were immunoprecipitated with sera from vaccinated mice. To our delight, a single labeled antigen reacted with pools of polyclonal antisera (Gwadz et al., 1979).

Next, monoclonal antibodies against P. berghei were produced. Mice were immunized by a nonorthodox procedure, that is, by repeated bites of infected mosquitoes (Vanderberg et al., 1970). In this way, we minimized the exposure of the mice to irrelevant antigens which contaminate sporozoites isolated from dissected salivary glands of mosquitoes. To prevent infection of the mice with malaria, the mosquitoes were X irradiated. The spleen cells of these mice were fused with a plasmacytoma using the technique of Kohler and Milstein (1975). The culture supernatants of the resulting hybridomas were screened to select those containing monoclonal antibodies directed against surface antigens of sporozoites. One monoclonal antibody (Fig. 4) immunoprecipitated precisely the same antigen as the serum of immune mice (Fig. 4), that is, a protein of M_r 44,000, which we designated Pb44 (Yoshida et al., 1980).

Dr. Yoshida and Dr. Potocnjak studied the neutralizing properties of this monoclonal antibody. In the experiment summarized in Table III, groups of mice received intravenous injections of different amounts of antibody and were challenged a few minutes later with 10^3 sporozoites. Most animals which received as little as 10 μg of antibody were protected. When infection occurred, the prepatent period was prolonged. The effect of the antibody was species specific. It did not neutralize sporozoites of Plasmodium yoeli nigeriensis, or react in vitro with sporozoites of primate or human malaria parasites.

The neutralizing activity of the antibody in vivo could have been mediated either directly through its interaction with the antigen, or could have resulted from secondary effects of the antigen–antibody reaction, such as complement fixation or phagocytosis of the parasite. To clarify this important point, monovalent (Fab) fragments of the antibodies were prepared, incubated with the parasite in vitro and the mixture injected into mice. As seen in Table IV, the Fab fragments were as effective as whole antibodies in the neutralization of sporozoites. Therefore, it appears that the primary reaction between Pb44 and antibody prevented further development of the parasite (Potocnjak et al., 1981).

Aikawa et al. (1981), at Case Western Reserve University, used the

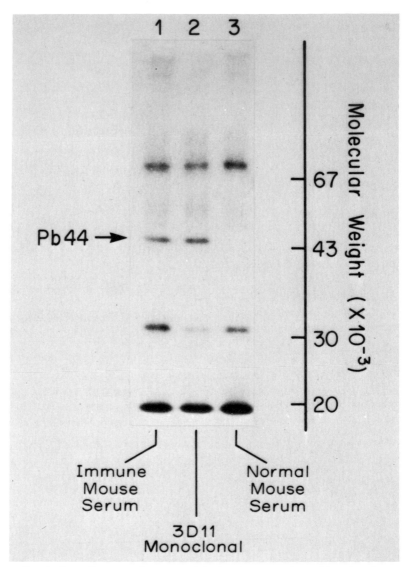

FIG. 4. Autoradiograms of extracts of *P. berghei* sporozoites subjected to immunoprecipitation and electrophoresis on SDS-polyacrylamide gels. Sporozoites were purified from salivary glands and radiolabeled with ^{125}I by the lactoperoxidase method. The extracts were immunoprecipitated with polyclonal antiserum from mice immunized by the bite of X-irradiated infected mosquitoes (Track 1), with the culture supernatants of a hybridoma (3D11) (Track 2), and with a normal mouse serum (Track 3). The same band of M_r 44,000 was specifically immunoprecipitated by 3D11 or by the polyclonal antiserum.

TABLE III

RESISTANCE OF MICE TO INFECTION WITH 10^3
P. berghei SPOROZOITES AFTER TREATMENT
WITH MONOCLONAL ANTIBODIES TO Pb44[a]

Dose of antibodies (μg/mouse)	Number infected/ number injected	Prepatent period (days ± SE)
300	0/5	—
100	0/5	—
50	1/5	7.0
25	1/5	6.0
10	0/5	—
None	5/5	5.2 ± 0.4

[a] Adapted from Potocnjak *et al.* (1981).

monoclonal antibody coupled to ferritin to localize Pb44 in the various developmental stages of the parasite. Pb44 is absent in blood stages and expressed in mature salivary gland sporozoites, where it is distributed uniformly over their entire surface membrane (Fig. 5). In contrast, in about half of the sporozoites from oocysts Pb44 is absent, and in the other half, Pb44 is found in few membrane patches. These observations provide an explanation for the failure of attempts to vaccinate mice with X-irradiated immature sporozoites from oocysts (Vanderberg, 1975) and show that Pb44 is indeed a stage-specific antigen whose function

TABLE IV

NEUTRALIZATION OF *P. berghei*
BY Fab FRAGMENTS OF MONOCLONAL ANTIBODY 3D11[a]

Sporozoites	Fab (μg/ml)	Number of mice infected/mice injected
P. berghei	1200	0/15
	240	0/15
	48	0/9
	24	5/5
	—	5/5
P. yoelii nigeriensis	1200	5/5
	—	5/5

[a] Adapted from Potocnjak *et al.* (1981).

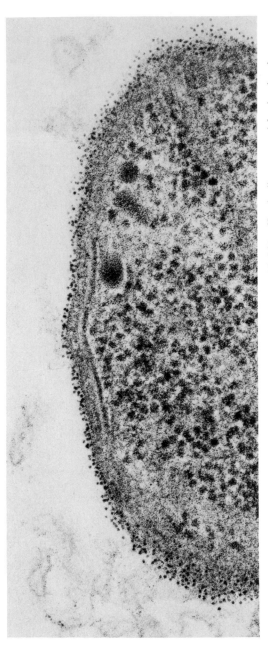

Fig. 5. End views of regular, idealized helical skeletal diagrams of Z-DNA and B-DNA. Heavier lines are used for the phosphate–sugar backbone. A guanine–cytosine base pair is shown by shading and the difference in the positions of the base pairs is quite striking; they are near the center of B-DNA but at the periphery of Z-DNA.

must be associated with the activities of mature salivary gland sporozoites.

An experiment performed by Dr. Potocnjak and Dr. Yoshida directly showed that the CSP reaction is mediated by the cross-linking of Pb44 by antibody. They compared the efficiency of Fab fragments and native monoclonal antibodies to mediate the CSP reaction. As shown in Table V, the minimal amount of intact antibodies necessary to give a CSP reaction is 12 μg/ml. In contrast, when living *P. berghei* sporozoites were incubated with 1500 μg/ml of Fab fragments of monoclonal antibody, no CSP reaction was observed. Addition of rabbit antibodies to mouse immunoglobulin restored the bivalency of the Fab fragments, and resulted in strong CSP reactions even when the concentration of Fab was as low as 2 μg/ml (Potocnjak *et al.*, 1981).

In short, a single monoclonal antibody displayed all properties of polyclonal antisera obtained from animals vaccinated with whole sporozoites. It identified a stage- and species-specific membrane antigen which is shed by the parasite when appropriately cross-linked. As will be documented later, the sporozoites of several other malaria parasites have proteins on their membranes which have similar characteristics; we named these circumsporozoite or CS proteins.

These findings raised the possibility of developing vaccines against malaria using purified CS proteins. The source of antigen posed a serious problem, however, since sporozoites can only be obtained from salivary glands of infected mosquitoes. To overcome this difficulty and to obtain large amounts of CS proteins, there are two possible ap-

TABLE V

CSP REACTIONS ARE A RESULT
OF THE CROSS-LINKING OF PB44[a]

Treatment of sporozoites	Minimal concentration of 3D11 for CSP reaction (μg/ml)
IgG alone	12
Fab alone	>1500
Fab + rabbit antimouse IgG	2

[a] Adapted from Potocnjak *et al.* (1981).

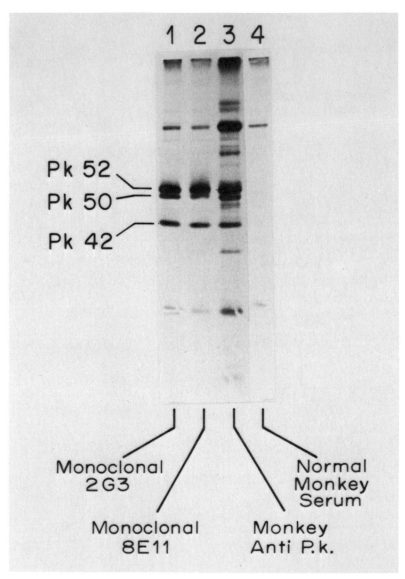

Fig. 6. Autoradiograms of extracts of *P. knowlesi* subjected to immunoprecipitation and electrophoresis on SDS-polyacrylamide gels. The purified sporozoites were labeled metabolically with [^{35}S]methionine. The extracts were immunoprecipitated with two monoclonal antibodies, 2G3 (Track 1), 8E11 (Track 2), with a polyclonal antiserum from a monkey immunized with X-irradiated sporozoites (Track 3), and with serum from a normal monkey (Track 4). The same three proteins with M_r 52,000, 50,000, and 42,000

proaches: genetic engineering, and/or synthesis of the portion of the molecule which contains the relevant epitopes. Fortunately, as shown below, both approaches may be feasible in this system.

Prior to applying recombinant DNA technology, we studied the biosynthesis of CS proteins in sporozoites of several malarial species (Yoshida *et al.*, 1981; Cochrane *et al.*, 1982; Nardin *et al.*, 1982). We illustrate here the results obtained by Dr. Cochrane using *P. knowlesi* sporozoites.

Sporozoites were maintained viable *in vitro* for several hours in the presence of radiolabeled methionine. Immunoprecipitation of parasite extracts with several monoclonal antibodies to the *P. knowlesi* CS protein revealed three identical specific bands, a doublet of M_r 52,000 (Pk52) and 50,000 (Pk50) and a third band of M_r 42,000 (Pk42). The same antigens were recognized by the serum of a rhesus monkey immunized with and protected against *P. knowlesi* sporozoites (Fig. 6). The results of pulse-chase experiments showed that the proteins with larger M_r (Pk52 and Pk50) are precursors of Pk42. Mild trypsinization of the intact parasite before extraction and immunoprecipitation resulted in deletion of the band of M_r 42,000 (Fig. 7), suggesting that Pk42 is located on the surface of the parasite (Cochrane *et al.*, 1982).

This type of experiment showed something of greater significance; that in mature, salivary gland sporozoites of several species of malaria parasites, between 5 and 15% of the labeled methionine incorporated into protein is found in the CS proteins. In other words, in this stage of development of malaria parasites, a large part of the biosynthetic machinery for making proteins is committed to the manufacture of a single surface polypeptide, the CS protein. These results suggested not only that CS proteins were important for the survival of the parasite in the host, but also that the corresponding mRNA would be present in large amounts.

This observation encouraged Dr. Nigel Godson and his students Joan Ellis and Luiz Ozaki to start cloning the genes of CS proteins, although the supply of sporozoites was very limited, since they had to be obtained from the salivary glands of individual mosquitoes. Using mRNA

---

were specifically immunoprecipitated. The polyclonal antiserum immunoprecipitated a few other polypeptides which could have originated from sporozoites or from contaminating microorganisms present in the preparation of the salivary gland sporozoites.

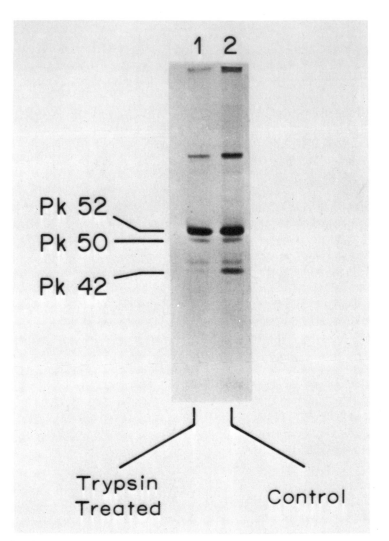

Fɪɢ. 7. Autoradiograms of extracts of *P. knowlesi* subjected to immunoprecipitation and electrophoresis in SDS-polyacrylamide gels. One sample of parasites was incubated with TPCK-trypsin at a concentration of 200 μg/ml for 5 minutes at 37°C. Then the trypsin-treated and untreated samples were extracted and immunoprecipitated with the monoclonal antibody 2G3. Compared with the control, the extract from trypsinized sporozoites showed a marked reduction in the intensity of PK42, but not of PK52 or PK50. An additional control showed that the polypeptides PK52 and PK50 are trypsin sensitive if the parasite is disrupted and extracted before enzymatic treatment (not shown).

from sporozoites of *P. knowlesi,* the simian malaria parasite, Joan Ellis prepared cDNA and introduced fragments into plasmids, and these into bacteria. Recently she found that some of the bacterial colonies are expressing portions of the polypeptide which contain the relevant protective antigenic determinants or epitopes (Ellis *et al.,* 1983).

There is good reason to believe that the results obtained with the *P. knowlesi* model will be applicable to the parasites of human malaria, *P. vivax* and *P. falciparum.* This view is based on the structural similarities of all CS proteins. Table VI provides the M_r and isoelectric points of CS proteins and intracellular precursors from sporozoites of rodent, simian, and human malarias. The M_r vary between 40,000 and 60,000. In every case, the pI of the surface peptide is lower than that of the two larger precursors, suggesting that during intracellular processing basic peptides are removed. Dr. Santoro and Dr. Ferreira compared the [^{35}S]methionine-containing tryptic peptides of different CS proteins, by reverse phase high-performance liquid chromatography. They found that several peptides had identical retention times, which strongly suggests structural similarity or identity (Santoro *et al.,* 1982).

The homology between the CS proteins is also revealed by immu-

TABLE VI

MOLECULAR WEIGHTS AND ISOELECTRIC POINTS
OF CS PROTEINS AND THEIR PRECURSORS[a]

Species	Molecular weight ($\times$ 10^3)	pI (range)
P. berghei	44 (CS)	4.7
	52	5.2–5.5
	54	
P. knowlesi	42 (CS)	4.9
	50	5.3–5.6
	52	
P. cynomolgi	48 (CS)	4.9
	56	5.2–5.5
	58	
P. falciparum	58 (CS?)	5.3
	65	5–6
	67	

[a] Adapted from Santoro *et al.* (1982).

nological methods. Indeed, some monoclonal antibodies to *P. knowlesi* cross-react with *P. falciparum* and *P. cynomolgi* (Cochrane *et al.*, 1982); antibodies to *P. cynomolgi* cross-react with *P. vivax* (A. Cochrane and J. Hii, unpublished observation); antibodies to *P. yoeli nigeriensis* cross-react with *P. berghei,* and, in this instance, even abolish their infectivity (N. Yoshida and R. S. Nussenzweig, unpublished observation).

The general resemblance between the CS proteins probably reflects a common function, most likely related to penetration of the parasite into the target cells. Dr. M. Hollingdale recently developed an *in vitro* system in which sporozoites adhere to, penetrate, and multiply inside fibroblast cell lines (Hollingdale *et al.*, 1981). They showed that in the presence of monoclonal antibodies against the CS protein of *P. berghei,* sporozoite attachment and penetration did not take place, and the intra-cellular stages, namely, the exoerythrocytic forms, did not develop (Hollingdale *et al.*, 1982). This was recently confirmed using sporozoites of the human malaria parasites *P. vivax* and *P. falciparum* (Hollingdale *et al.*, 1983).

While these *in vitro* studies were being performed, Dr. Nardin determined the effect of the monoclonal antibodies to the CS proteins of *P. falciparum* and *P. vivax* on sporozoite infectivity. In her experiments 10,000–20,000 sporozoites were incubated with the monoclonal antibodies or with Fab fragments and injected into chimpanzees, which are very sensitive to infection with these species of malaria parasite (Nardin *et al.*, 1982). Although complete neutralization was not achieved, and only a limited number of experiments could be performed, the results were very encouraging, especially since these were the first monoclonal antibodies raised against the CS proteins of human malaria. Two animals out of seven did not develop infection, and in the remaining five animals the prepatent period was greatly increased. Such an increase in prepatent period reflects considerable diminution in the number of sporozoites in the inoculum, perhaps more than 99% (Schmidt, 1982). Dr. J. Gysin recently performed neutralization experiments with the same monoclonal antibodies, using squirrel monkeys as recipients of *P. vivax* sporozoites, and found that in this host, which is less sensitive to infection than chimpanzees, the antibodies completely abolished parasite infectivity (J. Gysin and R. S. Nussenzweig, unpublished observation).

In summary, all CS proteins studied are structurally, antigenically, and functionally similar. It is likely, therefore, that the CS genes present areas of homology. This should facilitate their identification and cloning, which are necessary steps for the large-scale production of the polypeptide products by genetic engineering.

A sporozoite vaccine, however, does not necessarily have to be produced by the recombinant DNA technology. Two results suggest that a synthetic vaccine may be possible. First, the size of one of the DNA fragments isolated by Joan Ellis, which codes for the epitope of the CS protein of *P. knowlesi,* is quite small, and corresponds to no more than 100 amino acids (Ellis *et al.,* 1983). Second, several experiments by Dr. F. Zavala, Dr. Cochrane, and Dr. Nardin suggest that the CS proteins of all the malarial species examined have a single immunodominant region. They performed competitive binding assays between several monoclonal antibodies to a single CS protein, and observed the inhibitory effects they have on each other. The underlying principle of this assay is that monoclonal antibodies directed against different areas of an antigen molecule should not interfere with their respective binding capacity. Conversely, if the antibodies are directed against the same epitope, or epitopes which are topographically related, they will inhibit each other. Table VII illustrates the evidence for the presence of an immunodominant region in the CS proteins of *P. knowlesi, P. vivax,* and *P. falciparum* (Zavala *et al.,* 1983). The numbers represent percentage inhibition, and as shown, every one of the homologous monoclonal antibodies strongly inhibited the binding of the others.

Perhaps even more striking, most of the polyclonal antibodies present in the serum of animals which have been immunized with intact, irradiated sporozoites are directed against this same immunodominant region of the CS protein. Preincubation of crude extracts of *P. knowlesi* and *P. falciparum* sporozoites with single monoclonal antibodies to the corresponding CS proteins strongly inhibited the subsequent binding of polyclonal antibodies from the serum of humans or monkeys vaccinated with whole sporozoites (Zavala *et al.,* 1983). Therefore, it appears that the CS proteins are the most immunogenic constituent of sporozoites, and that the epitope recognized by the polyclonal and monoclonal antibodies is identical.

Another important observation was that in all systems every monoclonal antibody tested revealed a unique repetitive epitope. This was demonstrated by the ability of monomeric CS proteins to simul-

TABLE VII

EVIDENCE FOR THE PRESENCE OF AN IMMUNODOMINANT REGION ON CS PROTEINS[a]

P. vivax

Cold inhibitor (monoclonal antibody)	Percentage inhibition of binding to antigen of the radiolabeled monoclonal Ab				
	3D10	5D9	3C1	4E8	2F2
3D10	100	102	99	101	59
5D9	83	100	98	101	65
3C1	113	103	100	102	67
4E8	105	100	99	100	60
2F2	100	101	100	116	100
Control monoclonal	8	−6	−11	3	6
PBS-BSA	0	0	0	0	0

P. knowlesi

Cold inhibitor (monoclonal antibody)	Percentage inhibition of binding to antigen of the radiolabeled monoclonal Ab					
	5H8	2G3	8B8	8A8	8E11	6B8
5H8	100	99	101	115	105	121
2G3	96	100	87	78	106	103
8B8	95	94	100	106	107	125
8A8	86	83	94	100	105	128
8E11	65	59	86	70	100	105
6B8	88	85	91	95	104	100
Control monoclonal	6	0.4	0.5	8	0	0
PBS-BSA	0	0	0	0	0	0

P. falciparum

Cold inhibitor (monoclonal antibody)	Percentage inhibition of binding to antigen of the radiolabeled monoclonal Ab				
	3D6	2E7	1E9	2C11	2A10
3D6	100	98	99	95	75
2E7	98	100	102	99	90
1E9	100	103	100	100	99
2C11	104	100	99	100	100
2A10	110	102	106	8	100
Control monoclonal	2	0	−4	8	0
PBS-BSA	0	0	0	0	0

[a] Represented in this table are the results of competitive binding assays between monoclonal antibodies against CS proteins of *P. vivax*, left panel, *P. knowlesi*, center panel, and *P. falciparum*, right panel (Zavala *et al.*, 1983).

taneously bind two or more monoclonal antibodies in two-site immunoradiometric assays. In this type of assay the concentration of antigen is measured by means of two antibodies of different specificities. The first antibody is bound to a solid support, and serves to isolate and concentrate the antigen. The second antibody, directed against a different epitope, is labeled and serves to measure the concentration of bound antigen. Unexpectedly, as seen in Fig. 8, CS proteins can be detected

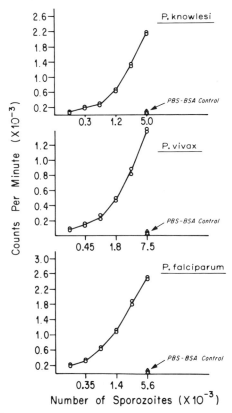

FIG. 8. Two-site/one-antibody immunoradiometric assays for detection of sporozoites. Sporozoite extracts were incubated in wells of microtiter plates coated with a monoclonal antibody to a CS protein. After washing, the amount of antigen bound to the solid phase was measured by adding to the wells an excess of the same monoclonal antibody radiolabeled with [125]I.

with a single monoclonal antibody; that is, antigen titrations can be done with a "two-site/one-antibody" instead of a "two-site/two-antibody" assay. It appears, therefore, that the single immunodominant region of CS proteins contains repetitive epitopes. In agreement with these observations, the nucleotide sequence of the cDNA clone from the *P. knowlesi* CS protein was found to contain multiple repeats coding for a sequence of amino acids which react with the monoclonal antibodies (Ellis *et al.*, 1983).

It is clear that the recurrent epitope of CS proteins is a potent immunogen, since every monoclonal antibody produced in our laboratory against sporozoites is directed against it. Moreover, the binding of Fab fragments of these antibodies to this structure neutralizes the infectivity of sporozoites. It is possible, therefore, that the small portion of the CS molecule represented in this epitope could be synthesized and used to produce protective immunity in the host.

What are the prospects that effective malaria vaccines can be developed solely on the basis of the CS proteins?

The main difficulty is that resistance to sporozoites does not confer resistance to blood stages, and if a few sporozoites escape the immune defenses, infection will develop. In several experimental models sterile immunity has been achieved by vaccination with sporozoites, but the effectiveness of the protection depended on the dose of parasites used for challenge. The higher this dose, the less effective the vaccination.

What is the size of the infective inoculum under natural conditions? The exact answer is not known. It may vary according to the endemic area, and the vector, but there is good reason to believe that in many instances this number is quite low, perhaps only a few hundred sporozoites (Pringle, 1966). If this estimate is correct, it is conceivable that a vaccine containing only sporozoite antigens could completely protect part of the exposed population. The remaining vaccinated individuals would be expected to develop a milder course of the disease due to the neutralization of a large proportion of the infective inoculum (McGregor, 1964). The effect would be magnified in those individuals having some degree of immunity to blood forms. Ideally, however, to be fully effective, a malaria vaccine should also contain protective antigens from the other stages of development of the parasite.

Another possible practical application of our findings is the use of monoclonal antibodies to detect sporozoites in mosquitoes. The choice of an effective strategy for control of malaria in endemic areas depends on the accurate determination of the proportion of infected mosquitoes, as well as on the identification of the main vector species. In the past the determination of infection rates of mosquitoes had to be carried out by laborious dissection and microscopic examination of salivary glands of individual mosquitoes. This was an almost impossible task in most areas, where less than 1/1000 *Anopheles* are infected. Another serious limitation of this methodology is that sporozoites are morphologically identical. Therefore, when *P. vivax* and *P. falciparum* and other malarias coexist, the identification of the parasite species by microscopy is impossible.

Dr. Zavala recently developed an immunoassay which serves not only to detect but also to identify and quantify with minimal effort, sporozoites in individual or pooled mosquitoes. The assay could not be simpler. As shown in Fig. 9, our favorite illustration, whole mosquitoes

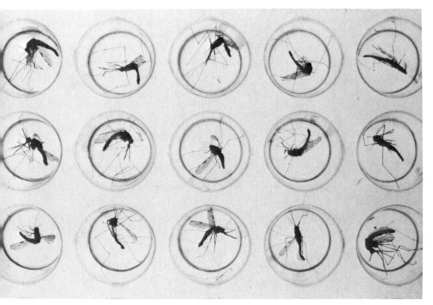

FIG. 9. The Zavala assay for detection of sporozoite-infected mosquitoes. The wells of a microtiter plate contain dried *Anopheles* mosquitoes. They are crushed, the wells washed, and radiolabeled monoclonal antibodies are added. The thorax and head were crushed, and the plates were frozen and thawed a few times. Then the wells were emptied, and ^{125}I-labeled monoclonal antibodies were added. After appropriate incubation and washings, the wells were counted in a gamma counter.

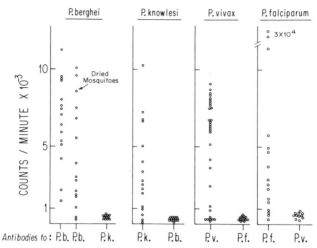

FIG. 10. Detection of malaria infection in populations of mosquitoes, some of which were infected with different species of malaria parasites. The circles represent individual mosquitoes. The results of the immunoassay demonstrate that the population of mosquitoes infected with the various malaria parasites was revealed by the homologous monoclonal antibodies, even if the mosquitoes had been kept dry for several days.

are anesthetized and put in wells of plastic microtiter plates. The thorax and head of the mosquitoes are crushed with wooden applicators. The wells are washed, and radiolabeled monoclonal antibodies are added. Figure 10 summarizes the results of tests performed on batches of mosquitoes, some of which were infected with different malaria species. As shown, the infected mosquitoes and the species of sporozoite were revealed in every instance. The sensitivity of this method is at least equal to that of microscopic examination. The infection can be detected in mosquitoes which have been killed with ether and kept dry for several days, which is of practical importance because this permits completion of the assays in a central laboratory outside the endemic areas (Zavala *et al.*, 1982).

The Zavala test was used by a team from New York University and the National Institutes of Health in an endemic area in The Gambia, West Africa, and the results confirmed the laboratory findings (Collins *et al.*, 1983). It should be pointed out that this assay may have a wider application. Similar methodology could be used to detect other human or animal parasites in crude extracts of vectors, provided that species-specific monoclonal antibodies of high affinity are available.

In conclusion, our studies in the malaria system show that parasites, in spite of their complexity and the high degree of adaptation to the host, are not invulnerable to immunologic attack. It is remarkable, however, that not a single vaccine against a parasite infection of man has yet been developed. Although this may be due in part to intrinsic difficulties, research in this area has not been proportional to the magnitude of the health problems involved. Fortunately, an increasing number of investigators in different areas of biology are discovering the beauty and challenge involved in uncovering the mechanisms of the host–parasite relationship. With the help of the powerful technologies now available, their work will probably lead to more rapid progress in the prophylaxis and therapy of these diseases and contribute to the disruption of the cycle of poverty, underdevelopment, and disease.

Acknowledgments

This article is a result of close to two decades of research performed in collaboration with colleagues from several institutions in the United States and abroad. We are grateful for their contributions. We thank Dr. M. Aikawa for the electron micrographs of sporozoites. We also acknowledge the editorial assistance of Ms. Joanne Joseph, Mr. Roger Rose, and Ms. Sharon Hecht and grants from the Agency for International Development, UNDP/World Bank/WHO Special Programme for Research and Training in Tropical Medicine, National Institutes of Health, and the Rockefeller Foundation.

References

Aikawa, M. Yoshida, N., Nussenzweig, R. S., and Nussenzweig, V. (1981). *J. Immunol.* **126,** 2494–2495.

Chen, D. H. (1974). Ph.D. thesis, New York University School of Medicine, (Microfilm No. 7SZ75-09).

Chen, D. H., Nussenzweig, R. S., and Collins, W. E. (1976). *J. Parasitol.* **62,** 636–637.

Clyde, D. F., McCarthy, V. C., Miller, R. M., and Hornick, R. B. (1973a). *Am. J. Med. Sci.* **266,** 398–403.

Clyde, D. F., Most, H., McCarthy, V., and Vanderberg, J. (1973b). *Am. J. Med. Sci.* **266,** 169–177.

Clyde, D. F., McCarthy, V., Miller, R. M., and Woodward, W. E. (1975). *Am. J. Trop. Med. Hyg.* **24,** 397–401.

Cochrane, A. H., Aikawa, M., Jeng, M., and Nussenzweig, R. S. (1976). *J. Immunol.* **116,** 859—867.

Cochrane, A., Santoro, F. Nussenzweig, V., Gwadz, R. W., and Nussenzweig, R. S. (1982). *Proc. Natl. Acad. Sci. U.S.A.* **79,** 5651–5655.

Cohen, S. (1982). *Br. Med. Bull.* **38,** 161–165.

Collins, F. H., Zavala, F., Graves, P., Cochrane, A., Gwadz, R. W., and Nussenzweig, R. S. (1983). Submitted.

Ellis, J., Ozaki, L. S., Gwadz, R. W., Cochrane, A. H., Nussenzweig, V., Nussenzweig, R. S., and Godson, G. N. (1983). *Nature (London)* **302**, 536–538.

Gwadz, R. W., Cochrane, A. H., Nussenzweig, V., and Nussenzweig, R. S. (1979). *Bull. WHO* **57**, 165–173, Suppl. 1.

Hollingdale, M. R., Leef, J. L., McCullough, M., and Beaudoin, R. L. (1981). *Science* **213**, 1021.

Hollingdale, M. R., Zavala, F., Nussenzweig, R. S., and Nussenzweig, V. (1982). *J. Immunol.* **128**, 1929–1930.

Hollingdale, M. R., Nardin, E. H., Tharavanij, S., Schwartz, A. L., and Nussenzweig, R. S. (1983). Submitted.

Kohler, G., and Milstein, C. (1975). *Nature (London)* **256**, 495–497.

McGregor, I. A. (1964). *Trans. R. Soc. Trop. Med. Hyg.* **58**, 80–92.

Mulligan, H. W., Russell, F. P., and Mohan, B. N. (1941). *J. Malar. Inst. India* **4**, 25–34.

Nardin, E. H., and Nussenzweig, R. S. (1978). *Nature (London)* **274**, 55–57.

Nardin, E. H., Nussenzweig, R. S., and Gwadz, R. (1979a). *Bull. WHO* **57**, 211–217 (Suppl.), 1.

Nardin, E. H., Nussenzweig, R. S., McGregor, C. A., and Bryan, J. (1979b). *Science* **206**, 597–599.

Nardin, E. H., Nussenzweig, R. S., Bryan, J. H., and McGregor, I. A. (1981). *Am. J. Trop. Med. Hyg.* **30**, 1159–1163.

Nardin, E. H., Nussenzweig, V., Nussenzweig, R. S., Collins, W. E., Harinasuta, K. T., Tapchaisri, P., and Chomcharn, Y. (1982). *J. Exp. Med.* **156**, 20–30.

Nimo, K. P., Agadzi, V., Asante, R., Biritwum, R., Jones, C., Morrow, R. H., Neill, A., Nelson, K., Owusu, J., Saakwamante, K., Smith, P. G., and Wupara, F. (1981). *Int. J. Epidemiol.* **10**, 73–85.

Nussenzweig, R. S., Vanderberg, J., Most, H., and Orton, C. (1967). *Nature (London)* **216**, 160–162.

Nussenzweig, R. S., Vanderberg, J. P., and Most, H. (1969a). *Mil. Med.* **134** (Suppl.), 1176–1182.

Nussenzweig, R. S., Vanderberg, J. P., Most, H., and Orton, C. (1969b). *Nature (London)* **222**, 488–489.

Nussenzweig, R. S., Vanderberg, J. P., Sanabria, Y., and Most, H. (1972a). *Exp. Parasitol.* **31**, 88–97.

Nussenzweig, R. S., Vanderberg, J. P., Spitalny, G., Rivera, C.I.O., Orton, C., and Most, H. (1972b). *Am. J. Trop. Med. Hyg.* **21**, 722–728.

Orjih, A. U., Cochrane, A. H., and Nussenzweig, R. S. (1981). *Nature (London)* **291**, 331–332.

Orjih, A. U., Cochrane, A. H., and Nussenzweig, R. S. (1982). *Trans. R. Soc. Trop. Med. Hyg.* **76**, 57–61.

Potocnjak, P., Yoshida, N., Nussenzweig, R. S., and Nussenzweig, V. (1981). *J. Exp. Med.* **151**, 1504–1513.

Pringle, G. (1966). *Trans. R. Soc. Trop. Med. Hyg.* **60**, 626–632.

Rieckmann, K. H., Beaudoin, R. L., Cassels, J., and Sell, K. (1979). *Bull. WHO* **57,** 261–265 (Suppl.), 1.

Santoro, F., Cochrane, A. H., Nussenzweig, V., Nardin, E. H., Nussenzweig, R. S., Gwadz, R. W., and Ferreira, A. (1982). *J. Biol. Chem.* **258,** 3341–3345.

Schmidt, L. H. (1982). *Am. J. Trop. Med. Hyg.* **31,** 609–611.

Shin, S. C., Vanderberg, J. P., and Terzakis, J. A. (1982). *J. Protozool.* **29,** 448–454.

Spitalny, G. L., and Nussenzweig, R. S. (1972). *Proc. Helminthol. Soc. Wash.* **39,** 506–514.

Vanderberg, J. P. (1975). *J. Parasitol.* **61,** 43–50.

Vanderberg, J. P., Nussenzweig, R. S., and Most, H. (1969). *Mil. Med.* **134** (Suppl.), 1183–1190.

Vanderberg, J., Nussenzweig, R. S., and Most, H. (1970). *J. Parasitol.* **56,** 350–351.

Yoeli, M., Vanderberg, J., Nawrot, R., and Most, H. (1965). *Am. J. Trop. Med. Hyg.* **14,** 927–930.

Yoeli, M., Upmanis, R. S., Vanderberg, J., and Most, H. (1966). *Mil. Med.* **131,** 900–914.

Yoshida, N., Nussenzweig, R. S., Potocnjak, P., Nussenzweig, V., and Aikawa, M. (1980). *Science* **207,** 71–73.

Yoshida, N., Potocnjak, P., Nussenzweig, V., and Nussenzweig, R. S. (1981) *J. Exp. Med.* **154,** 1225–1236.

Zavala, F., Gwadz, R. W., Collins, F. H., Nussenzweig, R. S., and Nussenzweig, V. (1982). *Nature (London)* **299,** 737–738.

Zavala, F., Cochrane, A. H., Nardin, E. H., Nussenzweig, R. S., and Nussenzweig, V. (1983). *J. Exp. Med.* **157,** 1947–1957.

BIOGENESIS OF THE OUTER MEMBRANE OF *Salmonella**

MARY JANE OSBORN

Department of Microbiology
University of Connecticut Health Center
Farmington, Connecticut

I. INTRODUCTION

T HE central problem in membrane biogenesis and the focus of current intense interest arises from the fact that biological membranes are not, by and large, self-replicating structures. That is, most membranes and membranous organelles are highly differentiated and functionally specific structures that lack all or part of the biosynthetic apparatus necessary for synthesis of their own unique complement of proteins and lipids. To a greater or lesser extent, then, polypeptides and lipids destined for a given target membrane must be synthesized elsewhere in the cell and in some manner identified and delivered to their sites of functional integration. This central question of mechanisms of targeting and translocation is most dramatically evident in the complexities of intracellular traffic in eukaryotic cells. However, gram-negative bacteria face a conceptually similar problem in assembly of the outer membrane of the cell envelope, and it is one aspect of this problem, the mechanism of translocation of lipopolysaccharide to the outer membrane of *Salmonella* that has particularly fascinated me.

The outer membrane is a highly specialized membranous organelle that lies outside the cytoplasmic (inner) membrane and the murein cell wall and forms the interface between the cell and its outside world. It is virtually inert metabolically and serves primarily as a selective barrier that excludes a variety of noxious substances, such as antibiotics and detergents, while allowing permeation of nutrient solutes to active transport systems of the inner membrane. This specialized function is

*Lecture delivered January 13, 1983.

87

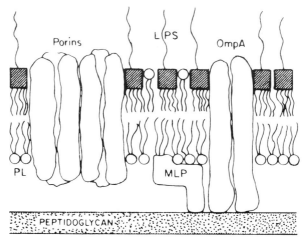

FIG. 1. Schematic organization of outer membrane. Mlp, Murein lipoprotein; LPS, lipopolysaccharide.

reflected in a highly specialized composition and molecular organization (Fig. 1). Characteristic components include a limited set of unusual major proteins, including the porin family and murein lipoprotein, and a unique major lipid, the lipopolysaccharide (Fig. 2). A detail that will be important to the present discussion is the extreme asymmetry of lipid distribution across the membrane, lipopolysaccharide being localized

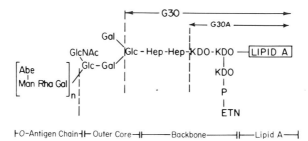

FIG. 2. Structure of *Salmonella typhimurium* lipopolysaccharide. Abe, Abequose; ETN, ethanolamine; Gal, galactose; Glc, glucose; GlcNAc, *N*-acetylglucosamine; Hep, L-glycero-D-mannoheptose; KDO, 2-keto-3-deoxy-octonate; Man, mannose; Rha, rhamnose. G30 indicates the incomplete chain of *galE* mutants and G30A, that of heptoseless mutants.

exclusively in the external leaflet and glycerophosphatide (principally phosphatidylethanolamine) correspondingly enriched in the inner leaflet.

The idiosyncratic and most intriguing aspect of outer membrane biogenesis derives from the fact that it is outside the cell and is literally walled off from the precursor pools and metabolic machinery of the cytoplasm. Thus, outer membrane is an extreme example of secondary assembly in which all constituents, lipid as well as protein, must be synthesized elsewhere and delivered to the outer membrane by specific export processes. The mechanism of export of outer membrane proteins has been a subject of lively interest in a number of laboratories and is well discussed in recent reviews (Emro et al., 1980; Ito et al., 1981; Randall and Hardu, 1982). My laboratory has focused on the lipid side of the problem, and this article will summarize our current ideas about the mechanism of translocation of lipopolysaccharide to the outer membrane.

II. Properties of Lipopolysaccharide Translocation

Early studies established that lipopolysaccharide is initially synthesized in the inner cytoplasmic membrane and rapidly, but secondarily, translocated to the outer membrane (Osborn et al., 1972). The phenomonology of the translocation process, as defined by in vivo pulse-chase and membrane fractionation techniques, is as follows:

1. Transfer of pulse-labeled lipopolysaccharide from inner to outer membrane is fast ($t_{1/2} = 1.2$ minutes at 32°C) and is unidirectional.

2. Translocation shows dependence of a potentially revealing type on lipopolysaccharide structure. The polysaccharide portion of the molecule is not important, since mutational amputation of the entire polysaccharide chain distal to the innermost KDO residues (see Fig. 2) has little or no effect on the rate of translocation. However, mutations interfering with synthesis and incorporation of KDO result in production of an incomplete precursor of lipid A that is translocated to outer membrane at greatly reduced rates (Osborn et al., 1980). Indeed, the resulting accumulation of the incomplete, KDO-deficient lipid in the inner membrane appears to be responsible for the conditional lethal phenotype exhibited by mutants temperature sensitive for KDO bio-

synthesis. Although the lipid A precursor lacks the saturated C_{12} and C_{14} fatty acyl residues of lipid A in addition to KDO (Rick *et al.*, 1978), these are apparently nonessential for translocation. Cells can be tricked into producing an underacylated lipopolysaccharide having a normal polysaccharide structure but the acyl chain composition of lipid A precursor, and this underacylated lipopolysaccharide is translocated at the wild type rate (Walenga and Osborn, 1980). We suspect, therefore, that the KDO residues are the required structural element, and we postulate that this unique sugar may serve as a recognition signal for some component of an as yet hypothetical translocation machinery.

3. The notion that lipopolysaccharide translocation is a facilitated process is also suggested by its energy dependence (Osborn *et al.*, 1984). Translocation of pulse-labeled lipopolysaccharide to outer membrane is abolished by uncouplers under conditions in which the membrane potential is collapsed but the ATP pool maintained. It is also strongly inhibited by arsenate under experimental conditions in which the ATP pool is depleted but the membrane potential is intact. Thus, lipopolysaccharide translocation may require, directly or indirectly, phosphate bond energy in addition to membrane potential. The requirement for maintenance of the membrane potential is a property shared by all processes of export to outer membrane, protein and phospholipid as well as lipopolysaccharide, but dependence on ATP has not been observed in other systems.

4. Synthesis and translocation of lipopolysaccharide is completely independent of *de novo* protein synthesis and continues for long periods of time in the presence of chloramphenicol at concentrations that abolish synthesis of total protein, including outer membrane proteins. These observations are important in excluding possible models in which lipopolysaccharide is obligatorily translocated in association with outer membrane proteins and rides piggyback on a protein export machinery.

5. Finally, immunoelectron microscopic studies by Mühlradt and colleagues (1974) have indicated that lipopolysaccharide translocation is site specific, occurring preferentially at regions of close contact between inner and outer membrane, the zones of adhesion initially described by Bayer (1968). On this basis it has been postulated by a number of workers that zones of adhesion may be structures specialized for delivery of materials—protein, phospholipid, and lipopolysac-

charide—to the outer membrane, and most models for biogenesis of outer membrane are based on this hypothesis.

III. Models of Lipopolysaccharide Translocation

The role postulated for zones of adhesion in outer membrane assembly is indeed an attractive one, but insight into molecular mechanisms has proven elusive. Indeed, zones of adhesion have remained a morphological construct in search of a biochemical correlate. Attempts at isolation and biochemical characterization have met with limited success, and electron microscopy has not yet revealed relevant details of ultrastructure. In the absence of evidence, imagination is unfettered and a variety of models of zones of adhesion have been proposed in various contexts with greater or lesser degrees of seriousness (Fig. 3). Although these models differ widely in their predictions as to routes and mechanisms of lipopolysaccharide translocation, all are based on two assumptions: first, that lipopolysaccharide is located exclusively in the external

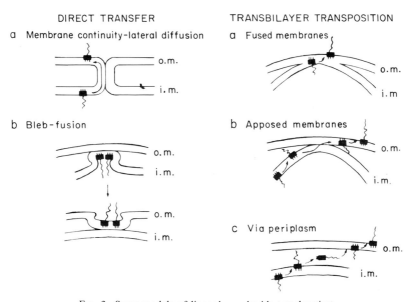

Fig. 3. Some models of lipopolysaccharide translocation.

leaflet of the outer membrane, and second, that the molecule is synthesized at the cytoplasmic face of the inner membrane where biosynthetic
enzymes would have direct access to intracellular precursor pools. The
first assumption has been experimentally validated (Mühlradt and Golecki, 1975; Funahara and Nikaido, 1980); the second, however, has not
previously been subjected to experimental test. If it is correct, translocation of lipopolysaccharide to outer membrane imposes a formal requirement for transposition of this bulky amphipath across two bilayers, and
it is in their solutions to this problem that the models differ. Some
accomplish delivery of lipopolysaccharide to the outer membrane by
lateral diffusion or vesicle blebbing, avoiding necessity for transmembrane flip-flop (Fig. 3, direct transfer). Others require one or two
transbilayer transpositions. Recent studies have led us to a working
hypothesis which is a variant of the apposed membrane model car-
tooned in Fig. 3. We postulate (1) assembly of lipopolysaccharide is
intrinsically a transmembrane vectorial process, in which early steps in
synthesis may occur at the cytoplasmic face of the inner membrane, but
terminal steps take place at the periplasmic face of the membrane; (2) as
a consequence of the topology of biosynthesis, translocation of
lipopolysaccharide to outer membrane takes place from the periplasmic
face of the inner membrane, presumably at zones of adhesion; and (3)
the overall process is facilitated and energy dependent.

IV. An Intermediate in Lipopolysaccharide Translocation

The idea that lipopolysaccharide synthesis is a transmembrane process is not novel. As early as 1966, Shands briefly reported immunoelectron microscopic evidence for the presence of lipopolysaccharide
at the periplasmic face of the inner membrane in penicillin spheroplasts
of Salmonella typhimurium. However, the significance of Shands' findings was then called into question by the realization that outer membrane lipopolysaccharide undergoes redistribution and randomization
upon disruption of the underlying murein at 37°C (Muhlradt and Golecki, 1975), i.e., conditions intrinsic to preparation of penicillin spheroplasts. We therefore undertook to reinvestigate by immunoelectron
microscopy the occurrence of lipopolysaccharide at the periplasmic face
of inner membrane and its potential role in translocation under conditions in which redistribution artifacts could be both recognized and

minimized (Mulford and Osborn, 1983). The experimental approach took advantage of the conditional lipopolysaccharide phenotype of *gal*E (UDPgalactose-4-epimerase) mutants of *S. typhimurium,* in which synthesis of wild-type lipopolysaccharide immunoreactive with anti-O antigen antibody is dependent on addition of exogenous galactose. Thus, lipopolysaccharide newly synthesized during a galactose pulse can be specifically detected and localized using ferritin or gold-conjugated anti-O specific IgG. To render the surface of the inner membrane accessible to antibody with minimal lipopolysaccharide redistribution, spheroplasts were prepared with lysozyme-EDTA at 2°C and were lightly prefixed with glutaraldehyde prior to immunolabeling. Preliminary controls for secondary redistribution of lipopolysaccharide were carried out as follows. One culture was grown in the presence of galactose for four generations and switched to galactose-free medium for the final generation of growth. All immunoreactive lipopolysaccharide was therefore at least one generation old and long since translocated to outer membrane. A second culture was exposed to galactose only during the last generation of growth such that immunoreactive lipopolysaccharide was of recent origin. Spheroplasts of this culture showed extensive ferritin labeling at the exposed periplasmic face of the inner membrane as well as the outer leaflet of the outer membrane. In contrast, the inner membrane of spheroplasts prepared from the redistribution control were entirely free of label, confirming that randomization of outer membrane lipopolysaccharide had not occurred. Interestingly, however, exposure of these control spheroplasts to 37°C for 1 minute prior to prefixation resulted in extensive redistribution of lipopolysaccharide to the periplasmic faces of both inner and outer membranes.

That the lipopolysaccharide observed at the periplasmic face constitutes an intermediate in translocation was established by immunoelectron microscopic pulse-chase experiments (Mulford and Osborn, 1983; Fig. 4) O-reactive lipopolysaccharide could be detected at the periplasmic face of the inner membrane within 20 to 30 seconds after addition of galactose, which corresponds to the earliest time at which radiolabeled lipopolysaccharide is found after addition of radioactive galactose, and accumulation of pulse-synthesized lipopolysaccharide at the inner membrane appeared to precede its buildup in outer membrane. In the experiment shown in Fig. 4, 80% of the total gold-conjugated IgG was found on the inner membrane at the end of a 50-second pulse.

During chase in the absence of galactose the inner membrane was rapidly depleted of immunoreactive lipopolysaccharide with a corresponding increase in outer membrane label (Fig. 4c–f). Analyses of grain density per unit length of membrane profile confirmed that the label appearing in outer membrane during chase was equivalent to that lost from inner membrane, and allowed estimation of an approximate half-time of translocation of 1.4 minutes, in good agreement with values derived from radioactive pulse-chase data.

V. TOPOLOGY OF LIPOPOLYSACCHARIDE ASSEMBLY

We conclude that newly synthesized lipopolysaccharide appears transiently at the periplasmic face of the inner membrane as an intermediate in translocation to outer membrane. However, these findings raise immediate question about the topology of lipopolysaccharide biosynthesis. Is the molecule, as initially assumed, synthesized at the cytoplasmic face of the membrane and secondarily transposed to the periplasmic face? Or must one postulate a more complex process of transmembrane synthesis? We believe the latter is the case, and that—at a minimum— the final steps in assembly of the molecule must take place at the periplasmic face. The evidence for this hypothesis is also immunoelectron microscopic.

The experimental approach was based on a peculiarity of lipopolysaccharide synthesis, namely, that O antigen and core lipopolysaccharide are synthesized independently and by different mechanisms. Specifically O antigen chains are assembled via a series of oligo and polysaccharide intermediates linked to undecaprenyl phosphate, and the O-specific polymer is finally transferred en bloc to previously completed core lipopolysaccharide. Thus, mutants blocked at intermediate stages of core biosynthesis continue to produce O antigen but lack the lipopolysaccharide attachment site (see Fig. 2). Under these conditions

---

FIG. 4. Kinetics of lipopolysaccharide pulse and chase. Strain G30 was pulsed with 40 μM galactose for 50 seconds and chased as described (Mulford and Osborn, 1983). Spheroplasts were labeled with gold-conjugated anti-O IgG. (a) Before addition of galactose; (b) 50-second pulse; (c) 30 seconds of chase; (d) 1 minute of chase; (e) 2 minute of chase; (f) 5 minute of chase. om, Outer membrane; im, inner membrane. Bars represent 100 nm.

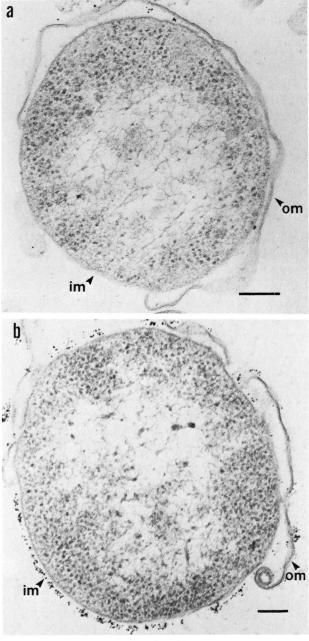

Fig. 4a and b.

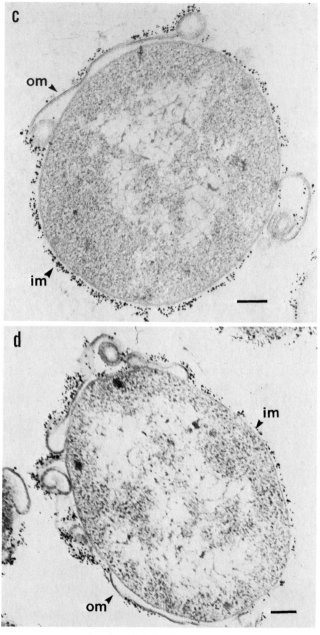

Fig. 4c and d. See legend on p. 94.

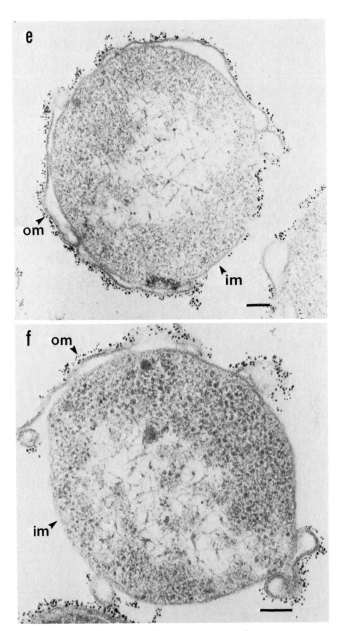

FIG. 4e and f. See legend on p. 94.

undecaprenyl phosphate-linked O polymer is the end product of O-antigen synthesis and can be localized by immunoelectron microscopy as above. The experiments (Mulford and Osborn, 1983) utilized a double mutant having a heptoseless core lipopolysaccharide (Fig. 2) and the *gal*E mutation to permit galactose-conditional synthesis of O antigen intermediates. O antigen was found exclusively at the periplasmic face of the inner membrane, and the kinetics of appearance paralleled that of O-reactive lipopolysaccharide. However, the maximal amount of immunolabeling was much reduced and the labeling pattern was stable to chase. It is known that accumulation of undecaprenylphosphoate-linked intermediates is limited by the small amounts of this lipid coenzyme in the membrane and that these intermediates are not translocated to outer membrane. The results strongly suggest that the final attachment of O antigen to core occurs at the periplasmic face of the membrane.

VI. Possible Mechanisms of Transmembrane Assembly

The mechanism of synthesis of O antigen is similar to that of cell wall peptidoglycan and both are homologous to the dolichol phosphate pathway for protein N-glycosylation of the rough endoplasmic reticulum. In each case, nucleotide sugar precursors on one side of a membrane are utilized for synthesis of a polymeric product on the other side of the bilayer. A priori, one can imagine at least three types of mechanism for such transmembrane synthesis (Fig. 5). As applied to lipopolysaccharide, the first (Fig. 5A) postulates synthesis of the lipid linked oligosaccharide repeating unit of O antigen by a series of membrane glycosyltransferases oriented at the cytoplasmic face of the inner membrane, followed by transmembrane flip-flop for polymerization at the periplasmic face and transfer to core lipopolysaccharide. The latter would also be independently assembled at the cytoplasmic face and transposed across the bilayer to the periplasmic face. Intuitive evaluation of the plausibility of this type of model depends in large part on one's willingness to accept the feasibility of the required transmembrane transpositions of glycolipids. At the least, it might be expected that flip-flop would require facilitation and expenditure of energy for kinetic efficiency. However, there are at least two potential mechanisms of transmembrane assembly that avoid this problem. According to one (Fig. 5B1), nucleotide sugars are transported to the periplasm for uti-

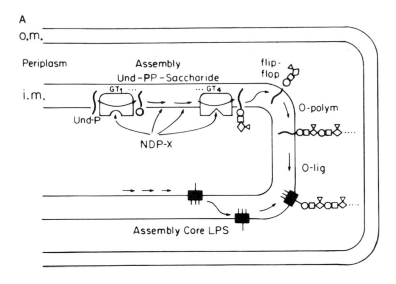

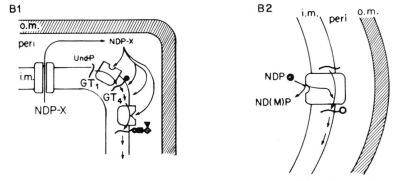

FIG. 5. Possible mechanisms for transmembrane assembly of O antigen and core lipopolysaccharide. Abbreviations: o.m. and i.m., outer and inner membrane; GT, glycosyltransferase; Und-P, undecaprenyl phosphate; NDP-X, nucleotide sugar. (A) Transmembrane flip-flop of oligosaccharide–lipid intermediate. (B) Assembly at the periplasmic face: (1) nucleotide sugar transport to periplasm; (2) transmembrane glycosyl translocase–transferase.

lization by periplasmically oriented transferases that carry out the entire biosynthetic sequence. Alternatively (Fig. 5B2), one might postulate a novel class of transmembrane translocase–transferase enzymes that would transfer glycosyl residues from nucleotide sugar donors, at the cytoplasmic face to acceptors at the periplasmic face. Recent evidence (Sommers and Hirschberg, 1982; Perez and Hirschberg, 1984) suggests that O-glycosylation of proteins in the Golgi apparatus may follow the second pathway—transport of nucleotide sugars to luminally oriented transferases—and this mechanism is not entirely implausible for the prokaryotic system since the outer membrane is poorly permeable to solutes the size of nucleotide sugars. The transmembrane topology and orientation of the dolichol pathway of rough endoplasmic reticulum still remains unclear.

VII. Transmembrane Orientation of Lipopolysaccharide Biosynthetic Enzymes

The bacterial system offers experimental advantages for studies on topology of membrane glycosyltransferases, in that both sides of the inner membrane can be rendered directly accessible to probes. It also suffers at present a major defect, in that the relevant enzymes have resisted purification and neither identifiable polypeptides nor specific antibodies are yet in hand for unequivocal determination of topology. For this reason, our preliminary studies (J. Gibson and M. J. Osborn, unpublished results) have relied on indirect and inherently messy techniques. Proteolytic inactivation and accessibility of enzymes to nucleotide sugar substrates were determined in intact spheroplasts (periplasmic face exposed) and inverted inner membrane vesicles (cytoplasmic face exposed) prepared by French press lysis. Two marker enzymes were probed: the CMP–KDO:lipid A transferase system (Munson et al., 1978) as marker for core lipopolysaccharide synthesis, and galactosyl-PP-undecaprenol synthetase (Osborn and Yuan Tze-Yuen, 1968), the first enzyme of O antigen synthesis. To our considerable surprise, the results retained for KDO transferase (Table I) were internally self-consistent and relatively unambiguous, and indicated that the enzyme was accessible to both protease and substrate only from the cytoplasmic side. It should be noted that accessibility of CMP–KDO to

TABLE I

TOPOLOGY OF BIOSYNTHETIC ENZYMES

	Protease sensitivity percentage inactivation		NDP sugar accessibility (pmol prod/min)	
	Spheroplasts	Inverted vesicles	Spheroplasts	Inverted vesicles
KDO: lipid A transferase	23	85	62	285
Und-PP-gal synthetase	34	32	3	16

the active site was measured by rate of transfer of KDO to endogenous lipid A precursor in spheroplast and vesicle preparations from a KDO-deficient mutant strain. Thus, a substantial fraction of the untranslocatable KDO-deficient precursor trapped in the inner membrane is available to the transferase, and is presumably located in the cytoplasmic leaflet of the membrane. The possibility that the defect in translocation of this molecule to outer membrane may reflect difficulty in preliminary transposition across the inner membrane is one of those ideas that are too good to be true, but it can be tested immunologically and such experiments are in preparation.

The results obtained with KDO transferase, while preliminary, are consistent with the first model of transmembrane assembly (Fig. 5A), synthesis of core lipopolysaccharide at the cytoplasmic face of the inner membrane followed by transmembrane transposition to the periplasmic face. Parallel assays of the first enzyme of O-antigen synthesis, carried out on the same preparations, allowed no such straightforward interpretation. Accessibility of the enzyme to UDPgalactose appeared to be restricted in spheroplasts relative to inverted vesicle preparations, but inactivation by a variety of proteases was partial (less than 40%) and equal from both sides of the membrane (Table I). We believe that these results merit only one conclusion, that more direct and unambiguous methods will be required to establish the transmembrane topology of O antigen synthesis in any convincing manner. Molecular cloning of key genes of the pathway, currently in progress, should allow amplification and identification of enzyme proteins and a more definitive approach.

VIII. CONCLUDING REMARKS

The work described here has provided us with a skeletal outline of a pathway of biogenesis and translocation of lipopolysaccharide, but the bones are as yet short on flesh. The analogy between inner membrane and rough endoplasmic reticulum in transmembrane assembly of saccharides is striking, and further elucidation of the transmembrane topology of lipopolysaccharide synthesis may provide insights into more general mechanisms. This aspect of the problem is clearly approachable with the clues presently in hand. However, we are still lacking any significant insight into the heart of the translocation problem, the mechanism whereby lipopolysaccharide is transferred from the periplasmic face of the inner membrane to the outer face of the outer membrane. A genetic approach may provide the most effective tool for opening a crack into this black box, and development of methods for selection of conditional mutants in lipopolysaccharide translocation is now in progress.

ACKNOWLEDGMENTS

Important contributions to the work described were made by many colleagues, and the author is indeed grateful to J. Gibson, P. Marino, R. McDade, C. A. Mulford, R. S. Munson, Jr., A. Progulske, P. D. Rick, and R. W. Walenga. This work was supported by USPHS Grant AI-08650.

REFERENCES

Bayer, M. E. (1968). *J. Gen. Microbiol.* **53,** 395–404.

Crowlesmith, I., Schindler, M., and Osborn, M. J. (1978). *J. Bacteriol.* **135,** 259–269.

Emro, S. D., Hall, M. N., and Silhavy, T. J. (1980). *J. Cell Biol.* **86,** 701–711.

Funahara, Y., and Nikaido, H. (1980). *J. Bacteriol.* **141,** 1463–1465.

Ito, K., Bassford, P. J., Jr., and Beckwith, J. (1981). *Cell* **24,** 707–717.

Mühlradt, P. F., and Golecki, J. R. (1975). *Eur. J. Biochem.* **51,** 343–352.

Mühlradt, P. F., Menzel, J., Golecki, J. R., and Speth, V. (1974). *Eur. J. Biochem.* **43,** 533–539.

Munson, R. S., Jr., Rasmussen, N. S., and Osborn, M. J. (1978). *J. Biol. Chem.* **253,** 1503–1511.

Osborn, M. J., and Yuan Tze-Yuen, R. (1968). *J. Biol. Chem.* **243,** 5145–5152.

Osborn, M. J., Gander, J. E., and Parisi, E. (1972). *J. Biol. Chem.* **247,** 3973–3986.

Osborn, M. J., Rick, P. D., and Rasmussen, N. S. (1980). *J. Biol. Chem.* **255,** 42456–4251.

Perez, M., and Hirschberg, L. B. (1984). *Fed. Proc., Fed. Am. Soc. Exp. Biol.* **44,** in press.

Randall, L. L., and Hardy, S. J. S. (1982). *In* "Modern Cell Bioloty" (B. Satir, ed.). Liss, New York.

Rick, P. D., Fung, L. W.-M., Ho, C., and Osborn, M. J. (1977). *J. Biol. Chem.* **252,** 4904–4912.

Shands, J. W. (1966). *Ann. N.Y. Acad. Sci.* **133,** 292–298.

Sommers, L. W., and Hirschberg, C. B. (1982). *J. Biol. Chem.* **257,** 10811–10817.

Walenga, R. W., and Osborn, M. J. (1980). *J. Biol. Chem.* **255,** 4257–4263.

LEFT-HANDED Z-DNA*

ALEXANDER RICH

Department of Biology
Massachusetts Institute of Technology
Cambridge, Massachusetts

F OR over 30 years we have had knowledge of the three-dimensional structure of DNA and we are familiar with the idea that it acts as an information carrier in biological systems. The nucleotides are regarded as bits of information and their sequence specifies some biological activity. The paradigm for carrying information rests in the genetic code: the relationship between nucleotide sequence in DNA, then RNA, and ultimately the sequence of amino acids in proteins. These ideas have provided the intellectual scaffold upon which the discipline of molecular biology has been built.

In recent years, this picture has been modified slightly. We have learned that the genome, especially in eukaryotes, is more complex. The protein coding sequences in DNA may account for less than 5% of the genome and considerable amounts of DNA seem to be involved in regulatory aspects of gene expression. We have learned that DNA is more complex than initially realized, especially in its structural features. It has been known for over 30 years that DNA can exist in two different right-handed double-helical forms, A- and B-DNA (Watson and Crick, 1953; Franklin and Goslin, 1953). Recently we have learned that it can also exist in a left-handed double helical form (Wang *et al.*, 1979). The right-handed conformations can accommodate any sequence of nucleotides, but the left-handed one forms most easily in sequences which have alternations of purines and pyrimidines. The fact that certain nucleotide sequences favor conformational changes in DNA leads to an extension of the information-carrying role of DNA.

In addition to carrying protein or RNA *coding information,* it can also carry *conformational information.* The latter phrase indicates that certain sequences facilitate conformational changes in DNA. The reversal

*Lecture delivered February 17, 1983.

of double helical twist favored by alternations of purines and pyrimidines is perhaps an extreme example of conformational information, but it is likely that other examples will be found (Rich, 1983).

I. Single Crystals and DNA Structure

The earlier structural work on DNA involved X-ray diffraction studies of fibers. These diffraction patterns have only limited resolution and are generally disordered to varying extents. Only in the past few years has it been possible to study the molecular structure of DNA by single-crystal X-ray analysis. This development is an outgrowth of advances in synthetic organic nucleotide chemistry which make it possible to produce oligonucleotides of defined sequence in quantities sufficient for crystallization experiments. Single crystals often diffract X rays at or near atomic resolution (~ 1 Å). Solution of these crystal structures provides a wealth of detail in contrast to the results of DNA fiber X-ray diffraction analyses. The first visualization of a double helix at atomic resolution was discovered in our laboratory in 1973 with crystalline dinucleoside monophosphates, which showed two right-handed base paired RNA fragments (Rosenberg et al., 1973; Day et al., 1973). Left-handed Z-DNA was discovered here in 1979 in a crystalline hexanucleoside pentaphosphate with the sequence d(CpGpCpGpCpG) (Wang et al., 1979). The crystal diffracted to 0.9 Å and its solution produced a large amount of experimental detail.

A variety of DNA conformations have now been visualized at or near atomic resolution. This includes the structure of B-DNA seen in a dodecamer (Wing et al., 1980) and several double-helical oligonucleotides which form A-DNA in single crystals (Shakked et al., 1981; Wang et al., 1982a,b; Conner et al., 1982). The significant features of these studies is that they provide precise structural information in which the sequence of nucleotides is seen to play a role in conformation. This reinforces the concept that DNA may contain conformational information as well as coding information.

Once we are aware that DNA can exist in various conformations, we are confronted with many questions. What induces conformational changes and what is their relation to each other? Are some conformations more stable in a physiological environment? Can we demonstrate that different conformations exist in vivo as well as in vitro? And finally, how are these changes used in biological systems? Here we will address several of these questions with respect to the left-handed Z conformation of the double helix.

II. A LEFT-HANDED DOUBLE HELIX

No one anticipated the structure of left-handed Z-DNA by using molecular model building, probably because it has several conformational features which distinguish it from right-handed B-DNA. In the first crystal structure analysis (Wang *et al.*, 1979), the double-helical hexanucleoside pentaphosphate molecules were found aligned along the crystal c axis; the molecule appeared to be a continuous helix running through the crystal. Figure 1 shows a van der Waals diagram of Z-DNA as seen in the crystal lattice. Three molecules are shown and there is a continuity of base pair stacking along the entire helical axis. In contrast to B-DNA, Z-DNA has one deep helical groove which is formally analogous to the minor groove of B-DNA. The concave major groove of B-DNA forms the convex outer surface of Z-DNA. The asymmetric unit in Z-DNA is a dinucleotide compared to a mononucleotide in B-DNA. The heavy line in Fig. 1 drawn between adjacent phosphate groups shows their zigzag organization in Z-DNA. This is because there are two different nucleotide conformations in Z-DNA. Figure 2 compares the conformation of deoxyguanosine in Z-DNA and B-DNA. In B-DNA, all of the bases have the anti conformation and a C2' endo pucker of the deoxyribose ring. In the Z-DNA crystal with alternating cytosine and guanine residues, the deoxycytidines all have the anti conformation while the deoxyguanosines are all syn with a C3' endo pucker. Every other residue in a Z-DNA molecule has the syn conformation. Figure 3 illustrates the conformation of nucleotide hexamers in the B and Z forms. The dinucleotide repeat in Z-DNA is due to the alternations of anti and syn conformations.

Z-DNA has 12 base pairs per helical turn, a pitch of 44.6 Å, and a diameter near 18 Å. In contrast, B-DNA typically has 10.5 base pairs per helical turn, a helical pitch of 34 Å, and a diameter of 20 Å. Z-DNA is thus slightly slimmer than B-DNA and has more base pairs per helical turn. Both Z-DNA and B-DNA consist of two antiparallel polynucleotide chains held together by Watson–Crick base pairs. However, the base pairs in the two structures have a different relationship to the

108   ALEXANDER RICH

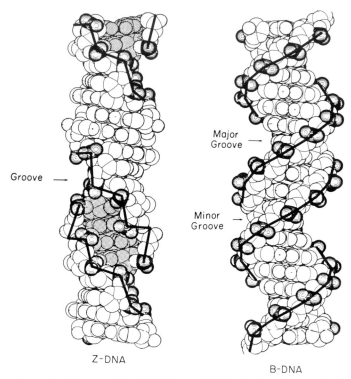

FIG. 1. van der Waals models of Z-DNA and B-DNA. The irregularity of the Z-DNA backbone is illustrated by the heavy lines that go from phosphate to phosphate residue along the chain. The Z-DNA is shown as it appears in the hexamer crystal. The groove in Z-DNA is quite deep, extending nearly to the axis of the double helix. In contrast, B-DNA has a smooth line connecting the phosphate groups and two grooves, neither one of which extends to the helix axis of the molecule.

sugar phosphate backbone, as shown in Fig. 4. DNA is drawn in the familiar ladder representation with the planar bases shown as flat plates. In converting a section of B-DNA to Z-DNA, the base pairs must flip over so that they are upside down relative to the orientation which they had in B-DNA. This flipping is brought about by rotating the purine residue about its glycosyl bond, from anti to syn. For the pyrimidines, both the base as well as the sugar rotate about. It is the rotation of every other sugar along the chain that produces the zigzag backbone conformation.

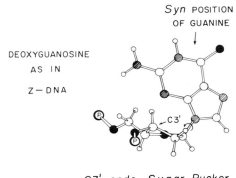

Syn POSITION
OF GUANINE

DEOXYGUANOSINE
AS IN
Z — DNA

C3' endo Sugar Pucker

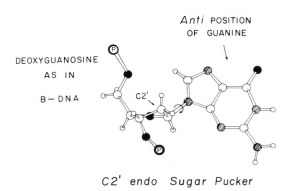

Anti POSITION
OF GUANINE

DEOXYGUANOSINE
AS IN
B — DNA

C2' endo Sugar Pucker

Fig. 2. Conformation of deoxyguanosine in B-DNA and in Z-DNA. The sugar is oriented so that the plane defined by C1'-O1'-C4' is horizontal. Atoms lying above this plane are in the endo conformation. The C3' is endo in Z-DNA while in B-DNA the C2' is endo. In addition, Z-DNA has guanine in the syn position, in contrast to the anti position in B-DNA. A curved arrow around the glycosyl carbon–nitrogen linkage indicates the site of rotation.

Figure 5 compares end views of Z-DNA and B-DNA. A shaded guanine–cytosine base pair is found in the center of B-DNA surrounded by the sugar phosphate chains. In Z-DNA, the base pair is located away from the center so that the guanine imidazole ring is found at the periphery. Several crystal structures of Z-DNA have been solved and they show some slight variations in conformation (Wang *et al.*, 1979, 1981; Drew *et al.*, 1980; Crawford *et al.*, 1981; Rich *et al.*, 1982; Fujii

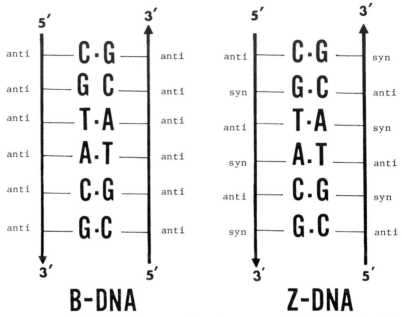

FIG. 3. The base conformations are shown for a segment of DNA in the B and Z conformations. Alternating residues in Z-DNA adopt syn and anti conformations. The three-dimensional structure of a hexamer with this sequence has been found to adopt the Z-DNA conformation (Wang *et al.*, 1984).

et al., 1982). Three different conformations have been seen, two of which are associated with slight alterations in the orientation of phosphate groups.

The stacking of base pairs on each other is different in Z-DNA and B-DNA as shown in Fig. 6. The stacking in Z-DNA is different in the sequence d(CpG) and in d(GpC), while in B-DNA they are similar. The d(CpG) sequence in Z-DNA has sheared base pairs so that the cytosine residues on opposite strands are stacked in the center of the molecule while the guanine residues are no longer stacking on bases. Guanine stacks upon the O1′ oxygen atoms of the sugar residues below. For the d(CpG) sequence there is a (−9°) rotation between successive base pairs, while the d(GpC) sequence has a −51° rotation. The helical axis passes through the center of the base pairs in B-DNA, producing a molecule with two grooves. In contrast, the Z-DNA helix axis falls outside the base pairs, producing a molecule with only one deep groove.

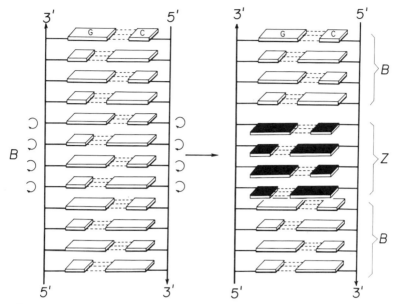

FIG. 4. A diagram illustrating the change in topological relationship if a four-base pair segment of B-DNA were converted into Z-DNA. The conversion is accomplished by rotation or flipping over the base pairs as indicated by the curved arrows. Rotation of the guanine residues about the glycosylic bond puts it into the syn conformation. For the deoxycytidine residues, both cytosine and deoxyribose are rotated.

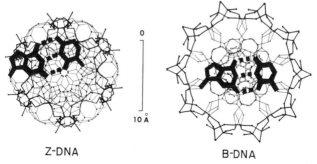

FIG. 5. End views of regular, idealized helical skeletal diagrams of Z-DNA and B-DNA. Heavier lines are used for the phosphate–sugar backbone. A guanine–cytosine base pair is shown by shading and the difference in the positions of the base pairs is quite striking; they are near the center of B-DNA but at the periphery of Z-DNA.

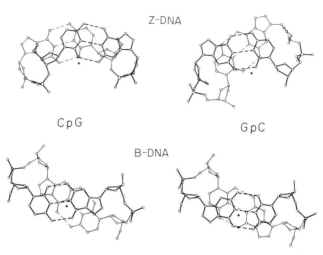

Fig. 6. A stacking diagram illustrating the overlap of successive bases along Z-DNA and B-DNA helix as viewed down the helix axis. The base pair drawn with heavier lines is stacked above the pair drawn with lighter lines. The left-hand column shows d(CpG) sequences of both Z-DNA and B-DNA, while d(GpC) sequences are on the right. The direction of the deoxyribose-phosphate chains is the same in all these diagrams. Note that the minor groove in B-DNA is found at the top while the analogous side of the base pairs is found at the bottom in Z-DNA. The black dot indicates the helical axis.

The Z-DNA structure was the first time that a syn conformation was used systematically in the formation of a polynucleotide structure. It has been known for many years that both purines and pyrimidines can rotate about their glycosyl bonds and these two conformations have been seen in a variety of crystallographic as well as solution studies. An early theoretical study (Haschemeyer and Rich, 1967) suggested that although purines could form the syn conformation without loss of energy, there was some steric hindrance to the formation of pyrimidine residues in syn. Experimental studies in solution generally indicate that purine residues can form syn conformations relatively easily but they are less common for pyrimidines (Davies, 1978). Since Z-DNA has every other residue along the chain in the syn conformation, it suggests that this conformation is more likely to be found in sequences with alternations of purines and pyrimidines. Although there is some energy loss due to close van der Waals crowding when pyrimidines are in the syn conformation, the energy loss is not very large.

A self-complementary Z-DNA structure with the sequence d(CpGpTpApCpG) (Fig. 4) has recently been solved to 1.2 Å resolution in which the cytosine residues have either methyl or bromine atoms attached to the C5 position (Wang *et al.*, 1984). The geometry of the AT base pairs in Z-DNA is similar to that of the CG base pairs with the adenine residues in the syn conformation and stacking interactions similar to those seen in Fig. 6. However, the water molecules in the helical groove of Z-DNA are disordered near the AT base pairs in contrast to the high level of ordering found in the solvent in the segments containing CG base pairs. The ordering is largely due to the presence of the amino group on the 2 position of guanine which hydrogen bonds to a water molecule and helps to organize others in the groove. The solvent disordering may be related to the fact that AT base pairs form Z-DNA less readily than CG base pairs.

III. Z-DNA in Solution

In 1972, Pohl and Jovin reported that the synthetic polydeoxynucleotide poly(dG–dC) went through a cooperative conformational change in solution when the concentration of salt was raised. In 4 M NaCl, the circular dichroism of the solution was nearly inverted compared to the spectrum in 0.1 M NaCl. Pohl and colleagues showed that the high-salt form of poly(dG–dC) could be induced by a variety of other factors including added alcohol (Pohl *et al.*, 1973; Pohl, 1976). The interpretation of this as a conformational change was reinforced by the observation that the Raman spectra of the high- and low-salt form of poly(dG–dC) differed considerably (Pohl *et al.*, 1973). Raman spectra measure the different types of vibrations of the components of macromolecules, including bond stretching and bending. Some of these vibrations are sensitive to conformational change. To a first approximation the Raman spectrum of a molecule is independent of whether it is fixed in a crystal lattice or tumbling free in solution. Raman spectroscopy is therefore a powerful tool for asking questions about the identity of a molecule in two different physical states. An analysis was carried out on the Z-DNA crystals (Thamann *et al.*, 1981), and it was discovered that the crystals had a Raman spectrum identical to that of the high-salt form of poly(dG–dC) and quite different from that of the low-salt form. From this it was inferred that the low-salt form represented right-handed B-DNA while the high-salt form was identified as Z-DNA. In solution, there is an equilibrium between right-handed and left-handed forms of DNA. The actual distribution between these two states is strongly influenced by environmental conditions as well as by the sequence of nucleotides.

In this equilibrium B-DNA is usually the lower energy state. However, Z-DNA can become the lower energy state when the system is modified in some way to stabilize it. The relative instability of Z-DNA compared to B-DNA is partly associated with the fact that the phosphate groups on opposite strands come closer together in Z-DNA than in B-DNA, as seen in Fig. 1. The distance of closest approach of the phosphate groups across the groove in Z-DNA is 7.7 Å compared to 11.7 Å across the minor groove in B-DNA (Wang *et al.*, 1981). Because the higher energy of Z-DNA has a large electrostatic component, it is not surprising that the initial observations concerning Z-DNA were made in solutions with high concentrations of salt, which reduce the phosphate–phosphate repulsion (Pohl and Jovin, 1972). Many factors are now known which stabilize Z-DNA or lower its energy so that the equilibrium shifts in its favor.

A number of chemical modifications have been discovered which influence the equilibrium (Rich *et al.*, 1984). One of the most important modifications from a physiological point of view is the methylation of cytosine C5 in CpG sequences. Behe and Felsenfeld (1981) found that poly(dG–m^{5}dC) exists as Z-DNA in a physiological salt solution, and B-DNA is less stable. The stabilization due to methylation can be understood by the manner in which the methyl group participates in hydrophobic bonding on the outer part of the Z-DNA double helix (Fujii *et al.*, 1982).

IV. NUCLEOTIDE SEQUENCES VARY IN THEIR TENDENCY TO FORM Z-DNA

Every other base in Z-DNA is in the syn conformation and Z-DNA formation is therefore favored in sequences containing alternations of purines and pyrimidines. Three kinds of regular polymers exist with simple alternations of purine and pyrimidine sequences: poly(dG–dC), poly(dC–dA)·poly(dG-dT), and poly(dA–dT). Poly(dG–dC) forms Z-DNA readily under various ionic conditions (Pohl and Jovin, 1972).

But, poly (dA–dC)·poly(dG–dT) does not form Z-DNA readily in solutions with elevated salt concentrations, although suggestive changes in the circular dichroism spectrum are found in high concentrations of CsF and in ethanolic solutions (Vorlickova *et al.*, 1982; Zimmer *et al.*, 1982). However, a Z-DNA type fiber diffraction pattern has been reported for poly(dC–dA)·poly(dG–dT) (Arnott *et al.*, 1980). As discussed below, DNA supercoiling provides a powerful force for Z-DNA formation and d(CA/TG)$_n$ segments can be stabilized as Z-DNA when cloned into circular plasmids (Nordheim and Rich, 1983b; Haniford and Pulleyblank, 1983). At present, attempts to demonstrate the formation of Z-DNA in poly(dA–dT) have been unsuccessful.

We can summarize the tendency of pyrimidine–purine dinucleotides to form Z-DNA in polymers as follows: CG > TG = CA > TA. As mentioned above, a structural basis for these differences has been found in the disordering of solvent water molecules in the helical groove near TA base pairs (Wang *et al.*, 1984).

V. SPECIFIC ANTI-Z-DNA ANTIBODIES

B-DNA and Z-DNA are in equilibrium under most physiological conditions: Z-DNA is in a higher energy state and is less stable than B-DNA, especially with linear DNA fragments. Synthetic poly(dG–dC) is stable as Z-DNA in 4 M NaCl, but in order to have it remain as Z-DNA in the lower ionic environment of a physiological medium some modifications are necessary. The imidazole ring of guanine, especially C8, is very accessible in Z-DNA compared to B-DNA. In B-DNA, C8-H is in van der Waals contact with the sugar–phosphate chain, but in Z-DNA it is on the outside of the molecule (Fig. 5). One of the first methods for stabilizing Z-DNA in a low-salt solution was through chemical bromination (Lafer *et al.*, 1981; Moller *et al.*, 1983). Poly(dG–dC) was placed in a 4 M salt solution where it assumed the Z-DNA conformation and Br$_2$ was added. The bromine reacts largely with the C8 position of guanine and to a lesser extent with the C5 position of cytosine. The bromine atom at C8 sterically prevents guanine from adopting the anti conformation (Bugg and Thewalt, 1969). When the salt is dialyzed away from brominated poly(dG–dC), it remains as Z-DNA. Only 1 guanine C8H atom in 3 is replaced by bromine and 1 cytosine in 6 has reacted to stabilize Z-DNA. Immunological experiments were carried out on this material by Lafer *et al.* (1981) who demonstrated that Z-DNA is a strong immunogen, producing antibodies with a high degree of specificity for Z-DNA. In contrast, B-DNA is a very poor immunogen. The organism probably becomes tolerant to B-DNA during the early stages of embryological development. It is likely that Z-DNA is not seen by the cells of the immune system during early embryogenesis. When DNA is released from cells which have broken down, nuclease cleavage probably converts any Z-DNA to B-DNA by releasing torsional strain. However, antibodies specific for Z-DNA arise in certain autoimmune disease states, and are found in both murine and human systemic lupus erythematosus (Lafer *et al.*, 1981, 1983a).

Monoclonal antibodies have been produced against Z-DNA (Moller *et al.*, 1982; Pohl, 1983; Thomae *et al.*, 1983). Some monoclonal antibodies bind to the base pairs on the surface of Z-DNA while others have a preference for the sugars and negatively charged phosphate groups. One of the interesting properties of polyclonal and some monoclonal antibodies against Z-DNA is that they combine with Z-DNA even in the presence of high concentrations of NaCl (Nordheim *et al.*, 1981; Lafer *et al.*, 1983b). This is particularly useful, as it makes it possible to work with polymers as well as plasmids in different salt concentrations. Varying the salt concentration can be used to control the degree of Z-DNA formation and the specificity and reactivity of the antibodies can be determined.

Anti-Z-DNA specific antibodies have been used to look for Z-DNA in cells, using the methods of indirect immune fluorescence. In these studies an anti-Z-DNA antibody raised in one species, for example, is added to a fixed cytological preparation. Then a second antibody is added which was raised in another species against the first antibody. The second antibody has a fluorescent chromophore conjugated to it, and it is visualized by illuminating the preparation at a wavelength which excites fluorescence. Photographs are taken in the emitting wavelength so that position of the initial antibodies can be seen. Several organisms have been studied and yield fluorescent patterns in their genomes (Rich *et al.*, 1984).

VI. STABILIZATION OF Z-DNA BY SPECIFIC PROTEIN BINDING

As Z-DNA is seen in a variety of biological tissues using indirect immune fluorescence, it raises the general question of how it is stabilized *in vivo*. High concentrations of salt are not generally found in most biological systems. However, some cations are especially effective in Z-DNA stabilization. The polyamines spermine and spermidine complex specifically to the outer surface of Z-DNA as visualized in the crystals (Wang *et al.*, 1979) and stabilize it through ionic interactions (Behe and Felsenfeld, 1981). Chemical modification of DNA, especially in eukaryotes, occurs in methylation of cytosine C-5 in CpG dinucleotides. Potentially, this may contribute to the *in vivo* stabilization of Z-DNA, but it is not clear whether the level of methylation is adequate.

The major molecules with which the nucleic acids interact are proteins, and a class of proteins exists which can bind specifically to left-handed Z-DNA but not to B-DNA. These proteins have been found in the nuclei of eukaryotic cells (Nordheim *et al.*, 1982a). Z-DNA binding proteins were initially isolated from the nuclei of *Drosophila* cells using the method of affinity chromatography. Brominated poly(dG-dC), stable in the Z form at low NaCl concentrations, was attached covalently to Sephadex G-25. The nuclei of *Drosophila* cells were lysed and the salt concentration was raised to 2 *M* in order to dissociate the proteins from nucleic acids. After removal of DNA, the proteins were precipitated with ammonium sulfate and redissolved in a physiological salt solution. B-DNA binding proteins were precipitated by addition of sonicated single- and double-stranded *Escherichia coli* DNA. The remaining proteins free of DNA were absorbed to an affinity column containing Br-poly(dG–dC)-Sephadex G-25. Proteins were eluted from the column with NaCl and fractions were assayed for binding to ^{3}H-labeled Br-poly(dG–dC) (Z-DNA) and ^{3}H-labeled poly(dG–dC) (B-DNA), using nitrocellulose filter binding. Naked DNA molecules pass through the holes in nitrocellulose filters but if proteins are bound to the DNA, it does not pass through. The first passage over the column yielded a mixture of B- and Z-DNA binding proteins (Fig. 7). A second passage yielded proteins that come off in a single peak. This had binding activity to the brominated poly(dG–dC) (Z-DNA) but not to poly(dG–dC) itself (B-DNA).

Polyacrylamide gel analysis of these proteins revealed five major bands and several minor bands. Some of the major bands can also be seen in a gel analysis of total unfractionated proteins from the *Drosophila* cell nucleus. The major bands migrated with apparent molecular weights greater than 70,000. It appears that not only are there numerous

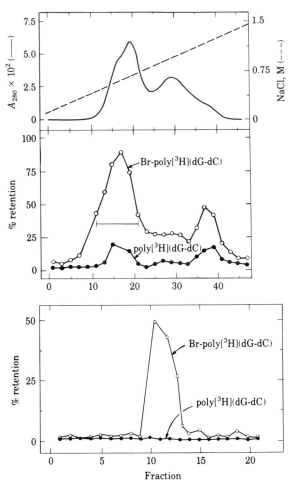

FIG. 7. Column chromatography of Z-DNA binding proteins from *Drosophila* nuclei. Two successive elution patterns are shown. In the upper one, the protein was eluted off the affinity column with increasing NaCl concentration. The large peak indicated by the horizonal bar was passed over the column a second time with the addition of more native and denatured *E. coli* DNA. Elution with 1 *M* NaCl yielded proteins with only Z-DNA binding seen in the nitrocellulose filter binding assay.

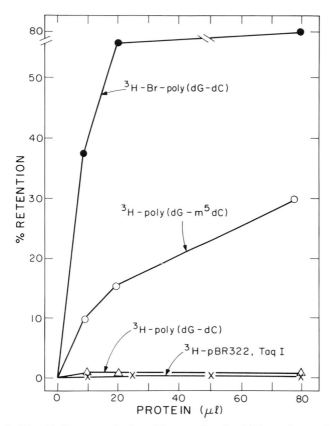

FIG. 8. Filter binding assays for four different radioactive DNA samples as a function of increasing amounts of Z-DNA binding proteins. The ³H-labeled Br-poly-pBR322 is in the Z-DNA form; ³H-labeled poly(dG-dC) and the *Taq*I digest of ³H-labeled pBR322 are in the B-DNA form. The methylated polymer ³H-labeled poly(dG-m⁵dC) was partially retained in this assay. All binding experiments were carried out in 150 m*M* NaCl.

species of Z-DNA binding proteins in the *Drosophila* nucleus, but some of them seem to be moderately abundant.

The binding activity of these proteins is shown in more detail in Fig. 8, where filter binding studies are shown with several polymers as a function of increasing amounts of Z-DNA binding proteins. Addition of Z-DNA binding proteins results in high retention of Z-DNA [Br-poly(dG–dC)] but there is no retention of B-DNA either in the form of poly(dG–dC) or a *Taq*I restriction enzyme digest of the plasmid pBR322 which produces DNA fragments of the same length as in the synthetic polynucleotides. These assays are carried out in 0.15 M NaCl, at which concentration the methylated polymer, poly(dG–m^{5}dC), still forms B-DNA but not Z-DNA. However, in the presence of the Z-DNA binding protein, the methylated polymer is retained on the filter. Precipitation of the methylated polymer by antibodies specific for Z-DNA has been studied in both the presence and absence of the Z-DNA binding protein. The results show that the Z-DNA binding proteins have effectively flipped the polymer from the B configuration to the Z configuration and held it there. In the presence of the Z-DNA binding proteins the antibody will bind to the polymer, but in their absence the antibody will not bind. The *Drosophila* proteins have the property of shifting the equilibrium between B-DNA and Z-DNA toward the Z-DNA side. Some experiments have been done which suggest that some of the proteins appear to have sequence-dependent Z-DNA binding properties (Nordheim *et al.*, 1982a).

These proteins are heterogeneous and are being characterized more fully. In general, one would anticipate that Z-DNA binding proteins are likely to be of two different types. The first type is that which recognizes Z-DNA by binding to its backbone. It would be relatively insensitive to sequence. A second type of protein would bind to the bases as well and it would be likely to be sensitive to sequence. These two different types of proteins appear to be found in an analysis of monoclonal antibodies (Moller *et al.*, 1982).

VII. Negative Supercoiling Stabilizes Z-DNA

Most DNA in biological systems is under topological constraint, which means that the long molecule is twisted about itself or supercoiled. Supercoiling exists whenever the number of turns of the double helix is not equal to the number of turns the molecule would have were it in a linear or relaxed form. *In vivo,* DNA is generally not found in a linear form but is either in a circular form as in plasmids or it is constrained in topological domains. In eukaryotes, this occurs because the DNA is attached periodically to the nuclear matrix. In bacteria a complex series of enzymes, called topoisomerases, keeps DNA in a negatively supercoiled or slightly underwound state. In eukaryotic chromatin the negative superhelical turns are largely taken up in the DNA coiling around nucleosomes so the DNA is not torsionally strained even though it is supercoiled. However, it is possible that some of the DNA is subjected to transient torsional stress. This would be especially true if nucleosomes dissociate when the chromatin is transcriptionally active.

Negatively supercoiled DNA has a higher free energy than relaxed DNA. The free energy of supercoiling is proportional to the square of the number of superhelical turns or the superhelical density. Superhelical density is the number of supercoils divided by the number of turns the double helix would have if the DNA were fully relaxed, as, for example, in a nicked or linearized plasmid. The free energy of supercoiling can be used to change the DNA, since processes that reduce the number of superhelical turns are energetically favored. In negatively supercoiled DNA, these processes include unpairing of bases with strand separation, unwinding of the double helix, as well as binding to proteins as in nucleosome formation. Another process that is facilitated in a negatively supercoiled plasmid is stabilization of Z-DNA (Peck *et al.*, 1982; Singleton *et al.*, 1982).

Figure 9 illustrates the effect on supercoiling of converting one turn

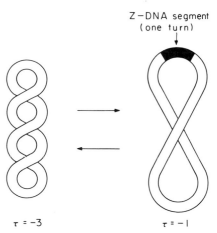

Z−DNA segment
(one turn)

$\tau = -3$ $\tau = -1$

FIG. 9. Schematic diagram in which the double helix is represented as a tubular structure. The diagram on the left represents a negatively supercoiled plasmid with three negative supercoil turns. In the diagram at the right, a 12-bp segment of B-DNA has converted to Z-DNA, and this results in a loss of two superhelical turns, from $\tau = -3$ to $\tau = -1$. The energy of supercoiling is used to stabilize Z-DNA.

of right-handed B-DNA into a left-handed Z-DNA segment. The negative supercoiling energy is adequate to stabilize one turn of left-handed Z-DNA. This effect can be visualized in a number of different experimental modes. One of the simplest is a filter binding experiment in which a negatively supercoiled plasmid is exposed to varying concentrations of anti-Z-DNA antibody and the complex is then passed through a nitrocellulose filter (Nordheim *et al.,* 1982b). If the plasmid is supercoiled sufficiently to induce the formation of Z-DNA, it is detected by retention of the plasmid–antibody complex on the filter (Fig. 10). Relaxed plasmids are not retained on the filter in the presence of the antibody. However, at a critical superhelical density, the plasmids begin to be retained, and as the number of negative superhelical turns increase we see a corresponding increase in the amount of retention. This experiment demonstrates the manner in which increasing

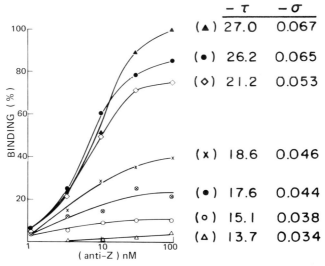

	$-\tau$	$-\sigma$
(▲)	27.0	0.067
(●)	26.2	0.065
(◇)	21.2	0.053
(×)	18.6	0.046
(●)	17.6	0.044
(○)	15.1	0.038
(△)	13.7	0.034

FIG. 10. The binding of radioactive negatively supercoiled plasmids to increasing concentrations of anti-Z-DNA antibodies is detected by nitrocellulose filter binding. The plasmid pLP32 is a derivative of pBR322 carrying a 32-bp insert of alternating CG sequences. The different curves represent antibody binding to the plasmids with different numbers of negative superhelical turns ($-\tau$) or superhelical density (σ), as listed in the columns next to the symbol. The number of negative superhelical turns is measured in agarose gels which separate different topoisomers.

negative superhelical densities result in the induction of Z-DNA formation as detected by the binding of anti-Z-DNA antibodies. The complex
of antibodies bound to negatively supercoiled plasmids can be visualized in the electron microscope. Figure 11 shows a number of fields
with dark staining globular antibodies attached to negatively supercoiled plasmids. In some cases, more than one antibody is seen (Nordheim *et al.*, 1982b).

The antibody binding sites can be precisely localized to map the
position of Z-DNA formation within a supercoiled plasmid. Glutaraldehyde crosslinking is used to fix the antibody on the DNA. This is
followed by restriction endonucleolytic DNA fragmentation and nitrocellulose filtration (Nordheim *et al.*, 1982b). DNA fragments containing the cross-linked antibody are retained on the filter and will thus be
missing from the filtrate which is analyzed by gel electrophoresis. We
can illustrate this experiment using the plasmid pBR322 with $(CG)_{16}$
spliced into it (Fig. 12). The *Hae*III restriction fragment which contains
the 32-base pair insert (12i, Fig. 12B) virtually disappears from the
filtrate, indicating Z-DNA formation in this segment.

When this experiment is carried out with pBR322 in the absence of
any insert, a 14-base pair segment of alternating purines and pyrimidines with one base pair out of alternation is found to form Z-DNA (Fig.
13). Further evidence for the formation of Z-DNA in this region of
plasmid pBR322 is shown by the fact that the cleavage of three restriction endonucleases (*Hae*III, *Hha*I, and *Sau*3A) are inhibited by the
presence of the antibody (Azorin *et al.*, 1983). It is also possible that the
Z-DNA segment may include an even larger segment than just the 14
base pairs of alternating purines and pyrimidines outlined in Fig. 13.
Further work will have to be done to determine the exact position of the
B–Z junction in order to be certain about the extent of the domain.
What is important here is that this approach provides an experimental
method which can be used for locating segments of Z-DNA in any
plasmid.

What are the implications in having one base pair out of purine–
pyrimidine alternation in this Z-DNA segment of pBR322? In this case
there is one cytosine residue in the syn conformation as well as 6
purines within the 14-bp dashed box of Fig. 13 The energy loss in
having occasional syn conformations of pyrimidine residues is not very
great; however, the systematic use of the pyrimidine syn conformation

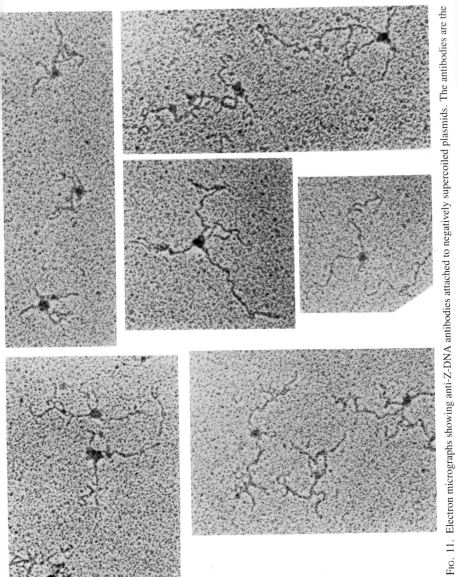

FIG. 11. Electron micrographs showing anti-Z-DNA antibodies attached to negatively supercoiled plasmids. The antibodies are the

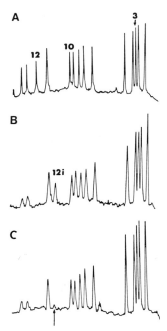

FIG. 12. Identification of Z-DNA segments cross-linked to anti-Z-DNA antibodies. The negatively supercoiled plasmids were restricted with *Hae*III endonuclease and passed through a nitrocellulose filter. The filtrate was analyzed on a polyacrylamide gel. The DNA fragments were stained with ethidium bromide, and the photograph was scanned on a densitometer. Electrophoretic migration was from right (top) to left (bottom), so that the larger fragments are at the right. (A) pBR322. (B) pLP32. The *Hae*III fragment 12 has the insert, and it becomes 12i. (C) pLP32 and antibody. The fragment 12i virtually disappears when the antibody is cross-linked to the negatively supercoiled plasmid.

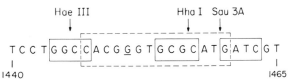

FIG. 13. The nucleotide sequences of pBR322 from residues 1440 to 1465. Enclosed in the dashed box is a 14-bp sequence of alternating purine and pyrimidine residues with one base pair (*G*) out of alternation. This corresponds to the proposed attachment site of the anti-Z-DNA specific antibody. The solid boxes contain the recognition sites for *Hae*III, *Hha*I, and *Sau*3A. These enzymes are blocked by the antibody.

would accumulate a significant bias against Z-DNA. In the pBR322 sequence, there is one site which contains 10 base pairs of alternating purines and pyrimidines and others contain 9 base pairs. Nonetheless, the first segment that we detect in our assay forming Z-DNA under negative superhelical stress is the one shown in Fig. 13. It is likely that the added length of the segment of Z-DNA contributes more stabilization than the destabilization associated with one cytosine residue in the syn conformation. This stabilizatin is probably related to the cooperativity of the B to Z conversion (Pohl and Jovin, 1972) and it is likely to be strongly dependent on the nucleotide sequence. A computer search of pBR322 reveals that there is no larger segment than the one shown in Fig. 13 with one residue out of alternation. However, another segment of 14 base pairs is found with one residue out of alternation which has not detectably formed Z-DNA at this superhelical density. Inspection of its sequence reveals that it has a higher proportion of AT base pairs and is thus less likely to form Z-DNA (Nordheim *et al.*, 1982b).

Experiments of this type demonstrate that negative supercoiling is a powerful factor in Z-DNA stabilization. However, it should be emphasized that the actual formation of Z-DNA *in vivo* will be strongly influenced by the presence of Z-DNA binding proteins which are also likely to stabilize Z-DNA to a considerable extent. Furthermore, they may significantly alter the distribution of Z-DNA which one would anticipate in the absence of the protein. The important biological consideration involves the interaction of negative supercoiling and torsional strain in DNA as well as the extent to which Z-DNA binding proteins are used.

VIII. Z-DNA IN SV40 AND TRANSCRIPTIONAL ENHANCERS

The methodology described above can be applied very simply to any circular genome to search for segments that can form Z-DNA. One of the circular eukaryotic DNAs frequently studied is that found in the DNA tumor virus, simian virus 40 (SV40). The 5243-bp viral genome codes for early and late proteins. The early proteins are important for DNA replication and transcription, while the late proteins are used for packaging the virus. The transcription of these proteins is regulated by a control region near the origin of replication at map position zero. Although the control region is less than a few hundred nucleotides, it carries out a number of functions including regulation of viral replication and transcription. It also contains a transcriptional enhancer, that is, a small segment of DNA which by its presence ensures a high level of transcriptional activity for the early transcriptional unit. Enhancers are cis-acting components of eukaryotic promoters that stimulate transcription in a manner relatively independent of position and orientation. Enhancers may represent entry sites for transcriptional factors onto DNA, possible RNA polymerase. Transcriptional enhancers are found in many viral and natural systems and they have been shown to enhance transcription by up to two orders of magnitude. In SV40, the transcriptional enhancer is associated with a region which contains two 72-base pair repeated segments (Benoist and Chambon, 1981; Gruss et al., 1981). Deletion of these 72-base pair repeats and some of the surrounding DNA inactivates the virus.

In infected host cells the SV40 genome exists in the nucleus as a nucleosomal chromatin structure called the minichromosome. The nucleosomes on the minichromosomes are not distributed at random over the DNA, but a nucleosomal free gap is found over the control region near the origin of replication (Varshavsky et al., 1981). Although negative superhelical turns are absorbed by the nucleosomes of the minichromosome, there has been a report of torsional strain in transcriptionally active SV40 minichromosomes (Luchnik et al., 1982).

Experiments were carried out to see whether Z-DNA forms in negatively supercoiled SV40 DNA. The protocol was similar to that described above. SV40 DNA was negatively supercoiled and retention on nitrocellulose filters was detected in the presence of Z-DNA antibodies (Nordheim and Rich, 1983a). SV40 DNA begins to be retained on the filter at a negative superhelical density of 0.045 when it is assayed in 150 mM NaCl. This is in the range of negative supercoiling that has been found in prokaryotic biological systems. At higher levels of negative supercoiling, the percentage retention on the nitrocellulose filter increases accordingly.

The sequences that form Z-DNA were determined using the technique described above. Negatively supercoiled plasmids were cross-linked to the anti-Z-DNA antibodies with 0.1% glutaraldehyde, and the initial experiments were carried out using the restriction enzyme MboII, which cuts the DNA into 17 pieces. One fragment was found to be retained on the filter, the segment which spanned the origin. Accordingly, two other restriction enzymes were added, *Bgl*I, which cuts precisely at map position zero, the origin of replication, and *Pvu*II, which cuts 273 base pairs away. This generates a fragment that covers most of the viral control functions. It can be seen that a densitometer scan of the DNA fragments in the filtrate (Fig. 14) is the same for the SV40 DNA in the absence and presence of the antibody except for the fact that the fragment 273 bp in length is significantly reduced. This experiment dramatically illustrates that although the plasmid contains over 5 kb of DNA, Z-DNA formation occurs only in the control region of the virus.

Additional experiments were carried out to locate more precisely the Z-DNA forming segments (Nordheim and Rich, 1983a). The position

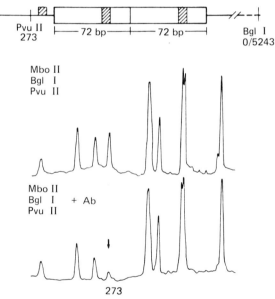

FIG. 14. Identification of the major region in the SV40 genome with potential for Z-DNA formation. Supercoiled SV40 circles were complexed with anti-Z-DNA antibodies and cross-linked. After digestion with restriction endonucleases *Mbo*II, *Bgl*II, and *Pvu*II, it was filtered. The filtrate was analyzed by gel electrophoresis and scanning with a densitometer. Glutaraldehyde cross-linking was performed in the absence (top) and presence (bottom) of anti-Z-DNA specific antisera (Ab). A clear reduction in scanning intensity can be seen in the 273-bp fragment which is located between the *Bgl*I and *Pvu*II cutting sites.

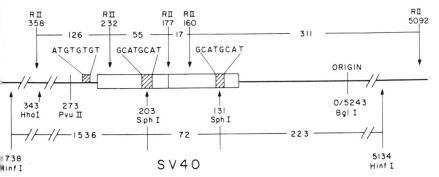

FIG. 15. Location of potential Z-DNA sites in the SV40 origin region. Crosshatched segments indicate the three major regions that can form Z-DNA in the SV40 genome and the base sequences of these sites are given. Cutting sites for several restriction endonucleases within this region are indicated, as well as the lengths of some restriction fragments. The 72-bp repeat segments are shown as rectangular boxes on the SV40 genome.

of the *Bgl*I, *Pvu*II, and other restriction sites around the control region of the virus is shown in Fig. 15. The same experiment with cross-linked antibodies was carried out using *Eco*RII cleavage, and retention on the nitrocellulose filter was observed of fragments containing 311, 55, and 126 base pairs. Analysis of the sequence of SV40 reveals that it has one segment containing nine base pairs of alternating purines and pyrimidines, and three segments containing eight base pairs. The nine-base pair segment contains the sequence ATAT and was not found to form Z-DNA. It is interesting that all three of the eight base pair segments are found in the control region as shown in Fig. 15. It seemed likely that these were the three regions forming Z-DNA in the three fragments which were retained on the filter paper following the *Eco*RII restriction digestion. Two of these sequences contain the recognition sequence for *Sph*I, and are found in the 72-base pair repeats. Another experiment was carried out which showed that binding the anti-Z-DNA antibody inhibited *Sph*I cleavage of negatively supercoiled SV40 DNA. These experiments lead us to believe that negatively supercoiled SV40 forms Z-DNA in three different segments in and near the 72-base pair repeats of the SV40 control region.

Experiments have been carried out on SV40 minichromosomes which reinforce the idea that Z-DNA may be forming in the 72-bp repeat regions at the *Sph*I site. If the minichromosomes are incubated with the Z-DNA affinity column material (brominated poly(dG–dC) attached covalently to Sephadex), proteins leave the minichromosome and become attached to the Z-DNA (Azorin and Rich, 1984). A prominent protein is seen of approximately 200,000 daltons. These proteins bind strongly to negatively supercoiled SV40 DNA, but not to the relaxed DNA. When they are bound they inhibit cleavage by *Sph*I and their removal from the minichromosome increases the accessibility of the *Sph*I restriction endonuclease to the minichromosome. Other restriction enzymes, however, are not affected by this protein removal. These experiments suggest that one or more Z-DNA binding proteins cover the enhancer region, especially near the *Sph*I site.

Transcriptionally active chromatin has many sites which are hypersensitive to DNase I digestion. In the SV40 minichromosome, two segments of hypersensitivity for DNase I cleavage have been identified within the control region covering the origin of replication and the transcriptional enhancer, respectively. Fine structure mapping of DNase I hypersensitive sites in the enhancer region (Cereghini *et al.,* 1983) identified DNase I cleavage sites. These were found to be approximately 25 base pairs on either side of the three hatched segments forming Z-DNA shown in Fig. 15 (Nordheim and Rich, 1983a). These hypersensitive sites on either side of the Z-DNA forming regions may have their positions determined in part by the presence of the Z-DNA binding proteins covering that region.

Mutational analyses have been carried out by several groups to characterize the boundaries of the SV40 enhancer element. The conclusions of these studies suggest that two of the three identified Z-DNA segments might be important for the physiological activity of the SV40 enhancer. A survey of other transcriptional enhancers showed that pairs of segments with the potential of forming Z-DNA are found in a number of transcriptional enhancers with 50 to 80 base pairs found between the two Z-DNA forming segments (Nordheim and Rich, 1983a). The distance between Z-DNA forming regions may reflect the formation of a structure in which the DNA is wrapped around a dimer of Z-DNA binding proteins so that both Z-DNA forming regions are in contact with the two dimer subunits. Formation of such a particle might be recognized by RNA polymerase or other transcriptional factors which could dislodge the Z-DNA binding proteins; the subsequent spontaneous conversion of the Z-DNA segments to B-DNA could produce a local increase in negative supercoiling which may alter local chromatin structure and facilitate entry of RNA polymerase onto the molecule. This speculative hypothesis points out the need for more detailed experimental analysis of the mechanism of transcriptional enhancement. It is possible that Z-DNA may be used in one class of enhancers, while other classes may achieve equivalent effects such as the generation of local superhelical stress using alternative mechanisms.

A wild-type variant of SV40 is found which contains only one copy of the 72-base pair repeat. This variant (SV40*) has been used to examine the effect of transitions and transversions in the Z-DNA forming regions on transcriptional enhancement and viral activity in experiments outlined in Fig. 16 (Herr *et al.*, 1984). Introduction of transitions

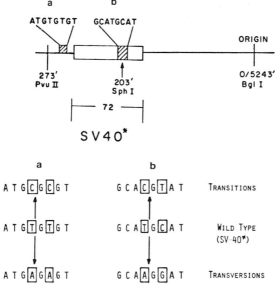

FIG. 16. A diagram of site-directed mutagenesis experiments to test the role of Z-DNA in a transcriptional enhancer. The SV40* wild type is used, which has only one copy of the 72-base pair repeat. Mutations are introduced into the two Z-DNA forming segments. Two pyrimidines are mutated in each Z segment. In the transitions, the thymines are changed to cytosine, or cytosine to thymine. In the transversions, thymines are changed to adenine and cytosine to guanine. The transversions no longer have the alternating purine–pyrimidine sequence which is favored for Z-DNA formation.

maintains the alternations of purines and pyrimidines and the potential for forming Z-DNA. These mutations do not result in a significant impairment of viral activity as measured by plaque formation. Furthermore, the transcriptional enhancer maintains its activity as assayed in a separate system. The introduction of transversions, however, has a marked effect on all of these activities. When the indicated transversions are introduced into both of the Z-DNA forming segments (Fig. 16), the virus is completely inactivated and the transcriptional enhancer loses its ability to activate transcription. The transversions break up the alternation of purines and pyrimidines which is favored in Z-DNA formation. These experiments together with the Z-DNA binding proteins that attach to the control support the idea that Z-DNA is involved in the SV40 transcriptional enhancer activity.

The experiments on SV40 provide the most detailed example to date of a specific biological role which may be carried out by Z-DNA. The use of site-directed mutagenesis in comparing the effects of either transitions or transversion on Z-DNA formation and the resulting phenotypic consequences may provide a valuable method for investigating a number of other systems as well.

IX. OTHER BIOLOGICAL ROLES FOR Z-DNA

Although we know a great deal about the structure and chemistry of Z-DNA, much less is known about how it acts in biological systems. It may act in a positive regulatory role, as in the transcriptional enhancer described above. However, it may also act as a negative regulatory element in the transcription of tRNA genes by RNA polymerase III (Hipskind and Clarkson, 1983). In these experiments a nine-base pair segment with the sequence TGCGCGTGC seems to prevent transcription *in vitro*. Its removal or replacement with a non-Z-forming sequence leads to tRNA transcription.

Z-DNA may also play a role in genetic recombination. Kmiec and Holloman (1984) have been studying synapsis formation in homologous circular plasmids as promoted by a *Rec*I protein from Ustilago. They have demonstrated the formation of Z-DNA in the region of the paranemic joint. Probably it forms there because the initial pairing of strands from the two homologous DNA circles introduces torsional strain. Formation of a segment of right-handed DNA is accompanied by formation of a compensatory segment of left-handed Z-DNA. This may be a general feature of this type of recombination.

In describing the potential role of Z-DNA, one can in principal think of two different effects, distal and proximal. Proximal effects are those associated with interactions in the immediate vicinity of the segment forming Z-DNA. Distal effects are those which may be distributed over long stretches of the genome, in which the role of Z-DNA in regulating the negative superhelical density of a DNA domain may be important in modifying its biological activity. In considering potential biological roles, it may be useful to recognize these two alternative modes of action.

The biological roles of Z-DNA will ultimately be understood in the context of identifying and characterizing the various proteins which interact with this left-handed form of the double helix. This field of protein characterization is just beginning. When it is fully developed we may find that Z-DNA is used quite widely in a variety of activities.

ACKNOWLEDGMENTS

This research was supported by grants from the National Institutes of Health, the American Cancer Society, the National Aeronautics and Space Administration, and the National Science Foundation.

REFERENCES

Arnott, S., Chandrasekaran, R., Birdsall, D. L., Leslie, A. G. W., and Ratliff, R. L. (1980). *Nature (London)* **283**, 743–745.

Azorin, F., and Rich, A. (1984). In preparation.

Azorin, F., Nordheim, A., and Rich, A. (1983). *EMBO J.* **2**, 649–655.

Behe, M., and Felsenfeld, G. (1981). *Proc. Natl. Acad. Sci. U.S.A.* **78**, 1619–1623.

Benoist, C., and Chambon, P. (198i). *Nature (London)* **290**, 304–310.

Bugg, C. E., and Thewalt, U. (1969). *Biochem. Biophys. Res. Commun.* **37**, 623–628.

Cereghini, S., Herbomel, P., Jounneau, J., Saragosti, S., Katinka, M., Bourachot, B., de Crombrugghe, M., and Yaniv, M. (1983). *Cold Spring Harbor Symp. Quant. Biol.* **47**, 935–944.

Conner, B. N., Takano, T., Tanaka, S., Itakura, S., and Dickerson, R. E. (1982). *Nature (London)* **295**, 294–297.

Crawford, J. L., Kolpak, F. J., Wang, A. H.-J., Quigley, G. J., van Boom, J. H., van der Marel, G., and Rich, A. (1981). *Proc. Natl. Acad. Sci. U.S.A.* **77**, 4016–4020.

Davies, D. B. (1978). *Prog. NMR Spectrosc.* **12**, 135–186.

Day, R. O., Seeman, N. C., Rosenberg, J. M., and Rich, A. (1973). *Proc. Natl. Acad. Sci. U.S.A.* **70**, 849–853.

Drew, H., Takano, T., Tanaka, S., Itakura, K., and Dickerson, R. E. (1980). *Nature (London)* **286**, 567–573.

Franklin, R. E., and Goslin, R. (1953). *Nature (London)* **171**, 740–742.

Fujii, S., Wang, A. H.-J., van der Marel, G., van Boom, J. H., and Rich, A. (1982). *Nucleic Acids Res.* **10**, 7879–7892.

Gruss, P., Dhar, R., and Khoury, G. (1981). *Proc. Natl. Acad. Sci. U.S.A.* **78**, 943–947.

Haniford, D. B., and Pulleyblank, D. E. (1983). *Nature (London)* **302**, 632–634.

Haschemeyer, A. E. V., and Rich, A. (1967). *J. Mol. Biol.* **27**, 369–384.

Herr, W., Gluzman, B., Nordheim, A., and Rich, A. (1984). In preparation.

Hipskind, R. A., and Clarkson, S. G. (1983). *Cell,* **34**, 881–890.

Kmiec, E. B., and Holloman, W. K. (1984). *Cell,* **36**, 593–598.

Lafer, E. M., Moller, A., Nordheim, A., Stollar, B. D., and Rich, A. (1981). *Proc. Natl. Acad. Sci. U.S.A.* **78**, 3546–3550.

Lafer, E. M., Valle, R. P. C., Moller, A., Nordheim, A., Schur, P. H., Rich, A., and Stollar, B. D. (1983a). *J. Clin. Invest.* **71**, 314–321.

Lafer, E. M., Moller, A., Valle, R. P. C., Nordheim, A., Rich, A., and Stollar, B. D. (1983b). *Cold Spring Harbor Symp. Quant. Biol.* **47**, 155–162.

Luchnik, A. N., Bakayev, V. V., Zbarsky, I. B., and Georgiev, G. P. (1982). *EMBO J.* **1**, 1353–1359.

Moller, A., Gabriels, J. E., Lafer, E. M., Nordheim, A., Rich, A., and Stollar, B. D. (1982). *J. Biol. Chem.* **257**, 12081–12085.

Moller, A., Nordheim, A., Kozlowski, S. A., Patel, D., and Rich, A. (1983). *Biochemistry* **23**, 54–62.

Nordheim, A., and Rich, A. (1983a) *Nature (London)* **303**, 674–679.

Nordheim, A., and Rich, A. (1983b). *Proc. Natl. Acad. Sci. U.S.A.* **80**, 1821–1825.

Nordheim, A., Pardue, M. L., Lafer, E. M., Moller, A., Stollar, B. D., and Rich, A. (1981). *Nature (London)* **294**, 417–422.

Nordheim, A., Tesser, P., Azorin, F., Kwon, Y. H., Moller, A., and Rich, A. (1982a). *Proc. Natl. Acad. Sci. U.S.A.* **79**, 7729–7733.

Nordheim, A., Lafer, E. M., Peck, L. J., Wang, J. C., Stollar, B. D., and Rich, A. (1982b). *Cell* **31**, 309–318.

Peck, L. J., Nordheim, A., Rich, A., and Wang, J. C. (1982). *Proc. Natl. Acad. Sci. U.S.A.* **79**, 4560–4564.

Pohl, F. M. (1983). *Cold Spring Harbor Symp. Quant. Biol.* **47**, 113–118.

Pohl, F. M., and Jovin, T. M. (1972). *J. Mol. Biol.* **67**, 375–396.

Pohl, F. (1976). *Nature (London)* **260**, 365–366.

Pohl, F. M., Ranade, A., and Stockburger, M. (1973). *Biochim. Biophys. Acta* **335**, 85–92.

Rich, A. (1983). *Cold Spring Harbor Symp. Quant. Biol.* **47**, 1–12.

Rich, A., Quigley, G. J., and Wang, A. H.-J. (1982). *In* "Biomolecular Stereodynamics" (R. H. Sarma, ed.), pp. 35–52. Adenine Press,

Rich, A., Nordheim, A., and Wang, A. H.-J. (1984). *Annu. Rev. Biochem.* **53**, 781–846.

Rosenberg, J. M., Seeman, N. C., Kim, J. J. P., Suddath, F. L., Nicholes, H. B., and Rich, A. (1973). *Nature (London)* **243**, 150–154.

Shakked, Z., Rabinovich, D., Cruse, W. B. T., Egert, E., Kennard, O., Sala, G., Salisbury, S. A., and Viswamitra, M. A. (1981). *Proc. R. Soc. London Ser. B* 479–486.

Singleton, C. K., Klysik, J., Stirdivant, S. M., and Wells, R. D. (1982). *Nature (London)* **299**, 312–316.

Thamann, T. J., Lord, R. C., Wang, A. H.-J., and Rich, A. (1981). *Nucleic Acids Res.* **9**, 5443–5457.

Thomae, R., Beck, S., and Pohl, F. M. (1983). *Proc. Natl. Acad. Sci. U.S.A.* **80**, 5550–5553.

Varshavsky, A. J., Sundin, O., and Bohm, M. (1981). *Nucleic Acids Res.* **5**, 5931–5938.

Vorlickova, M., Kypr, J., Stokrova, S., and Sponar, J. (1982). *Nucleic Acids Res.* **10**, 1071–1080.

Wang, A. H.-J., Quigley, G. J., Kolpak, F. J., Crawford, J. L., van Boom, J. H., van der Marel, G., and Rich, A. (1979). *Nature (London)* **282**, 680–686.

Wang, A. H.-J., Quigley, G. J., Kolpak, F. J., van der Marel, G., van Boom, J. H., and Rich, A. (1981). *Science* **211**, 171–176.

Wang, A. H.-J., Fujii, S., van Boom, J. H., and Rich, A. (1982a). *Proc. Natl. Acad. Sci. U.S.A.* **79**, 3968–3972.

Wang, A. H.-J., Fujii, J. H., van Boom, J. H., van der Marel, G. A., van Boeckel, S. A. A., and Rich, A. (1982b). *Nature (London)* **299**, 601–604.

Wang, A. H.-J., Hakoshima, T., van der Marel, G., van Boom, J. H., and Rich, A. (1984). *Cell,* **37**, 321–331.

Watson, J. D., and Crick, F. H. C. (1953). *Nature (London)* **171**, 737.

Wing, R., Drew, H., Takano, T., Broka, C., Tanaka, S., Itakura, K., and Dickerson, R. E. (1980). *Nature (London)* **287**, 755.

Zimmer, C., Tymen, S., Marck, C., and Guschlbauer, W. (1982). *Nucleic Acids Res.* **10**, 1081–1091.

VIRUSES, GENES, AND CANCER*

J. MICHAEL BISHOP

George W. Hooper Foundation
and
Department of Microbiology and Immunology
University of California Medical Center
San Francisco, California

I. INTRODUCTION

The more I learn about the fine structure of the mammalian cell and the complexities of intracellular and intercellular interactions and controls, the more I am convinced that detailed understanding of the malignant process and practical control based on understanding will never be possible (Burnet, 1976).

1983 may be the year in which carcinogenesis is finally understood . . . .Nobody now alive should confidently expect to be cured of a cancer . . .by what is soon to be discovered about the mechanisms of malignancy. . . . *But,* there is a chance. . . ! Oncogenes are the single most important finding in all of cancer research over many decades. . . . Scientists (may) learn how to manipulate (oncogenes) to protect or treat patients within the next two to five years (The New York Times, 1983).

ONE person in four will develop cancer, one in five will die of the disease. These are tragic dimensions, but they are no larger than the intellectual challenge cancer presents. Every minute, 10 million cells divide in our bodies. Usually, the divisions occur in the right way, at the right time and place, governed by mechanisms to which we cannot yet even give names. When the governance fails, cancer arises. Why does the governance fail? How does it fail? What hope do we have of penetrating the complexities of the cancer cell? Is there a way to solve the riddle of neoplastic growth?

In 1866, Paul Broca sketched the pedigree of his wife's family (Broca, 1866). Since the motive to publish was as great then as it is now, we still have that pedigree, and from it, we can see why Broca believed he had discovered an hereditary diathesis to cancer. The in-

*Lecture delivered March 17, 1983.

137

sight seems to have attracted little attention in Broca's time. During the century that followed, however, biologists began to seek genetic explanations for tumorigenesis. Now the quest has reached fruition: the long-imagined cancer genes have been brought to view. They were unearthed first by a simplification—the use of viruses that cause cancers in animals.

The harvest from this simplification has been abundant beyond all expectation. Tumor viruses have revealed to us a set of genes whose activities may lie at the heart of every cancer, no matter what its cause. We view these genes as the keyboard on which many different carcinogens can play, whether they are chemicals, X rays, the ravages of aging, or even viruses themselves. An enemy has been found; it is part of us; and we have begun to understand its lines of attack.

There is a subtlety here that deserves emphasis. The revelations of which I speak do not address the issue of whether viruses may cause some human cancers: that is another pursuit with its own challenges and recent flourish. I speak instead of how viruses have been used as experimental tools to ferret out universal processes that may cause a cell to run amok.

II. RETROVIRUSES AND CANCER GENES

We owe much of our recent progress in cancer research to the retroviruses, whose genes are carried in RNA but are copied into DNA by reverse transcriptase during viral growth (Temin and Baltimore, 1972). The outlines of this process provide a microcosm of carcinogenesis (Fig. 1). Once the viral genes have been copied into DNA, the viral DNA is inserted (or "integrated") into the chromosomal DNA of the host cell. Then, in a foolhardy act, the cell uses its own machinery to express the viral genes. These events hold two separate possibilities for carcinogenesis. First, the integration of viral DNA is potentially mutagenic: it can damage important cellular genes, and it can influence their expression (Varmus, 1982). We call this "insertional mutagenesis," and we will see later that it may indeed cause tumors. Second, some retroviruses carry genes which can themselves be carcinogenic: expression of any of these single genes appears to be sufficient to give rise to cancerous growth (Bishop and Varmus, 1982). We call these genes *oncogenes* (for obvious reasons) and their value to us is beyond mea-

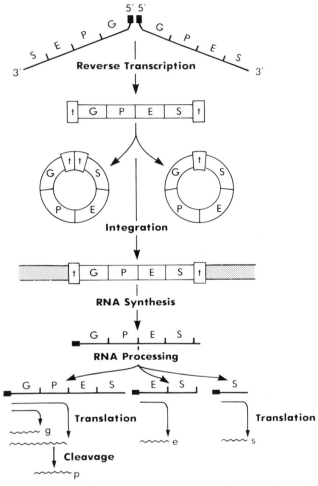

FIG. 1. The molecular life cycle of retroviruses. The scheme uses the replication of Rous sarcoma virus as a prototype. RNAs are denoted by single lines, DNAs by double lines. t denotes terminal redundancy, G the *gag* gene, P the *pol* gene, E the *env* gene, and S the *src* gene of the virus (see Vogt, 1977). Lower case letters denote the protein products of these genes.

sure: they are the keys with which we hope to unlock the closet in which cancer has sheltered its ugly secrets.

As these principles emerged, a marvelous and wholly unanticipated symmetry also came to light. The oncogenes carried by retroviruses, and the cellular genes whose mutation by viral insertions may initiate tumorigenesis, belong to overlapping (perhaps consubstantial) families. In studying the one, we also study the other. This symmetry will pervade all that I have to say.

How do we know that oncogenes exist, and how are they used to study cancer? Let me chart this terrain by reviewing what we have learned of four retroviral oncogenes. Each presents its own challenges and lessons.

III. THE ONCOGENE *src*

We begin with that most honored of oncogenes, *src*—so called because of the tumors (sarcomas) that it induces. By some accounts, *src* came to us from a poultry market of New York's East Side. Like many other good things in tumor virology, it found its way to the public eye through the auspices of the Rockefeller University. Now we know it to be one of four genes in the Rous sarcoma virus, and it is the only gene required for the virus to induce tumors; the three remaining genes are devoted solely to viral growth.

We first learned of *src*'s existence from experiments with genetics (Martin, 1970; Vogt, 1977). It is possible to damage *src* in such a way that the action of the gene becomes vulnerable to heat: at one temperature (usually $\sim 35°C$), the gene is active; at a higher temperature (usually $\sim 39°C$), the gene is quickly inactivated. If cells are affected by a temperature-sensitive *src* at the lower temperature, they convert to cancerous growth within 12 hours. By merely shifting the temperature to a higher level, the cells can be ''cured''—returned to normal growth because *src* has been inactivated. By manipulating the temperature, the cells can be taken through a potentially unending cycle: transformation to cancerous growth, followed by curing, transformation again, ad infinitum. From these experiments, we learn that a viral gene is responsible for cancerous growth, that the gene must be continuously active if cancerous growth is to persist, and that the gene probably works by directing the synthesis of a protein.

As an aside, I note that whenever I describe these wondrous events to general audiences, I am inevitably asked whether the properties of temperature-sensitive mutants underlie the use of heat to treat cancer. Despite my best efforts, I often cannot bring my questioners to see that the temperature-sensitive mutant is an artifice, an invention whose properties nevertheless tell us something of nature's real ways. It is one of the great failures of our culture that the general public (among whom I must include most medical students) are so innocent of the ways of science. They have been denied the ecstasy of understanding it should be their privilege to share.

We can make *src* more palpable by using the procedures of recombinant DNA to isolate the gene free of any other genetic impedimenta (Czernilofsky *et al.*, 1980; Delorbe *et al.*, 1980). The tiny piece of DNA bearing *src*, and only *src*, can then be inserted into cells, where it will commence the production of its protein and elicit cancerous growth. Here is graphic evidence that the action of *src* alone is sufficient to cause cancer, and here is eloquent testimony to the experimental value of oncogenes. We need identify only a single gene product—a single protein—a single biochemical activity—to get our first view of how a cancer cell arises.

We have that first view for *src*, and the vista is rich with promise and puzzles. The protein produced under the instructions of *src* (pp60^{v-src}) nestles against the inner surface of the plasma membrane of the cell (Willingham *et al.*, 1979; Courtneidge *et al.*, 1980), where it catalyzes a familiar chemical reaction: the transfer of phosphate ions to proteins—"protein phosphorylation" (Collett and Erikson, 1978; Levinson *et al.*, 1978). The details of this reaction are *not* so familiar: it is the amino acid tyrosine that is phosphorylated by the kinase activity of pp60^{src}, not the more conventional sites of serine and threonine (Hunter and Sefton, 1980). And pp60^{v-src} is itself a phosphoprotein (Levinson *et al.*, 1978; Collett *et al.*, 1979), with a phosphoserine at residue 17 and a phosphotyrosine at residue 416 (Smart *et al.*, 1981). It has been possible to dissect the protein into two separate functional domains (Fig. 2): one binds the protein to the plasma membrane by means not yet clear and resides near the amino terminus (Krueger *et al.*, 1980; Levinson *et al.*, 1981); the other carries the kinase activity and is restricted to the carboxy half of the protein (Levinson *et al.*, 1981; Oppermann *et al.*, 1981b). You will shortly see that these assignments are more than trivial details.

When the "protein kinase" activity of *src* was discovered, it sent the

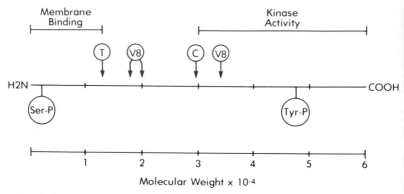

Fɪɢ. 2. The topography of pp60^{v-src}. Sites of preferential cleavages by proteases are denoted by T (trypsin), V8 (*Staphylococcus aureus* protease), and C (chymotrypsin).

thrill of precognition down the spines of biochemists because we have come to view protein phosphorylation as one of the chief means by which the activities of cells can be controlled. By phosphorylating numerous cellular proteins, the *src* enzyme might rapidly change myriad aspects of cell structure and growth. Now the race is on to find which cellular proteins are phosphorylated, which are the targets for the deadly onslaught. For the moment, the race can be fairly described as turtle against turtle: it has been a slow and vexing business that has taxed our best technologies to the limit.

A few of the target proteins have been identified. One is found on the plasma membrane of the cell, just as is the *src* enzyme itself (Fig. 3). The protein in question was discovered by Radke *et al.* (1980). It is very abundant within the cell, has a molecular weight of 36,000, and apparently resides on the cytoplasmic aspect of the plasma membrane (Courtneidge *et al.,* 1983). These details embody our ignorance. Though we can isolate the protein in quantity, dissect it in fine chemical detail, and track it to its residence within the cell, we still know nothing of what it does and hence nothing of why its phosphorylation by *src* might be important to tumorigenesis. It is a mystery, for the moment at least, how chemical reactions at the outer boundaries of the cell can influence events at the very heart of the cell's nucleus. And we remain totally ignorant of how these events lead to cancerous growth. But, a door has been opened.

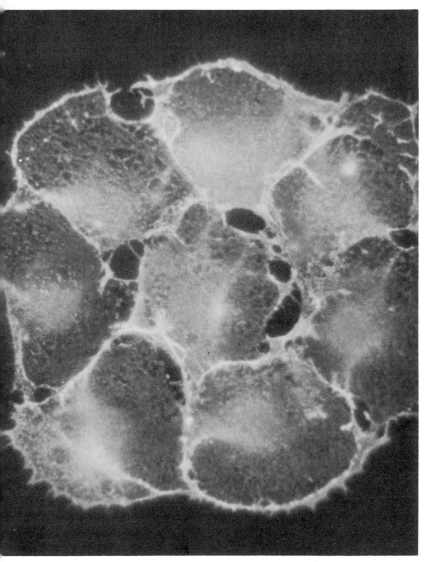

FIG. 3. Subcellular localization of a protein substrate for *src*. Epithelial cells in culture were examined by immunofluorescence, using antibody prepared against the 36-kilodalton substrate for $pp60^{v\text{-}src}$ described by Radke *et al.* (1980). For details, see Courtneidge *et al.* (1983). The figure was taken from unpublished work of K. Alitalo.

IV. The Biogenesis of pp60$^{v\text{-}src}$

As the door opened, nuances emerged to tease the biochemist's wits. For example, the biogenesis of pp60^{src} follows a hitherto unappreciated route (Fig. 4). The protein is synthesized on free polyribosomes, yet eventually makes its way to the plasma membrane (Courtneidge and Bishop, 1983). While in the cytoplasm, it is bound to two cellular proteins with masses of 89 and 50 kilodaltons, respectively, phosphorylated on serine, and possibly devoid of detectable kinase activity (Brugge *et al.*, 1981; Oppermann *et al.*, 1981a; Courtneidge and Bishop, 1983). Approximately 15 minutes after synthesis, pp60 has left the complex and joined the plasma membrane, where it is now phosphorylated on both serine and tyrosine, and displays kinase activity. The 89-kilodalton cellular protein is incidentally a major heat-shock protein of the host cell (Oppermann *et al.*, 1981c), an unexpected fact whose significance we have yet to plumb. And the 50-kilodalton protein is thought to be a substrate for phosphorylation by pp60 (Gilmore *et al.*, 1982).

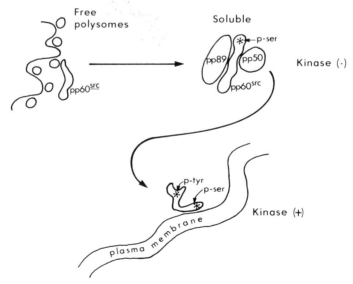

Fig. 4. The biogenesis of pp60$^{v\text{-}src}$. The scheme arises from experimental findings described by Brugge *et al.* (1981) and Courtneidge and Bishop (1983).

Why does this complex form? What is its purpose? We do not know, but fantasy urges us to suspect that the complex may preserve pp60 from the ravages of the cytoplasm, restrain the kinase activity until the desired subcellular compartment has been reached, and transport pp60 specifically to the plasma membrane. It is provocative that at least two other oncogene products—tyrosine–specific kinases as well—appear to reach the plasma membrane by the same route. Whether other membrane proteins traverse this route, whether we may have blundered onto a more general highway to the plasma membrane, remains for the future to tell.

This scheme in turn draws our attention to the phosphorylation of tyrosine in $pp60^{src}$. By what means does this phosphorylation arise, and to what end is it directed? The first question remains unanswered. My guess is that there are at least two classes of tyrosine-specific kinases in eukaryotic cells: those that phosphorylate tyrosine in pp60 and related tyrosine kinases, and those like pp60 itself that phosphorylate other classes of proteins, and in so doing, may elicit neoplastic growth. These are not trivial matters, because we need to know in which substrates to look for the important chemical signals that mandate phosphorylation by pp60 and its nefarious cousins.

V. Phosphorylation of Tyrosine in $pp60^{v\text{-}src}$

We have better experimental purchase on the possible purpose of the tyrosine phosphorylation in pp60. In collaboration with Art Levinson and his colleagues, Mark Snyder has converted the codon encoding the Tyr-416 residue in *src* to Phe, which we suppose to be innocuous and surely invulnerable to phosphorylation (Snyder *et al.*, 1983). The presence of the mutation has been documented by DNA sequencing, the mutated gene rigged for expression within cells by insertion into a vector where its transcription is driven by an SV40 virus promoter and terminated by a retroviral polyadenylation site. The results of these machinations came as a bit of a surprise (Table I): the mutated gene was unimpaired in its ability to transform cells to neoplastic growth, and to produce fully active protein kinase. Some phosphorylation of the protein on Tyr remained—not at residue 416, of course, but elsewhere in the molecule. The location of that phosphorylation and its contribution (if any) to the function of $pp60^{src}$ are matters for the future. These

TABLE I

PROPERTIES OF RSV MUTANT SF-1[a]

	Wild type	Mutant SF-1
Residue 416	Tyr	Phe
Transformation (BALB/c)	+	+
Agar clones (BALB/c)	+	+
$pp60^{v-src}$	+	+
p-Ser $pp60^{v-src}$	+	+
p-Tyr $pp60^{v-src}$	+	10%
p-Tyr kinase (src)	+	+

[a] Mutant SF-1 contains phenylalanine rather than tyrosine at residue 416 of $pp60^{v-src}$. For details, see Snyder *et al.* (1983).

findings diminish the likelihood that phosphorylation of Tyr in pp60 serves any significant physiological purpose and emphasize the need to examine phosphorylation sites in legitimate substrates for the *src* kinase.

VI. THE ONCOGENE *erb*-B

src is not the only door opening on carcinogenesis. Consider the avian erythroblastosis virus (AEV), a virus that causes both erythroleukemias and sarcomas in birds (Beug *et al.*, 1982). The tumorigenicity of AEV has been attributed to either or both of two loci within the viral genome, known as *erb*-A and *erb*-B (Bishop and Varmus, 1982). *erb*-A is expressed by translation from a genomic-length messenger RNA and *erb*-B from a spliced subgenomic mRNA (Sheiness *et al.*, 1981). What do each of these loci contribute to tumorigenesis by AEV? To answer this question, Linda Sealy created mutations in the molecularly cloned genome of AEV: *deletions* that affect either *erb*-A or *erb*-B, and *frame-shift* mutations that interrupt translation at the beginning of *erb*-A, and at either the beginning or near the end of *erb*-B. The mutated DNA was then introduced into permissive chicken cells to recover virus, and Sealy soon learned that *erb*-A may be an almost silent passenger in AEV. She could account for the transforming potential and tumorigenicity by the action of *erb*-B alone.

Bjorn Vennstrom and his colleagues studied similar deletion mutants and reached similar conclusions (Frykberg *et al.*, 1983). Now the all-important issue became the identity of the protein encoded by *erb*-B.

Translating the subgenomic mRNA for *erb*-B, Martin Privalsky found a protein of 61-kilodalton mass that he suspected was encoded by *erb*-B (Privalsky and Bishop, 1982). He verified his suspicions by the use of hybridization arrest of translation, in which DNA fragments derived from defined regions of the AEV genome were hybridized to mRNA prior to translation (Fig. 5). As expected, fragments derived from within *erb*-B blocked the synthesis of the 61-kilodalton protein; the protein is indeed encoded by *erb*-B. But is this protein produced from an authentic mRNA or, by unhappy accident, from a mere fragment of the viral genome? Privalsky assaulted this problem by using a

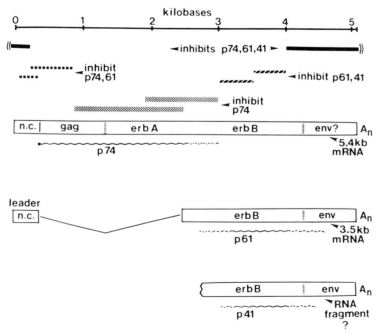

Fig. 5. Mapping the *erb*-B gene by hybrid-arrested translation. The figure illustrates the genesis of proteins from *erb*-A and *erb*-B by translation of mRNAs *in vitro* and the arrest of this translation by restriction fragments of DNA representing portions of the AEV genome. For details, see Privalsky and Bishop (1982).

DNA fragment representing the spliced leader of the messenger, but none of the protein coding domain. The leader fragment blocked synthesis of the 61-kilodalton protein, making it likely that the protein indeed hails from an authentic message (Privalsky and Bishop, 1982).

These are experiments entirely in test tubes. To breathe life into a protein, we must find it within cells, and to do that, we would best have antibodies directed against the protein. The preparation of antibodies against pp60^{src} required heroic exertions by Joan Brugge and Ray Erikson (1977). But those were earlier times. We were able to avoid the demands of heroism by the use of molecular cloning. In collaboration with Art Levinson and J. P. McGrath, we inserted a portion of *erb*-B into a plasmid vector that could produce astonishing quantities of protein in bacteria. The product was then used to immunize rabbits, and the resulting antisera precipitated two major proteins from either fibroblasts or erythroblasts transformed by AEV (Privalsky *et al.*, 1983). Both of these proteins appeared larger than 61-kilodaltons, yet peptide maps revealed that both were indistinguishable from the 61-kilodalton protein made *in vitro*. The use of tunicamycin solved this puzzle. When glycosylation of proteins was inhibited with the drug, we recovered a 61-kilodalton protein from infected cells—a protein whose peptide map again was identical to that of the 61-kilodalton protein translated from *erb*-B *in vitro* and to the maps of the 65/68-kilodalton proteins recovered from undisturbed infected cells. The 65/68-kilodalton proteins bound to lentil lectin and could be metabolically labeled with radioactive mannose, thus affirming that these are glycosylated proteins. We were doubly sure that these proteins were specified by *erb* because they were shorter by suitable amounts when we infected cells with Linda Sealy's frame-shift mutant that terminates translation near the end of *erb*-B (Privalsky *et al.*, 1983).

The glycoprotein encoded by *erb*-B has a perplexing compartmentalization within the cell. During synthesis, the protein is glycosylated and inserted into dense membranes; there most, if not all of it, then remains for the balance of its 12- to 24-hour life span (Fig. 6). We are for the moment not fully persuaded that any of the protein reaches the plasma membrane, although we have on occasion sighted miniscule quantities of the protein there, in a more highly modified form than any of the *erb*-B protein we find within the cell (Fig. 6). We are bewildered by this course of events. Is the *erb*-B protein an enzyme or not? What-

Translation on Dense Membranes——— p61^{ERB-B}

Modification in Dense Membranes——— gp65-68^{ERB-B}

Modification and Transit to
Plasma Membrane——————— gp70-72^{ERB-B}

FIG. 6. Compartmentalization of the glycoprotein encoded by v-*erb*-B. The figure illustrates unpublished results from Martin Privalsky. Proteins are designated with p if unmodified, with gp if glycosylated. Molecular weights of the proteins are given as units $\times 10^{-3}$.

ever could it be doing during its lengthy sojourn within intracellular membranes? And by what foul play does this sojourn elicit neoplastic growth. *src* this is not!

Or is it? Examination of the amino acid sequence of *erb*-B (predicted from DNA sequence) has uncovered an unanticipated and extensive homology with *src* and other tyrosine-specific protein kinases, all within the domain we know to harbor the kinase activity of pp60^{src}. Over 40% of the amino acids are shared by the two proteins through this domain (M. Privalsky, unpublished data). Is the product of *erb*-B a protein kinase? Not by any previous estimate. Not according to our frantic exertions when we revisited this issue in response to the revelations of nucleotide sequence. Perhaps our tools are too blunt. The matter requires further nurture, and it is surely grist for the mill of the evolutionary biologist.

VII. THE ONCOGENE *myb*

So far our quest has uncovered protein kinases and glycoproteins. But there is even more to this story. The oncogene *myb* of avian myeloblastosis virus induces myeloblastic leukemias in birds and transforms myelomonocytic hemopoietic cells in culture (Moscovici, 1975; Beug *et al.*, 1982). This gene, too, is expressed by translation from a spliced mRNA smaller than the viral genome (Gonda *et al.*, 1980). We sought the product of *myb* with a now familiar drill (Klempnauer *et al.*, 1983): translation of the mRNA *in vitro* to produce a 45-kilodalton protein whose synthesis could be blocked by hybridization arrest with fragments of DNA derived from within *myb* and precipitation of the same protein from infected cells, using antisera raised against *myb* antigen produced in bacteria. Peptide maps secured the identity between the cellular and synthetic proteins. The *myb* protein obtained from cells is phosphorylated, but we have no reason at present to believe that the protein is itself a kinase.

In striking contrast to what has gone before, the product of *myb* is a *nuclear* protein, as revealed by both immunofluorescence and biochemical fractionation of infected cells (K.-H. Klempnauer, unpublished data). Here is a distinctive door to the mechanisms of leukemogenesis, but what the passageway beyond will hold we cannot for the moment even imagine.

VIII. The Oncogene *myc*

The myelocytomatosis viruses are among the most versatile and virulent viral carcinogens known, inducing renal and hepatic carcinomas, endotheliomas, sarcomas, and myelocytic leukemias (Beug *et al.,* 1982). The oncogene of these viruses (v-*myc*) takes various topographical forms in different viral strains; the protein product of the gene varies accordingly—it may be fused to portions of other viral proteins or expressed independently. Using antisera prepared with our Genentech allies (this time, Wendy Colby and Art Levinson), Kari Alitalo identified the sundry products of v-*myc* in cells transformed by several strains of myelocytomatosis viruses (Table II). The menagerie of *myc* proteins is of concern primarily to tumor virologists, but two general points emerge. First, among the *myc* products we have found is a 58-

TABLE II

Gene Products of *myc*

	Proteins	Reactivity with anti-*myc* serum	Genetic composition of protein	Subcellular location
MC29 virus	P110	+	*gag–myc*	Nucleus
OK-10 virus	P200	+	*gag–pol–myc*	Nucleus
	p58	+	*myc*	Nucleus
MH-2 virus	P100	−	*gag–pol* (?)	?
	p58	+	*myc*	Nucleus

kilodalton protein that apparently represents the full coding potential of *myc*. Second, no matter what their topography, the *myc* proteins are located in the nuclei of transformed cells—a finding that echos in a haunting manner the intracellular location of the *myb* protein. Is this a coincidence? Two genes (*myc* and *myb*) that can assault the same hemopoietic lineage (myelomonocytic) attack in the same compartment of the cell.

IX. The Diversity of Retroviral Oncogenes

There are now at least 19 different retroviral oncogenes in our armamentarium, each capable of inducing specific forms of neoplasia, each encoding a protein whose action apparently wreaks the mischief (Bishop and Varmus, 1982). These genes have shown us that single, dominant genetic loci can convert cells to neoplastic growth. The demonstration may be misleading, since workaday tumorigenesis is thought to arise from several discrete events within the emerging tumor cell. This is a caveat that we cannot neglect, and it will return to trouble us again later in the story. Nevertheless, it is from retroviral oncogenes that we have gained our most promising glimpse of biochemical mechanisms leading to neoplastic growth, and we would be fools to ignore the lessons these genes may teach us. The first of these lessons has been rendered (Fig. 7). Oncogenes and their products display a provocative diversity: some oncogenes encode protein kinases, some surely do not; some attack in the nucleus of the cell, some at the plasma membrane, some within the cytoplasm.

There is little correlation between what we now know of how transforming proteins act and their tumorigenicities (Fig. 7). Four tyrosine-specific protein kinases induce sarcomas, but a fifth does not. Two glycoproteins that settle into what may be juxtanuclear membranes induce erythroleukemia, but a third elicits sarcomas instead. And three nuclear proteins cause a bewildering array of tumors that defeat any effort at synthesis.

What does this diversity signify? That there is more than one way to create a cancer cell, of course. But a greater truth may lie beyond. It seems likely that the growth of cells is regulated by an interdigitating network that spans from the surface of the cell to the heart of the nucleus. If that network were touched at any point by an adverse influ-

TUMORIGENICITY	ONCOGENE	PROPERTIES OF PRODUCT
SARCOMAS	SRC YES FPS/FES ROS	TYR-SPECIFIC PROTEIN KINASE ON/IN PLASMA MEMBRANE
B-LYMPHOMA	ABL	
CARCINOMAS, SARCOMAS AND MYELOCYTIC LEUKEMIA	MYC	NUCLEAR PROTEINS
MYELOBLASTIC LEUKEMIA	MYB	
OSTEOSARCOMAS	FOS	
ERYTHROLEUKEMIAS	ERB-B SFFV-ENV	JUXTANUCLEAR(?) MEMBRANE GLYCOPROTEINS
SARCOMAS	FMS	
ERYTHROLEUKEMIAS AND SARCOMAS	RAS	GTP-BINDING PROTEIN ON/IN PLASMA MEMBRANE
SARCOMAS	MOS	PHOSPHOPROTEIN IN CYTOSOL

FIG. 7. The proteins encoded by retroviral oncogenes. SFFV denotes the spleen focus forming virus found in the Friend virus complex. Oncogenes are designated by a standard nomenclature (Bishop and Varmus, 1982).

ence and tilted out of balance, cancerous growth might arise. Perhaps the several forms of oncogenes mirror different components of this normal regulatory network, revealing to us how the network performs its vital functions. By studying oncogenes, we are likely to be learning of both cancerous and normal growth at one and the same time. It is an old adage of medical science that study of the abnormal can reveal the normal.

X. UNVEILING CELLULAR ONCOGENES

When the exploration of viral oncogenes began, it was only a hope that their mechanisms of action might prefigure abnormalities in cancers of many origins. That hope approached reality with the discovery that the oncogenes of retroviruses are but wayward copies of what we now call "protooncogenes" or, more explicitly, "cellular oncogenes," found in all vertebrates and, perhaps, all metazoan organisms (Bishop, 1983). Table III provides a partial summary, to dramatize the point and to reveal the extraordinary evolutionary conservation these genes have enjoyed. (I suppose that survival over 1000 million years is cause for enjoyment.)

The cellular origins of retroviral oncogenes came as a surprise to many, but in retrospect, there had been ample warning that something unusual was afoot. First, oncogenes are not required for the replication of retroviruses, and it is therefore difficult to imagine that they emerged from evolution in concert with the remainder of the viral genome. Second, the large variety of tumors induced by different retroviruses, and the specificity with which each virus elicits tumors, posed a striking contrast with the tumorigenic properties of DNA tumor viruses. Third, the early literature carried explicit suggestions that retroviruses could acquire new capabilities for tumorigenicity while replicating in animals.

We now know that protooncogenes are cellular genes, not viral genes in disguise; and we know that they are expressed during normal growth and development, giving rise to proteins quite similar to those produced by their viral offspring. By pursuing these genes and their proteins, we are peering deep into the recesses of evolutionary time. As the structures of the genes began to unfold, we learned that they display two forms of evolutionary kinship—vertical and horizontal.

Vertical kinship is exemplified by the *src* genes isolated from DNAs

TABLE III

Molecular Paleontology of Cellular Oncogenes: A Sampler

Species	Divergence (Myrs)[b]	Cellular oncogenes[a]							
		src	*fps*	*myc*	*erb*	*myb*	*abl*	*mos*	*ras*
Human	—	+	+	+	+	+	+	+	+
Mouse	70	+	+	+	+	+	+	+	+
Chicken	325	+	+	+	+	+	+	+	+
Fish	425	+	?	+	+	+	?	?	?
Drosophila	>600	+	+	+	?	?	+	?	+
Escherichia coli	>600	−	−	−	−	−	−	−	−

[a] +, Gene detected; −, gene not detected; ?, testing not finished.

[b] Myrs, millions of years.

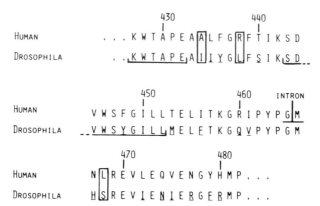

FIG. 8. Evolutionary conservation of cellular *src*. Residues in the deduced amino acid sequence are numbered as in pp60$^{v\text{-}src}$ (Czernilofsky *et al.*, 1983). Unpublished data were provided by Richard Parker, Graeme Mardon, and Michael Simon. [Fifty-six residues, 68% full conversion, 95% structural conversion (McLachlin).]

of humans and *Drosophila* by molecular cloning. The two genes can be recognized easily as kindred souls. Figure 8 illustrates a comparison through the heart of the protein kinase domain. According to conventional rules, the two amino acid sequences are related to the extent of almost 95%!

The *horizontal* kinships of protooncogenes became evident from relationships we had not fully anticipated (Fig. 9). The various genes that specify tyrosine-specific protein kinases (five, at last count), and even some that allegedly or indisputably do not (*mos, erb*-B, and a serine protein kinase of mammals), give evidence of having been constructed from common building blocks—"lego-units" I call them, under the influence of what currently litters my own house. Sometime in the distant past, in an organism perhaps too primitive for even the fossil record to hold, a single gene sired the beginnings of this complexity and all that it connotes. We have here a tiny but perceptible fragment from the historical record of the human race, which harbors all of these genes.

XI. TRANSDUCTION OF CELLULAR ONCOGENES BY RETROVIRUSES

Oncogenes enter the genomes of retroviruses by novel molecular gymnastics whose details are just now coming into focus. A complex

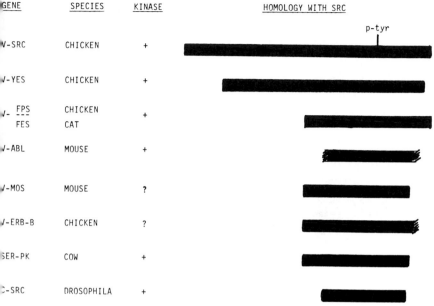

GENE	SPECIES	KINASE	HOMOLOGY WITH SRC
V-SRC	CHICKEN	+	
V-YES	CHICKEN	+	
V- FPS / FES	CHICKEN / CAT	+	
V-ABL	MOUSE	+	
V-MOS	MOUSE	?	
V-ERB-B	CHICKEN	?	
SER-PK	COW	+	
C-SRC	DROSOPHILA	+	

Fig. 9. A family of protein kinases and related genes. The comparisons are based on data compiled from Barker and Dayhoff (1982) and unpublished results of Martin Privalsky and Robert Ralston. Black bars denote extents of detectable homology with *src*, assessed with amino acid sequences.

("split") cellular gene becomes reorganized into a contiguous unit and inserted into the viral genome. It seems likely that transduction by retroviruses in this manner is a rare accident of nature, and there is no reason to believe that the accident is limited to cellular oncogenes. But the event is nevertheless of profound consequence for cancer research. In an extraordinary act of benevolence, retroviruses have brought to view cellular genes whose activities may be vital to natural tumorigenesis; it might have required many decades more to find these genes among the morass of the mammalian genome; instead, we have the oncogenes made manifest in viruses, excerpted from amidst the morass, and available for close scrutiny.

How do retroviruses acquire their copies of cellular oncogenes, and how might the mechanism of acquisition contribute to the malevolence of the pirated genes? Figure 10 illustrates representative models which exploit distinctive features of the retroviral life cycle. The scheme on

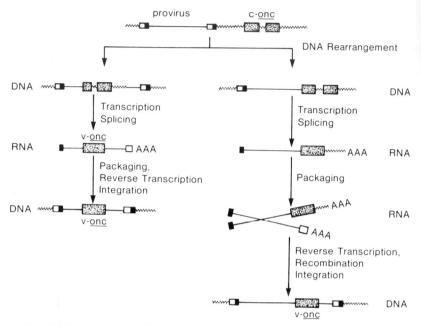

Fig. 10. Transduction of cellular oncogenes by retroviruses. The scheme is described in the text.

the right is the prevailing model, which arose mainly from studies of c-*src* by Ron Swanstrom and Richard Parker (Swanstrom *et al.*, 1983). It begins with the integration of a retroviral provirus, fortuitously positioned upstream of a cellular oncogene. A deletion then fuses the provirus and cellular gene into a hybrid transcriptional unit. The deletion eliminates the terminator of transcription from the provirus and, very likely, the promoter for transcription from the cellular gene. Transcription and RNA processing can now produce a chimeric RNA that includes the signals for packaging of RNA into virions, and a spliced version of the cellular gene. Encapsidation of the chimeric RNA into a heterozygous virus particle sets the stage for subsequent recombination that can complete the transductive act. Heterozygosity is possible because the genomes of retroviruses are characteristically diploid—a fact that has been invoked to explain the high frequency with which retroviruses recombine among themselves—they thrive on incest.

Transduction as we now envision it could inflict damage on the transduced gene in at least two ways. First, exclusion of portions of the cellular gene could drastically change the coding unit. Second, two error-prone polymerases participate in replication of the transduced gene: RNA polymerase II and reverse transcription. We have it on good authority that reverse transcriptase is prodigiously mutagenic (Gopinathan *et al.*, 1979), and I presume that the same may be true of RNA polymerase when it shares the responsibility for replicating genes—as it does in the life cycle of retroviruses.

Four testable predictions flow from the model. First, there is no need that the entirety of the cellular gene be transduced. Indeed, it is unlikely that the entire gene will be transduced because it is preferable to exclude its signals for initiation and termination of transcription. Second, the leftward (and chronologically first) recombination occurs between DNA forms of the viral genome and the cellular gene. It can therefore take place in cither an intron or an exon of the cellular gene, but it will be particularly telling if it occurs in an intron because we can then recognize the nature of the event in retrospect. Third, the rightward (and chronologically second) recombination is likely to occur within an exon of the cellular gene because it employs a spliced version of the cellular gene throughout the transduced domain.

We can examine and sustain each of these predictions by recourse to *myb*. Karl-Heinz Klempnauer sequenced both the viral and cellular versions of *myb* (Klempnauer *et al.*, 1982). From the sequence, and from mapping of splice sites on viral and cellular *myb* RNAs, we could deduce the following (Fig. 11): (1) seven separate segments of the cellular gene can be joined at prototypic splice junctions to reconstitute the viral gene; not a nucleotide has been lost; (2) at the left, recombination occurred in an intron of cellular *myb*; at the right, within an exon. Neat package though this is, we do not have the final answer. For example, work in Hidesaburo Hanafusa's laboratory raises the possibility that the rightward recombination during the transduction of *src* occurred in an intron of the cellular gene (Takeya and Hanafusa, 1983), casting stern doubt on the latter part of the prevailing model for transduction. Is *anything* ever easy?

What fraction of the cellular *myb* gene has been transduced? We cannot tell from the sequence alone, so Klempnauer proceeded to identify the protein product of cellular *myb*. The antisera developed for

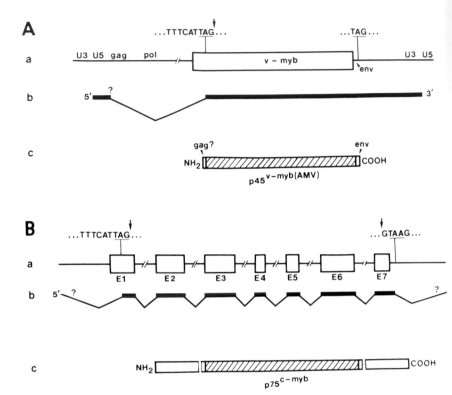

FIG. 11. v-*myb* is a truncated version of c-*myb*. The drawings depict the structure (a), transcription (b), and translation (c) of v-*myb* (A) and c-*myb* (B). Vertical arrows denote sites of splicing, E specifies a region of homology between v-*myb* and c-*myb*.

identification of the viral *myb* protein proved equal to the task, precipitating a single protein from various hemopoietic cells with great specificity (Klempnauer *et al.*, 1983). Peptide mapping confirmed the identity of the protein. But, the protein has a molecular weight of 75,000, not 45,000 as found for the viral gene product (Fig. 11). We are led to the conclusion that a substantial portion of the cellular gene has been excluded from the virus and that the viral and cellular *myb* proteins may therefore differ appreciably in their functional properties, although we do know that the cellular *myb* protein, like the viral protein, is located in the nucleus (K.-H. Klempnauer, unpublished data).

TABLE IV

Products of Cellular Oncogenes

Oncogene	Protein	Alleged function	
		Cellular gene	Viral cognate
c-*src*	60K	Tyr kinase	Tyr kinase
c-*fps*	98K	Tyr kinase	Tyr kinase
c-*abl*	150K	?	Tyr kinase
c-*ras* (Ha/Ki)	21K	?	?
c-*fes*	92K	?	Tyr kinase
c-*myb*	75K	?	?
c-*myc*	58K	?	?

XII. The Functions of Cellular Oncogenes

Pursuit of the proteins encoded by cellular oncogenes has not been an easy task. They often comprise only a tiny fraction of all the proteins in the cell; they are accordingly very difficult to find and characterize. Table IV summarizes most of the successes to date; in each instance, there is similarity (but never identity) between the viral and cellular forms of the proteins. What role do cellular oncogenes play in the daily affairs of normal cells? Why are they there? We suspect that they may figure in differentiation. The suspicion has two origins. First, retroviral oncogenes attack different tissues with great specificity (Table V). It is

TABLE V

Specificity in the Action of Oncogenes[a]

Oncogene	Cell	Product	Transformation
src	Fibroblast	+	+
	Macrophage	+	−
myb	Myeloblast	+	+
	Fibroblast	+	−

[a] Viral oncogene products were detected by immunoprecipitation. + denotes presence of the protein or transformation by the protein, − the absence of the protein or failure to transform.

as if each oncogene were designed to work only in certain types of cells. For example, Rous sarcoma virus can infect macrophages. *src* is expressed, pp60 is produced in substantial quantities, the kinase of pp60 appears fully active, yet the macrophage remains little changed—ignorant of the momentous events to which it is host. The converse is true for *myb*, whose protein we now believe is produced in both macrophages and fibroblasts infected with AMV, yet only the macrophage becomes transformed.

It is also true that most retroviral oncogenes meddle with differentiation; in the purest examples, the oncogene freezes the course of differentiation—the tumor that emerges is composed of ostensibly normal cells, growing relentlessly because they have been forbidden to mature (Graf *et al.*, 1978). Like father, like son: we cannot ignore the possibility that the effects of viral oncogenes on differentiation are but caricatures (and fairly accurate caricatures, at that) of what cellular oncogenes are normally intended to do. This is an exciting prospect, if true, because we presently have very little purchase on the molecular genetics of differentiation and embryogenesis. What a marvelous dividend it would be if retroviruses have revealed to us not only touchstones of carcinogenesis, but clues to the control of normal development as well.

These are not easy ideas to test. Let me illustrate one promising strategy. We know a great deal about the development of the humble fruit fly; we have unusually facile access to its genetic apparatus; we know that the fly possesses cellular oncogenes; and we are quickly learning where these genes are located on the chromosomes of the fly. For example, a gene that we believe is *src* has been found at position 64B on the third *Drosophila* chromosome, where it encodes an enzyme (a tyrosine-specific protein kinase) very similar to that produced from the viral or even the human *src* gene (Hoffman-Falk *et al.*, 1983; Simon *et al.*, 1983)! From decades of painstaking research by geneticists, we know how to damage or remove this gene. Thus, sometime within the near future, we hope to learn what happens to the growth and development of *Drosophila* when it has been deprived of the services of *src*. This is an exciting prospect, and the strategy should be applicable to other cellular oncogenes as well.

For the moment, we know only that the expression of many cellular oncogenes is restricted to certain developmental lineages (Gonda *et al.*,

1982) and can fluctuate during the course of differentiation (Muller *et al.*, 1982). Correlations of this sort point to a role for cellular oncogenes in development, but they do not illuminate that role for us. Illumination may come from the incisive genetical strategies offered by *Drosophila*—or perhaps by the creation of transgenotes in mammals.

XIII. CELLULAR ONCOGENES AS CANCER GENES

From all that has gone before, there has emerged a theoretical construct that guides some of the most vibrant current research in cancer. It appears that every vertebrate cell contains a family of genes (more than 20, I would guess, but perhaps less than 100) which may become oncogenes when transplanted into retroviruses. Since viral oncogenes profoundly affect growth and development, we suspect that their cellular parents might be involved in the regulation of normal cell division and differentiation. And it seems an easy leap of faith to suggest that all agents of carcinogenesis (chemicals, irradiation, aging, even viruses) wreak their havoc by acting on cellular oncogenes, either by augmenting their activity or by changing their function in some way.

Do cellular oncogenes participate in all forms of tumorigenesis? Are they a common keyboard for all the players in carcinogenesis? The evidence is incomplete, circumstantial, provocative, and of several kinds.

First, direct manipulation of *cellular oncogenes* has revealed that these genes can indeed be tumorigenic. At least two cellular oncogenes (c-*mos* and c-Ha-*ras*) can convert cells to tumorous growth if they are first purified by molecular cloning, attached to signals that command the genes to work at high speed, and then reinserted into cells (Blair *et al.*, 1981; Chang *et al.*, 1982).

Second, deletion mutants of viral oncogenes can be repaired by recombination with homologous cellular oncogenes. This astonishing feat was first accomplished with *src* by Hidesaburo Hanafusa (1981), and it has since been repeated with at least two other oncogenes (Ramsay *et al.*, 1982; Frykberg *et al.*, 1983). Since the repaired oncogene generally regains tumorigenicity, we must conclude that the makings of an active oncogene lurk in thin disguise in the cellular gene.

Third, even retroviruses that do not have oncogenes of their own appear to exploit cellular oncogenes to produce tumors. This first came to view from studies of B cell lymphomas induced in chickens by a retrovirus that has no oncogene. Genesis of the lymphomas apparently begins when the incoming viral DNA inserts in the vicinity of a resident cellular oncogene (Neel *et al.*, 1981; Payne *et al.*, 1981), whose identity was first established as c-*myc* by W. Hayward and his colleagues (1981). Insertion on either side will do (Payne *et al.*, 1982), a fact that astounds and provokes molecular biologists but need not bother others. As a result of the insertions, the previously dormant cellular oncogene is aroused to vigorous action, and this apparently sets the cell upon its way to cancerous growth.

There can be no doubt that the expression of c-*myc* is enhanced. The antisera prepared for study of the viral gene product has been used by Kari Alitalo to find the protein encoded by c-*myc*—a 58-kilodalton protein (p58^{c-myc}) whose abundance is increased 20- to 100-fold in the virus-induced lymphomas. On superficial inspection, at least, the version of p58^{c-myc} produced in at least several of the lymphomas does not differ from the version found in various normal cells of chickens: insertion of viral DNA may have enhanced the expression of c-*myc* without noticeably damaging the coding domain of the gene.

The number of viruses that may cause tumors by this means is large (it may even include viruses other than retroviruses), and the variety of tumors they cause is remarkable—we may find new oncogenes by tracking these viruses into cellular DNA.

My next examples take us into the human cancer cell itself—treacherous ground for the experimentalist because the human cancer cell can be studied only in retrospect. (One of my colleagues has likened the exploration of human tumor cells to an archaeological dig; we cannot watch tumorigenesis from its very beginning, as we can with our tumor virus models!) Many human tumor cells display abnormalities of their chromosomes. It has long been postulated and generally denied that these abnormalities might have a causative role in producing the tumors. Now our views are changing rapidly because the studies of cellular oncogenes and chromosomal abnormalities have conjoined in remarkable ways.

Some human tumor cells contain either of two forms of related chromosomal abnormalities (Schimke, 1982): double-minute (DM) chromosomes that are much smaller than normal chromosomes, have no centromeres, and thus distribute themselves haphazardly when the cell divides; and homogeneously staining regions (HSR)—areas of chromosomes that have lost all structural features, all "banding pattern." We know from previous studies not concerned with oncogenes that double-minute chromosomes and homogeneously staining regions are manifestations of amplified DNA (Schimke *et al.*, 1978). A region of chromosome encompassing many genes begins to multiply in number: from 1 copy to 5, to 100, to 1000 or beyond. The reasons for the multiplication are not known, but the amplified DNA survives and continues to multiply only if it serves some purpose in the cell. The amplified DNA eventually departs the chromosome, giving rise to double-minute chromosomes, and these in turn—according to current (but suspect) theory—reenter chromosomes to form homogeneously staining regions.

We began our exploration of gene amplification with human tumor cells that arose from a carcinoma of the colon, but which actually represent malignant neuroendocrine cells that secrete endocrine products, and are known as APUDomas because of other biochemical properties (Quinn *et al.*, 1979). Double-minute chromosomes were present in this tumor at the time of its resection; the HSRs arose as the cells were propagated in culture. Kari Alitalo and Manfred Schwab have shown that the double-minute chromosomes and homogeneously staining regions do indeed represent amplified DNA, and among this DNA is an old friend (or enemy, depending on your perspective): the cellular oncogene *myc* (Alitalo *et al.*, 1983). Hybridization *in situ* located the cellular *myc* gene for us (Fig. 12): the gene has been amplified from its usual single copy to almost 50 copies and is now spread across the entire HSR on both arms of what was once the X chromosome. Since *myc* normally resides on chromosome 8 (Neel *et al.*, 1982), the amplified DNA has also been transposed—double jeopardy for the cell, if you will.

Amplification of DNA increases the number of templates from which RNA can be copied, and indeed, these tumor cells make 50 times the usual amounts of *myc* RNA (Alitalo *et al.*, 1983); the cellular oncogene is vastly overexpressed, as it is in the chicken lymphomas I described before. We cannot yet say what role, if any, the overexpression of cellular *myc* has played in the genesis of the APUDoma tumor, but I remind you that DM chromosomes survive in cells only if they serve some selective advantage. What that selective advantage might be, I

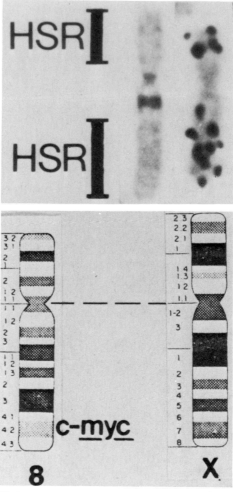

Fig. 12. Amplified c-*myc* genes are located in homogeneously staining regions of chromosomes. The top panel depicts hybridization *in situ* to amplified c-*myc* in homogeneously staining regions on an X chromosome in COLO320 cells (see Alitalo *et al.*, 1983). The bottom panel illustrates details of human chromosomes 8 and X.

cannot even conjure, but who could doubt the importance of pursuing these findings further? Where there is smoke, there may be fire.

Nor is this an isolated case. With Donna George at The University of Pennsylvania, we have examined the mouse adrenocortical tumor Y1 that possesses double-minute chromosomes and HSRs. Again, we find a known cellular oncogene among the amplified DNA: Kirsten c-*ras* this time, rather than *myc,* amplified 50-fold over its usual single-haploid copy, located on the HSR and on the double-minute chromosomes, and expressed at high levels (Schwab *et al.,* 1983).

Evidence of amplified DNA is proving to be a far more common feature of primary tumors than was formerly appreciated. I suspect that the search for oncogenes among these amplifications will soon be a growth industry. Our latest capital gain has been the discovery of abnormally amplified DNA that seems to be shared by numerous human neuroblastomas (M. Schwab, unpublished date).

Another major form of chromosomal abnormality found in human tumors is known as translocation: one portion of a chromosome breaks away and joins another, different chromosome. A remarkable number of these translocations involve chromosomes that carry one or more of the known cellular oncogenes (Table VI). Taken alone, of course, the apparent correlations are trivial. But recent work around the globe has taught us that we must take these correlations seriously and examine them one by one. In Burkitt's lymphoma of humans, in roughly analogous tumors of mice, and in human chronic myelogenous leukemia, chromosomal translocations move a known cellular oncogene from one chromosome to another and, in doing so, may affect the structure and/or function of the oncogene—the precise consequences of the translocations are for the moment being hotly debated (Klein, 1983; Rowley, 1983). The demonstration that cellular oncogenes are translocated in chronic myelogenous leukemia is particularly gratifying because it represents a molecular sounding of the Philadelphia chromosome ($22q^-$), whose discovery years ago raised the first alert that consistent forms of chromosomal damage might figure in tumorigenesis (Nowell and Hungerford, 1960).

In a very different strategy, pioneered by Robert Weinberg, recent experiments have apparently succeeded in detecting the activity of oncogenes taken directly from human tumor cells (Cooper, 1982; Wein-

TABLE VI

CHROMOSOMAL TRANSLOCATIONS IN HUMAN NEOPLASMS
AND CELLULAR ONCOGENES: CHANCE OR NECESSITY?[a]

Neoplasm	Translocation	Cellular oncogenes
ALL	8; 14	*myc/mos* (8)
	11; 14	Ha-*ras* (11)
	4; 11	Ha-*ras* (11)
	9; 22	*abl* (9)
AML	8; 21	*myc/mos* (8)
AMML	6; 11	*myb* (6); Ha-*ras* (11)
APML	15; 17	*fes* (15)
CML	9; 22	*abl* (9); *sis* (22)
Burkitt's lymphoma	2; 8	*fos* (2); *myc/mos* (8)
	8; 14	*myc/mos* (8)
	8; 22	*myc/mos* (8); *sis* (22)
Lymphoma	8; 14	*myc/mos* (8)
	11; 14	Ha-*ras* (11)
Ovarian carcinoma	6; 14	*myb* (6)
Parotid mixed tumors	3; 8	*myb* (6)
Renal carcinoma	3; 8	*myc/mos* (8)
	3; 11	Ha-*ras* (11)

[a] ALL, acute lymphocytic leukemia; AML, acute myelogenous leukemia; AMML, acute myelomonocytic leukemia; APML, acute promyelocytic leukemia; CML, chronic myelogenous leukemia. Numbers in parentheses denote the chromosomes on which cellular oncogenes are located. For a summary, see Rowley (1983).

berg, 1982). DNA from a variety of tumors can be used to convert mouse or rat cells to neoplastic growth, as if the DNA contained an active oncogene of the sort we were once accustomed to finding only in viruses. The variety of human tumors in which active oncogenes have been detected by this means is arresting; notice that these may be dominant oncogenes because they appear to commandeer the recipient rodent cells without regard to the controls those cells contain. When the responsible human genes were identified for several types of human tumors, they were again old friends cum enemies: members of the *ras* cellular oncogene family already known to us from the study of retroviruses. A remarkable circle had been closed.

XIV. The Genesis of Cancer Genes

How might a protooncogene (a compliant member of the cellular citizenry) become an oncogene (an unruly and lethal enemy within)? Either the gene is unleashed from its usual controls—outlandish or inappropriate expression of an otherwise normal gene is the fatal flaw, or mutation might change the structure of the gene and the protein it encodes, giving rise to abnormal function. A brief reprise will bring you abreast of how these competing views are faring.

We presently know of two distinct settings in which enhanced expression appears to be the order of the day (Table VII): induction of cellular oncogenes by insertion of either retroviral DNA or perhaps transposable DNA of other sorts and augmented expression consequent to gene amplification. Four different cellular oncogenes have been so implicated.

But direct mutation of cellular oncogenes has also blustered into view from experiments that have captured recent newspaper headlines with monotonous frequency. Within the active oncogene isolated from the cells of a human bladder carcinoma, there resides a single mutation that changes a single amino acid in the protein product of the gene (Reddy *et al.*, 1982; Tabin *et al.*, 1982; Taparowsky *et al.*, 1982). By all available accounts, this solitary change converts a harmless cellular protooncogene to an active oncogene.

Dramatic though it is, this example may be but the tip of a large

TABLE VII

Enhanced Expression of Protooncogenes in Neoplastic Cells

Tumor cells	Enhanced protooncogene	Mechanism
Avian B lymphoma	c-*myc*	Insertional mutagenesis
Avian erythroleukemia	c-*erb*	Insertional mutagenesis
Mouse mammary carcinoma	?	Insertional mutagenesis
Human promyelocytic leukemia	c-*myc*	Gene amplification
Human APUdoma	c-*myc*	Gene amplification
Mouse adrenal tumor	c-Ki-*ras*	Gene amplification
Mouse plasmacytoma	c-*mos*	DNA rearrangement

iceberg. For example, it appears ever more likely that most (if not all) retroviral oncogenes are not merely copies of their cellular progenitors, but instead are mutated and sometimes truncated in ways that could modify their function and account for their oncogenic potential. Consider these examples: neoplastic transformation by *src* does not require large doses of the viral gene product, perhaps because the viral and cellular versions of the *src* protein are manifestly different in several details (Smart *et al.*, 1981; Swanstrom *et al.*, 1983; Takeya and Hanafusa, 1983); the viral and cellular forms of the *myb* gene differ by a large amount, as I explained earlier; and efforts to transform cells in culture with transcriptionally active but otherwise unmodified c-*src* have failed (R. Parker, unpublished results). For the moment, it appears that when the final results are in, we will have it both ways. Enhanced expression of normal cellular oncogenes and mutational conversion to abnormality may both play their parts.

The genesis of cancer is not a simple matter. More than one event is required. So we should be cautious in speaking of oncogenes as if their sole activity can account for tumorigenesis. But we should not neglect the possibility that the identification of oncogenes offers us the tools with which to enumerate and recognize several separate steps in tumorigenesis. The B cell lymphomas in chickens can again serve as a model. We already know of *two* oncogenes active in this tumor: c-*myc*, whose expression has been enhanced by insertional mutagenesis—presumably the earliest event in the genesis of this tumor, and a different gene, uncovered by Geoffrey Cooper, recognized only by using the assay with mouse cells, and perhaps representing a later step in tumorigenesis (Cooper, 1982; Goubin *et al.*, 1983). We can also look forward to explorations of what part cellular oncogenes might play in the heritable susceptibilities to tumorigenesis that engendered the first dim images of cancer genes.

XV. Conclusions

What then have we learned, one century after Broca constructed his prescient diagram?

1. That a common set of cellular genes may contribute to the genesis of all tumors, whatever their cause.

2. That we have the means to learn how these genes act, and that in so doing, we may solve not only the riddle of the cancer cell, but the riddles of normal growth and development as well.

We owe much of this to the study of viruses found in chickens— beasts not renowned for glamour. There is here a lesson that scientists must continually relearn, and that scientists should make great effort to teach to the public at large. The proper conduct of science lies in the pursuit of nature's puzzles, wherever they may lead. We *cannot* pre- judge the utility of scholarship, we can only ask that it be sound. We cannot always assault the great problems of biology at will; we must remain alert to nature's clues and seize on them whenever and wherever they appear.

Where will our clues lead us in the quest for prevention and therapy of cancer? We cannot say. No one should yet predict whether and when we might be turning oncogenes off and on at will. We are not even yet certain that oncogenes are the key we hope they are. There may be lifetimes of toil ahead before we know, or we might know tomorrow.

I return to where I began. Cancer research is a peculiarly public endeavor. Those of us who labor in cancer research look to our fellow citizens for mandate and support; they in turn look to us for an honest accounting of our affairs and for hope. These are anxious times: the dollar now dictates what we can and cannot do to an extent that is damaging and demoralizing. But we must resist the temptation to offer unwarranted promises; we must sustain the mutual trust between scien- tist and citizen that has fueled the triumphs of biological science in our time; we must adhere to the rigor from which those triumphs sprang.

> Science is the only way we have of shoving truth down the reluctant throat. Only science can overcome . . . differences in seeing and believing. . . . Man cannot live by contemplative receptivity and artistic creation alone. As well as every word proceeding from the mouth of God, (man) needs science (Huxley, 1963).
>
> Things have been learned painfully and incompletely in the pursuit of science. Only in the wider tasks of homanity will their use be found (Bernal, 1939).

ACKNOWLEDGMENTS

The author is indebted to Janine Marinos for preparation of the manuscript; to the National Cancer Institute and the American Cancer Society for research support; to Lois Fanshier, Joyce Futa, Jean Jackson, Suzanne Ortiz, Rubye Ponder, Nancy Quintrell, Lois Serxner, and Karen Smith for all manner of help; to the students and postdoctoral fellows who have been yeast for the daily bread of an aging scientist; to K.I.B. for daily bread and other sustenance; to Warren Levinson for vital help in the early years; to Leon Levintow for his longstanding friendship and encouragement; and to Harold E. Varmus, with whom much of the work described in the article was conceived and directed.

REFERENCES

Alitalo, K., Schwab, M., Lin, C. C., Varmus, H. E., and Bishop, J. M. (1983). *Proc. Natl. Acad. Sci. U.S.A.* **80,** 1707.
Barker, W. C., and Dayhoff, M. O. (1982). *Proc. Natl. Acad. Sci. U.S.A.* **79,** 2836.
Bernal, J. D. (1939). "The Social Function of Science," p. 415. Routledge, London.
Beug, H., Hayman, M. J., and Graf, T. (1982). *Cancer Surv.* **1,** 205.
Bishop, J. M. (1983). *Annu. Rev. Biochem.* **52,** 301.
Bishop, J. M., and Varmus, H. E. (1982) *In* "Molecular Biology of Tumor Viruses, Part III" (R. A. Weiss, N. Teich, H. E. Varmus, and J. Coffin eds.), p. 999. Cold Spring Harbor Press, Cold Spring Harbor, New York.
Blair, D. G., Oskarsson, M., Wood, T. G., McClements, W. L., Fischinger, P. J., and Vande Woude, G. G. (1981). *Science* **212,** 941.
Broca, P. P. (1866). *In* "Traite des Tumeurs," p. 80. Asselin, Paris.
Brugge, J. S., and Erikson, R. L. (1977). *Nature (London)* **269,** 346.
Brugge, J. S., Erikson, E., and Erikson, R. L. (1981). *Cell* **25,** 363.
Burnet, F. M. (1976). "Immunology, Aging and Cancer," p. 136. Freeman, San Francisco, California.
Chang, E. H., Furth, M. E., Scolnick, E. M., and Lowy, D. R. (1982). *Nature (London)* **479,** 479.
Collett, M. S., and Erikson, R. L. (1978). *Proc. Natl. Acad. Sci. U.S.A.* **75,** 2021.
Collett, M. S., Erikson, E., and Erikson, R. L. (1979). *J. Virol.* **29,** 770.
Cooper, G. M. (1982). *Science* **218,** 801.
Courtneidge, S., and Bishop, J. M. (1983). *Proc. Natl. Acad. Sci. U.S.A.* **79,** 7117.
Courtneidge, S. A., Levinson, A., and Bishop, J. M. (1980). *Proc. Natl. Acad. Sci. U.S.A.* **77,** 3783.
Courtneidge, S. A., Ralston, R., Alitalo, K., and Bishop, J. M. (1983). *Mol. Cell. Biol.* **3,** 340.
Czernilofsky, A. P., Levinson, A. D., Varmus, H. E., Bishop, J. M., Tischer, E., and Goodman, H. M. (1980). *Nature (London)* **287,** 198.
Czernilofsky, A. P., Levinson, A. D., Varmus, H. E., Vishop, J. M., Tischer, E., and Goodman, H. (1983). *Nature (London)* **301,** 736.
DeLorbe, W. J., Luciw, P. A., Goodman, H. M., Varmus, H. E., and Bishop, J. M. (1980). *J. Virol.* **36,** 50.
Frykberg, L., Palmieri, S., Beug, H., Graf, T., Hayman, M. J., and Vennstrom, B. (1983). *Cell* **32,** 227.
Gilmore, T. D., Radke, K., and Martin, G. S. (1982). *Mol. Cell. Biol.* **2,** 199.
Gonda, T. J., Sheiness, D. K., Fanshier, L., Bishop, J. M., and Moscovici, M. G. (1980). *Cell* **23,** 279.

Gonda, T. J., Sheiness, D. K., and Bishop, J. M. (1982). *Mol. Cell. Biol.* **2,** 617.

Gopinathan, K., Weymouth, L., Kunkel, T., and Loeb, L. (1979). *Nature (London)* **278,** 857.

Goubin, G., Goldman, D. S., Luce, J., Neiman, P. E., and Cooper, G. M. (1983). *Nature (London)* **302,** 114.

Graf, T., Ade, N., and Beug, H. (1978). *Nature (London)* **275,** 496.

Hanafusa, H. (1981). *Harvey Lect.* **75,** 255.

Hayward, W. S., Neel, B. G., and Astrin, S. M. (1981). *Nature (London)* **290,** 475.

Hoffman-Falk, H., Einat, P., Shilo, B.-Z., and Hoffman, F. M. (1983). *Cell* **32,** 589.

Hunter, T., and Sefton, B. M. (1980). *Proc. Natl. Acad. Sci. U.S.A.* **77,** 1311.

Huxley, A. (1963). "Literature and Science," pp. 39 and 79. Harper, New York.

Klein, G. (1983). *Cell* **32,** 311.

Klempnauer, K. H., and Bishop, J. M. (1983). *J. Virol.,* **48,** 565.

Klempnauer, K. H., Gonda, T. J., and Bishop, J. M. (1982). *Cell* **31,** 453.

Klempnauer, K. H., Ramsay, G., Bishop, J. M., Moscovici, M. G., Moscovici, C., McGrath, J. P., and Levinson, A. D. (1983). *Cell* **33,** 345.

Krueger, J. G., Wang, E., Garber, E. A., and Goldberg, A. R. (1980). *Proc. Natl. Acad. Sci. U.S.A.* **77,** 4142.

Levinson, A., Oppermann, H., Varmus, H. E., and Bishop, J. M. (1978). *Cell* **15,** 561.

Levinson, A., Courtneidge, S. A., and Bishop, J. M. (1981). *Proc. Natl. Acad. Sci. U.S.A.* **78,** 1624.

Martin, G. S. (1970). *Nature (London)* **227,** 1021.

Moscovici, C. (1975). *Curr. Top. Microbiol. Immunol.* **71,** 79.

Muller, R., Slamon, D. J., Tremblay, J. M., Cline, M. J., and Verma, I.M. (1982). *Nature (London)* **299,** 640.

Neel, B. G., Hayward, W. S., Robinson, H. L., Fang, J. M., and Astrin, S. M. (1981). *Cell* **23,** 323.

Neel, B. G., Jhanwar, S. C., Changanti, R. S. K., and Hayward, W. S. (1982). *Proc. Natl. Acad. Sci. U.S.A.* **79,** 7842.

Nowell, P. C., and Hungerford, D. A. (1960). *Science* **132,** 1497.

The New York Times. (1983). Sunday, February 20, p. 1.

Oppermann, H., Levinson, A. D., Levintow, L., Varmus, H. E., Bishop, J. M., and Kawai, S. (1981a). *Virology* **113,** 736.

Opperman, H., Levinson, A. D., and Varmus, H. E. (1981b). *Virology* **108,** 47.

Oppermann, H., Levinson, W., and Bishop, J. M. (1981c). *Proc. Natl. Acad. Sci. U.S.A.* **78,** 1067.

Payne, G. S., Courtneidge, S. A., Crittenden, L. B., Fadly, A. M., Bishop, J. M., and Varmus, H. E. (1981). *Cell* **23,** 311.

Payne, G. S., Bishop, J. M., and Varmus, H. E. (1982). *Nature London)* **295,** 209.

Privalsky, M. L., and Bishop, J. M. (1982). *Proc. Natl. Acad. Sci. U.S.A.* **79,** 3958.

Privalsky, M. L., Sealy, L., Bishop, J. M., McGrath, J. P., and Levinson, A. D. (1983). *Cell* **32,** 1257.

Quinn, L. A., Moore, G. E., Morgan, R. T., and Woods, L. K. (1979). *Cancer Res.* **39,** 4914.

Radke, K., Gilmore, T., and Martin, G. S. (1980). *Cell* **21,** 821.

Ramsay, G. M., Enrietto, P. J., Graf, T., and Hayman, M. J. (1982). *Proc. Natl. Acad. Sci. U.S.A.* **79,** 6885.

Reddy, E. P., Reynolds, R. K., Santos, E., and Barbacid, M. (1982). *Nature (London)* **300,** 149.

Rowley, J. D. (1983). *Nature (London)* **301,** 290.

Schimke, R. T. (1982). "Gene Amplification." Cold Spring Harbor Press, Cold Spring Harbor, New York.

Schimke, R. T., Kaufman, R. J., Alt, F. W., and Kellems, R. F. (1978). *Science* **202,** 1051.

Schwab, M., Alitalo, K., Varmus, H. E., Bishop, J. M., and George, D. (1983). *Nature (London)* **303,** 497.

Sheiness, D., Vennstrom, B., and Bishop, J. M. (1981). *Cell* **23,** 135.

Simon, M. A., Kornberg, T. B., and Bishop, J. M. (1983). *Nature (London)* **302,** 837.

Smart, J. E., Oppermann, H., Czernilofsky, A. P., Purchio, A. F., Erikson, R. L., and Bishop, J. M. (1981). *Proc. Natl. Acad. Sci. U.S.A.* **78,** 6013.

Snyder, M. A., Bishop, J. M., Colby, W., and Levinson, A. D. (1983). *Cell* **32,** 891.

Swanstrom, R., Parker, R. C., Varmus, H. E., and Bishop, J. M. (1983). *Proc. Natl. Acad. Sci. U.S.A.* **80,** 2519.

Tabin, C. J., Bradley, S. M., Bargmann, C. I., Weinberg, R. A., Papageorge, A. G., Scolnick, E. M., Dhar, R., Lowy, D. R., and Chang, E. H. (1982). *Nature (London)* **300,** 143.

Takeya, T., and Hanafusa, H. (1983). *Cell* **32,** 881.

Taparowsky, E., Suard, Y., Fasano, O., Shimizu, K., Goldfarb, M., and Wigler, M. (1982). *Nature (London)* **300,** 762.

Temin, H. M., and Baltimore, D. (1972). *Adv. Cancer Res.* 129.

Varmus, H. E. (1982). *Cancer Surv.* **1,** 309.

Vennstrom, B., and Bishop, J. M. (1982). *Cell* **28,** 135.

Vogt, P. K. (1977). *In* "Comprehensive Virology" (H. Fraenkel-Conrat and R. R. Wagner, eds.), p. 341. Plenum, New York.

Weinberg, R. A. (1982). *Adv. Cancer Res.* **36,** 149.

Willingham, M. C., Jay, G., and Pastan, I. (1979). *Cell* **18,** 125.

CHROMOSOME MODIFICATIONS AND CANCER*

RUTH SAGER

Department of Microbiology and Molecular Genetics
Harvard Medical School
and
Dana-Farber Cancer Institute
Boston, Massachusetts

THE Harvey Society has a long and distinguished tradition of lectures in research areas relevant to medical science. I feel honored by the invitation to participate. My topic is insights from genetic analysis into the origin of tumor cells. By way of introduction I wish to acknowledge the intellectual roots of the approach I have taken, which stems initially from the work of my mentors, Marcus Rhoades and Barbara McClintock. They each set a tremendous example of intellectual curiosity, originality, and lack of concern for fashions in science. They followed their experimental leads and their intuition. And specifically relevant to the subject of this lecture, they demonstrated the power of cytogenetic analysis: that is, the combination of genetic analysis with detailed studies of chromosome changes. Although they worked at the level of cell and organism, they encouraged molecular approaches and molecular interpretations. The research to be discussed in this lecture is based conceptually on the working hypothesis sumarized in Table I.

I. MULTISTEP ORIGIN OF TUMOR-FORMING CELLS

Tumor cells arise in a series of steps initiated by damage to DNA, which leads to genomic changes. The damage may occur in a variety of different ways but will lead toward tumorigenesis only if it has two essential consequences: (1) to overcome growth control so that the cells begin to divide, and (2) to destabilize the chromosomes so that they undergo not merely one, but successive waves of chromosome changes.

*Lecture delivered April 21, 1983.

TABLE I

MULTISTEP ORIGIN OF TUMOR-FORMING ABILITY

Initial DNA damage
    Induced by radiation, chemicals, viruses, or inherited genetic factors
    Leads to faulty growth control and loss of chromosome stability

Chromosome breakage and rearrangement
    Continuing rounds of cell division
    Continuing process of genomic rearrangement
    Genetic and phenotypic changes cascade as novel rearrangements arise

Accelerated evolution of tumor-forming cells
    Genomic rearrangements generate new phenotypes
    Selection favors proliferating and well-adapted cells
    Specific phenotypes succeed in different tissues

The increasing malignancy seen clinically as neoplastic progression is the consequence of continuing genomic rearrangements, which serve to generate genetic and phenotypic changes. Because these rearrangements occur with a high frequency, they lead to the accelerated evolution of tumor cells selected from the heterogeneous array of phenotypes including cell lethals that are produced.

The chromosomes of tumor cells typically show many rearrangements, some of them closely correlated with the tumor type. Decreased DNA methylation in tumor cells compared with the normal cells of origin has also been reported. In our studies, chromosome changes and methylation changes have been found in the same experimentally induced tumors. These results raise the possibility that underlying the correlations there may be a common mechanism.

II. CHLOROPLAST DNA AND THE POWER OF METHYLATION

Marcus Rhoades had done a series of elegant genetic experiments which showed the existence of non-Mendelian genes in corn, supporting and extending the findings in other plants made by many investigators beginning with Correns and Baur (reviewed in ref. 1). Although the concept of non-Mendelian genes was very unpopular among geneticists at the time, I was convinced of their reality and decided to work on this problem, using the single-celled microbial plant called *Chlamydomo-*

nas. Some aspects of this work, especially concerned with DNA methylation, are still continuing in my laboratory at present.

At that time there were two major questions: (1) what is the molecular identity of non-Mendelian genes, and (2) what is the molecular mechanism of non-Mendelian inheritance. The first question, the identity of non-Mendelian genes, was answered with our discovery of high-molecular-weight chloroplast DNA with an average base composition very different from nuclear DNA (2). Subsequently, in studies over a period of about 12 years, my co-workers and I showed that chloroplast DNA is the physical carrier of genes affecting chloroplast development, and we mapped these genes into a single circular DNA chromosome or linkage group (3).

The discovery of chloroplast DNA led to the discovery of mitochondrial DNA by other investigators, and opened up the field of organelle genetics now ongoing in many laboratories. It also clarified the molecular basis of what had been called "nucleo-cytoplasmic (genetic) interactions."

So the first question was answered: the molecular identity of non-Mendelian genes was shown to be self-coding DNA molecules carrying unique sequences and located in chloroplasts and mitochondria. The next question concerned the molecular mechanism responsible for the non-Mendelian pattern of inheritance. The essence of the problem is very simple. Nuclear genes are segregated according to Mendelian rules, but chloroplast genes exemplified in *Chlamydomonas* are transmitted to all progeny from the female parent. This phenomenon is called maternal inheritance, and the question is how does it work.

Our first clue came from DNAs extracted from vegetative cells and from gametes, i.e., differentiated vegetative cells that are capable of mating (Fig. 1). The chloroplast DNA in the zygote (top tracing) has undergone a density shift compared to the homologous DNA extracted from vegetative cells (bottom tracing). The chloroplast DNA from zygotes has become about 5 mg/cm^3 lighter in its bouyant density in CsCl$_2$ than that of the vegetative cells from which the gametes arose. This shift is very unusual, and indicates that some other cellular constituent has become attached to the DNA and is floating it, so to speak. This effect can occur by addition of methyl groups to cytosine residues in DNA. In a series of experiments we found that the ch1DNA of the female (mt^+) gametes had indeed become methylated. Furthermore, corresponding DNA in the male (mt^-) gametes was not methylated.

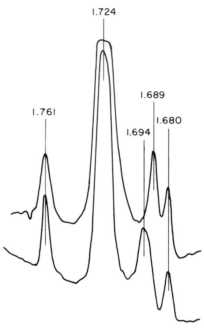

FIG. 1. Microdensitometer tracings of UV absorption bands of DNA after Cscl₂ densi-ty equilibrium centrifugation. (Top trace) DNA from 24-hour zygotes. (Bottom trace) DNA from vegetative cells. Outside peaks are markers; SP-15 DNA at 1.761 g/cm³ and poly[d(A-T)] at 1.680 g/cm³. Nuclear DNA (overload) at 1.724 g/cm³, chloroplast DNA at 1.694 g/cm³ in bottom trace, and at 1.689 g/cm³ (shifted density) in top trace (44,000 rpm, 20 hours, 25°C) (3).

This difference in methylation of the male and female gametes was shown in a number of experiments, one of which is illustrated in Fig. 2. In this experiment, a radioactive precursor of 5-methylcytosine (5mC) was used to prelabel the cells in a pair of reciprocal crosses: female labeled × male unlabeled, and female unlabeled × male labeled. Figure 2(top) shows the result when the female parent was prelabeled. In the DNA from 6-hour zygotes, the peak in the position of 5mC has a substantial label. This result was the first definitive evidence for DNA methylation in chloroplast DNA. Figure 2(bottom) shows that in the reciprocal cross, when the male parent was prelabeled, there was no label in the position of 5mC. This result was very exciting. It was the first evidence for a functional role of DNA methylation in any organism

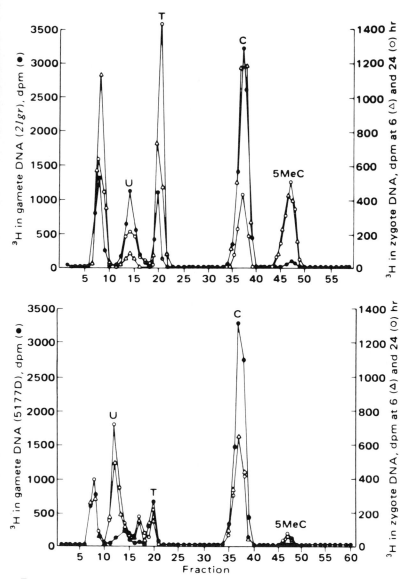

Fig. 2. Chloroplast DNAs from gametes and zygotes in which one parent was pre-labeled with deoxycytidine. One strain was prelabeled with [G-³H]deoxycytidine (50 μCi/ml), gametes were prepared and fused with unlabeled gametes of the other strain, and zygotes were sampled at 6 and 24 hours. Chloroplast DNAs were purified and hydrolyzed with formic acid, and bases were separated on HPLC Aminex A-6 column. Positions of marker bases are shown: U, unknown; T, thymine; C, cytosine; 5MeC, 5-methylcytosine. Peak at left is void volume, containing [³H]deoxyribose. (Upper) Strain 21gr (*mt*⁺) labeled. (Lower) Strain 5177D (*mt*⁻) labeled (4).

TABLE II

MATERNAL INHERITANCE OF CHLOROPLAST DNA:
THE METHYLATION-RESTRICTION HYPOTHESIS

Ch1DNA of mt^+ (female) gametes is methylated at particular recognition sites, and protected against restriction occurring in zytgotes
Ch1DNA of mt^- (male) is *not* methylated at those sites, and not protected against restriction
Ch1DNA of mt^- (male) origin is degraded in zygotes, leading to maternal inheritance of chloroplast genes
In *mat-1* mt^- (male) mutants, ch1DNA is methylated and is *not* degraded in zygote, leading to biparental inheritance of chloroplast genes
In *me-1* mutants, ch1DNA of mt^+ (female) is further methylated in gametes but ch1DNA of *me-1* mt^- (male) is not, leading to maternal inheritance

other than bacteria, and it provided a molecular basis by which DNA coming from two different parents could be distinguished in the zygote after fusion—one was tagged with methyl groups, the other was not (4).

The next question was how did the methylation affect maternal inheritance? We knew from bacterial studies that methylation could protect DNA against degradation by special restriction enzymes capable of chopping up unmethylated DNA, and in further experiments we showed that degradation of unmethylated chloroplast DNA from the male parent was precisely what was happening in *Chlamydomonas*. Further clarification came from studies of mutants, *mat-1* (5) and *me-1* (6). The results are summarized in Table II.

This work has demonstrated a powerful biological function for DNA methylation, which we have called *selective silencing,* that is, the ability of methylation to regulate gene transmission and expression (7). In maternal inheritance, the mechanism is irreversible—the unmethylated DNA is destroyed. But in other systems, differential methylation can regulate gene expression in a reversible way (8). This phenomenon is highly relevant to the cancer problem.

III. TUMOR FORMATION BY CHEF CELLS: AZACYTIDINE-INDUCED CHANGES IN METHYLATION AND CHROMOSOMES

Our studies with mammalian cells, beginning in 1975, have focused on the analysis of genetic changes underlying the phenomenon of tumor formation. The choice of cells was very important: they had to be

TABLE III

PROPERTIES OF CHEF/18 CELL LINE

Permanent cell line
Stable diploid
Nontumorigenic
High cloning efficiency ($\sim$ 40%)
Convenient growth rate (15-hour generation time)
Anchorage dependent
Grows well on serum-free defined medium

diploid, with a normal chromosome complement, and they had to be nontumorigenic. No such cell line was known. Human cells were unsatisfactory because of senescence. However, we were very fortunate in obtaining from Dr. George Yerganian a population of diploid Chinese hamster embryo fibroblastic cells.

By cloning and subcloning this population, the doubly cloned CHEF/18-1 cell line was established (9). Some of its properties are listed in Table III. In addition to their chromosome stability and nontumorigenicity, another very surprising property was revealed when the cells were grown briefly in the presence of the drug 5-azacytidine (azac). This drug has been shown to decrease the extent of DNA methylation and, at the same time, to induce mesenchymal differentiation (10). We wondered whether decreased methylation might induce tumor formation in CHEF cells.

We found that azacytidine had a powerful effect on CHEF cells, inducing differentiation of various mesenchymal cell types (11). An apparent multitude of different cell types were observed in the dishes, but as yet our studies have been restricted to the adipocyte pathway. Cells were isolated that gave rise to preadipocytes after a short treatment with azacytidine. Preadipocytes (PAs) are cells committed to become adipocytes but that show no obvious morphological difference from the stem cells of origin. They can be grown indefinitely in serum so long as they do not become confluent. Several clones and subclones of azaC-induced preadipocytes were established for further study. We found further that adipocytes were inducible by another method—namely, growth with a high amount of insulin (10 μg/ml). The role of insulin in differentiation is a fascinating story by itself, but only the data relevant to this article will be included here.

TABLE IV

TUMORIGENICITY OF PREADIPOCYTE CLONES
DERIVED FROM CHEF/18[a]

Aza-cytidine induced		Insulin induced	
Cell line	Tumors/sites[b]	Cell line	Tumors/sites[b]
IV-1	2/2	II-1	0/6
IV-1/1	2/4	II-2	8/16
1/2	9/12	2/1	6/8
IV-2	2/2	2/2	1/4
2/1	0/4	2/3	0/6
2/2	5/6	II-3	0/6
IV-5	2/6	3/2	0/4
		3/3	0/4
		II-5	0/2

[a] From Harrison et al. (12).
[b] 5×10^6–1×10^7 cells/site.

As shown in Table IV, azaC preadipocyte clones and subclones were found to be tumorigenic in the nude mouse assay system, whereas most of the insulin-induced lines were nontumorigenic (12). One insulin-induced clone, II-2, segregated both tumor-forming and non-tumor-forming subclones; and one azaC-induced subclone IV-2/1 was nontumorigenic.

The high efficiency of tumor formation was particularly surprising, since other experiments in progress were demonstrating the stability of CHEF/18 cells, and the difficulty of making them tumorigenic with chemical mutagens. The mutagenized cells will be discussed more fully later. With the preadipocyte the question arose whether decreased methylation itself was responsible for the tumorigenicity, and if so, whether the insulin-induced PAs were also hypomethylated. It became necessary to measure methylation, but bulk methylation changes are not very revealing. What could be used as a probe of specific methylation? To approach this question, a number of cDNA probes of specific genes were chosen to look for methylation changes in DNAs that had been cleaved with methylation-sensitive enzymes. The tested genes included β-globin, β-actin, dihydrofolate reductase, preproinsulin, Ha-*ras,* and Ki-*ras* (12).

TABLE V

COMPARISON OF INSULIN- (II) AND AZACYTIDINE- (IV) INDUCED
PREADIPOCYTE (PA) CLONES[a]

Cells	Tumor formation[b]	Chromosome	Methylation change[c]		
			INS	HA	KI
CHEF/18	0/36	Normal	−	−	−
Insulin PAs (II)					
II-1, II-3, II-5	0/28	Normal	−	−	−
II-2	8/16	Normal and 3q+	−	±	−
Tumor-derived IIs		+3q	+	+	+
Azacytidine PAs (IV)	20/26	+3q	+	+	+
Tumor-derived IVs		+3q	+	+	+

[a] From Harrison *et al.* (12).

[b] Tumors/site.

[c] (−) Means that *Msp*I and *Hpa*II restriction fragment patterns are the same as control, CHEF/18; (+) means decreased methylation.

Results with three of these gene probes are summarized in Table V. With some exceptions, similar decreases in methylation were seen with all three probes, detected by comparison of gene-specific restriction fragment patterns after digestion with the methylation-resistant *Msp*I and paired methylation-sensitive *Hpa*II enzymes. The patterns seen in the control, CHEF/18, were also found in the nontumorigenic insulin-induced preadipocytes, whereas decreased methylation at specific sites was seen in the azaC-induced preadipocytes and in the tumor-derived lines (12). Although less uniform, the results with the other probes also showed decreased methylation in tumor derived cells.

The decreases observed in methylation of scattered genes suggests that widespread decreases in methylation have occurred in the tumor-derived cells, whether they result from prior treatment with azacytidine or not. This result tells us that methylation changes are occurring in the origin of tumor cells. It should be noted that the methylation decrease affects not only Harvey and Kirsten *ras* genes, which are purported oncogenes, but also genes such as β-globin that is not functioning at all in these cells. Apparently the relationship between methylation and gene expression is not simple. What is clear is the strong correlation between decreased methylation and acquisition of tumor-forming ability.

The Giemsa banded karyotypes of these tumorigenic and tumor-induced PAs were examined (12), and something quite unexpected was revealed: a virtually complete correlation between tumor-forming ability and the presence of an extra 3q, that is, an extra copy of the long arm of chromosome 3. In some instances there were additional chromosome changes; in other cell lines no additional changes were detected. This correlation of tumor-forming ability with the presence of $+3q$ suggests that a gene or gene with strong effects on tumor formation is located on 3q. Similar karyotypes have been seen in other tumor-derived CHEF cells from other experiments (13).

What I have related so far supports the generalization with which this article began, namely that chromosome rearrangements and methylation changes both appear to be involved in the origin of tumor cells. The fact that methylation changes occur at many sites suggests that the expression of many genes may be altered in the process of tumorigenic transformation. The extra copy of chromosome 3q may result in extra gene products with tumor-inducing effects. Also the loss of the extra copy of the short arm of chromosome 3 may be quite important. Trisomy for the whole chromosome 3 was rarely seen in these cells. Perhaps the short arm carries suppressors of genes on the long arm. Clearly the potential exists for multiple gene changes.

IV. Tumor Formation by CHEF Cells: How Many Steps?

Multiple changes occurring during tumorigenesis of CHEF cells is precisely what was found. Let us now consider studies of the tumor-forming ability of CHEF/18 cells after treatment with various mutagens (14). CHEF/18 cells are very resistant to becoming tumorigenic, as shown in Table VI. The spontaneous occurrence of tumorigenicity has a frequency of less than 3×10^{-9}; and after mutagenesis it is still less than 10^{-8}. In contrast, the frequency of spontaneous single-gene mutations (e.g., $hprt^+ \rightarrow hprt^-$) in CHEF/18 is about 5×10^{-7}, and in EMS-treated cells it is 100-fold higher. Thus, it is evident that CHEF/18 cells do not become tumorigenic as the result of a single-gene mutation. In this study, transformed mutants were also selected by growth in low serum or in suspension, and these transformed mutants were hardly more tumorigenic than the unselected populations (14).

TABLE VI

TUMOR-FORMING ABILITY OF MUTAGEN-TREATED CHEF/18 CELLS[a]

Experiment	Mutagen	Percentage kill	Tumor take	Time (months)
CHEF/18	None	—	0/34	
CHEF/18 Expt 20	400 EMS	92	1/6	5
CHEF/18 Expt 21	200 EMS	86	1/6	5
CHEF/18 Expt 38	200 EMS	44	0/7	
CHEF/18 Expt 39	$10^{-5}M$ MNNG	46	1/6	$6\frac{1}{2}$
CHEF/18 Expt 67	0.4 4-NQO	85	0/18	

[a] From Smith and Sager (14).

Thus, CHEF/18 cells are stably nontumorigenic. They appear to be buffered against tumor formation. What might be the mechanism of this resistance? One mechanism is genetic suppression of tumor formation. Our evidence comes from cell fusions between tumorigenic and nontumorigenic cells, as summarized in Table VII, in which the cell hybrids were initially non-tumor forming (9). This phenomenon was first described by Henry Harris and George Klein using mouse cells, and more recently, suppression has been shown to be particularly stable in human cell hybrids in studies by Harold Klinger and independently by Eric Stanbridge (reviewed in 15). The "takehome" lesson from these suppression studies is that suppressor genes may be very important in the protection against tumorigenesis at the cellular level and that suppression must be overcome to permit tumor formation. Whether

TABLE VII

SUPPRESSION OF TRANSFORMATION AND TUMORIGENICITY
IN CHINESE HAMSTER CELL HYBRIDS[a]

	CHEF/18	CHEF/16	Hybrids	Suppression
Morphology	N	TR	Intermediate	Partial
Growth in methocel	$<10^{-5}$	40–60%	10^{-3}–10^{-5}	Complete[b]
Growth in hydron	−	+	−	Complete
Tumorigenicity	$<10^{-8}$	>90%	10^{-2}–10^{-4}	Complete[b]

[a] From Sager and Kovac (9).

[b] Small subset regains tumorigenicity and ability to grow in methocel.

suppressor genes are the dominant alleles of recessive oncogenes or are genes with other functions remains unknown at this time.

The results discussed so far support two concepts: (1) that genetic changes leading to tumorigenesis involve both genes that promote tumor formation and genes that suppress tumor formation, and (2) that at the molecular level, two kinds of events are involved: changes in chromosome organization, and changes in metylation patterns in which tumor cells are less methylated than are normal cells.

V. TUMOR FORMATION BY CHEF CELLS: UPTAKE OF TUMOR DNA

The next step is the identification of specific genes involved in these processes. A set of presumptive genes that induce tumor formation has been described, the cellular genes that resemble the transforming genes of retroviruses, so called oncogenes (16). Two of them were already mentioned, namely the Harvey and Kirsten *ras* genes, that showed decreased methylation in tumor cells (Table V).

We recently reported that CHEF/18 cells are good recipients of DNA including genomic DNA from EJ cells (17). EJ cells are a human cell line originally derived from a bladder carcinoma. DNA from EJ cells has been successful in transforming NIH/3T3 cells, and a fragment of DNA called the EJ gene has been cloned out of the total genomic DNA on the basis of its ability to transform NIH/3T3 cells (16). The cloned gene was found to be closely related to the transforming gene Ha-*ras* of the Harvey retrovirus Ha-MSV. Subsequently, it was reported that the cloned EJ gene differed from its normal homolog by only a single amino acid substitution (18). This result has led to the widely held view that a single amino acid change in a single gene is sufficient to convert a normal cell into a tumor cell. This view flies in the face of a vast amount of evidence that tumorigenic transformation is a multistep process, and has led to a genuine paradox. The EJ cells from which the transforming DNA was isolated have about 91 chromosomes, greatly rearranged. Since these cells have undergone so many genomic changes, it cannot be assumed that the cloned EJ gene was responsible for or even involved in the origin of the human bladder tumor.

Since CHEF/18 cells are so resistant to chemically induced transformation, it seemed important to study their response to the EJ DNA. Data in Table VIII show that CHEF/18 cells transformed by genomic

TABLE VIII

Tumorigenicity of Foci Induced by Transfer of EJ DNA into CHEF/18 Cells[a]

Experiment	Foci tested	Foci cells producing tumors in nude mice		Tumor take	EJ DNA in tumor-derived cells
f-29	5	2	29-5	6/8	+
			29-11	1/8	+
f-100	4	3	100-6	4/4	+
			100-13	4/4	+
			100-16	4/4	+
f-101	1		1	3/6	N.T.[b]
f-102	1		1	4/6	N.T.

[a] From Sager et al. (19).
[b] N.T., Not tested.

DNA from EJ cells are tumorigenic in the nude mouse. We then asked whether the single reported gene change is sufficient to transform CHEF cells. To answer this question, chromosomes and DNA were examined from several tumor-derived populations of CHEF/18 cells made tumorigenic by transfection with genomic EJ DNA (19). The chromosomes of one of these are shown in Fig. 3. There is an HSR, or amplification region, in chromosome 2q, and by *in situ* hybridization, the EJ gene was localized in this region (19).

Cells from other tumors recovered in this experiments showed other chromosome changes including an HSR in the long arm of a third copy of chromosome 4, a t(2;9) translocation, and the presence of extra centromeric fragments. At the DNA level, as shown in Fig. 4, the EJ DNA that had been transfected into CHEF cells was amplified in some tumor-derived cell lines, rearranged and partially deleted in others (19).

The conclusion from these studies is that genomic DNA from EJ cells *does* induce tumor formation in CHEF/18 cells, but that the tumor-derived cells show amplification and other changes in the EJ sequence and in the chromosome complement. It cannot be concluded that the EJ gene alone has converted CHEF/18 cells to tumor cells. The EJ gene clearly plays a role, but the relation to other genetic changes occurring in these cells remains an open question. These results illustrate the value of using diploid stably nontumorigenic cells as recipients in the genetic

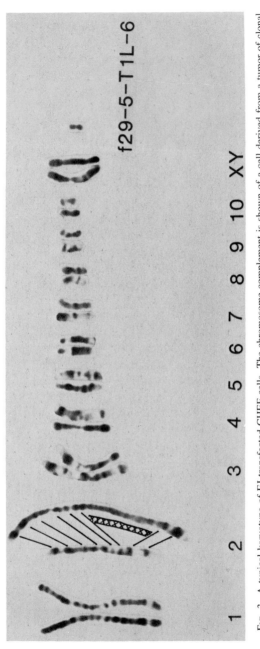

Fig. 3. A typical karyotype of EJ-transfected CHEF cells. The chromosome complement is shown of a cell derived from a tumor of clonal origin grown from a focus of CHEF/18 cells transfected with genomic EJ DNA. One copy of chromosome 2 contains an extensive HSR; and a centromeric fragment is present in addition to the diploid complement. (From Sager *et al.*, 19.)

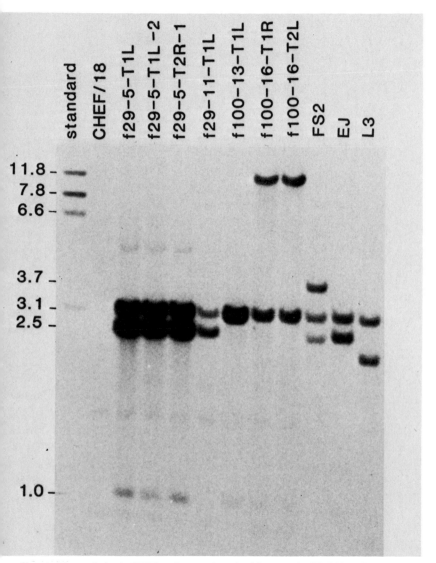

Fig. 4. Tumor-derived CHEF cells transfected with genomic EJ DNA. Genomic DNAs were extracted from a series of tumor-derived cell populations, digested with *Bam*HI + *Sst*I, electrophoresed on 1% agarose, transferred to nitrocellulose paper, and hybridized with the 6.6 kb EJ gene from pEJ. (From Sager *et al.*, 19.)

analysis of tumorigenesis. Small chromosomal changes can be detected by light microscopy, and the appearance of tumor-forming cells following DNA transfer provides material for the identification of multiple genetic changes.

VI. Human Cancer and the Future of Cancer Research

What are the implications of this work for the origin of human cancer? Human cells are much more resistant to becoming tumorigenic than are rodent cells. Various calculations indicate that human cells are about 10,000 to 100,000 times as resistant as mouse cells. If this resistance has a cellular basis, as opposed, for example, to immune surveillance or hormonal effects, then it should be possible to study it by transfection. Are human cells more resistant to transformation by the EJ gene than Chinese hamster cells? To answer this question, transfection of CHEF/18 cells was compared with transfection of a population of foreskin-derived normal human cells (established in our laboratory) using plasmids carrying the EJ gene (21,22).

The principal results are summarized in Table IX. The pEJ plasmid contains the EJ gene in pBR322, and the pSVgptEJ plasmid contains both the EJ gene and a bacterial gene *gpt* that confers resistance to the drug mycophenolic acid (20). The advantage of the latter plasmid is that one can select for drug resistance and then examine the resistant colo-

TABLE IX

Transfection of CHEF/18 and Normal Human Cells
by Cloned EJ DNA[a]

| | Recipient cells | | | |
| | CHEF/18 | | Human | |
DNA	Yield[b]	Tu[c]	Yield[b]	Tu[c]
pEJ	>10^2	+	0/04	—
pSVgptEJ	>10^2	+	~10 nontransformed drug-resistant colonies	N.T.Y.

[a] From Sager *et al.* (21, 22).
[b] Foci or colonies per μg transforming DNA.
[c] Tumorigenicity in nude mouse assay.

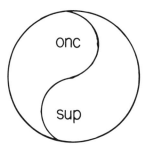

FIG. 5. Suppressor genes and oncogenes expressed as the Yin and Yang of cancer.

nies for expression of the EJ gene. Both plasmids are highly effective in CHEF/18 cells, but neither one has yet transformed the human cells (21,22). These results are still preliminary, but they support the idea that human cells have special mechanisms that protect them from tumorigenesis. Those mechanisms may include chromosome stability and multiple suppressor genes that inhibit the tumorigenic transformation.

The goal of cancer research is to protect ourselves against tumorigenic transformation in any of our cells. The experiments I have described suggest some novel approaches. For example, our experiments suggest that in addition to losing growth control, cells must undergo chromosome breaks, rearrangements, and methylation changes to become tumor cells. So far, cancer chemotherapy has focused on uncontrolled growth itself, and thereby has imperiled normal growing cells in cancer patients. A new approach might focus on the special subset of growing cells with damaged or aberrant chromosomes, and destroy them preferentially. Another line of research, which seems particularly exciting to me, focuses on genes that suppress tumor formation, which might be called antioncogenes. I think the evidence is strong enough to justify the view expressed in Fig. 5 that suppressor genes and oncogenes are the Yin and Yang of cancer. The identities and functions of both classes need to be investigated, which means there is a great deal of research out there still to be done.

ACKNOWLEDGMENTS

I gratefully acknowledge the enthusiasm, hard work, and inspiration contributed by many colleagues and co-workers including assistants, associates, students, and fellows, to the research I have described. In particular, I thank Zenta Ramanis, Dorothy Lane, Constance Grabowy, and Dr. Yoshihiro Tsubo, M. R. Ishida, Will Burton, and Hiroshi Sano for their devotion to *Chlamydomonas,* and Patricia Kovac, Anthony Anisowicz,

Esther Soudry, Lewis Chodosh, Dr. Robert Kitchin, Dr. Chris Marshall, Dr. Inder Gadi, Dr. Janie Harrison, Dr. Kiyoji Tanaka, Dr. Ching Lau, and Dr. Barbara Smith for sharing our adventures in the world of cell culture and medical research.

This work was supported principally by grants from the NIH, and made possible by the expressed confidence of numerous participants in the grant award process, whom I take this opportunity to thank.

REFERENCES

1. Sager, R. (1972). "Cytoplasmic Genes and Organelles." Academic Press, New York.
2. Sager, R., and Ishida, M. R. (1963). *Proc. Natl. Acad. Sci. U.S.A.* **50,** 725–730.
3. Sager, R. (1977). *Adv. Genet.* **19,** 287–340.
4. Burton, W. G., Grabowy, C., and Sager, R. (1979). *Proc. Natl. Acad. Sci. U.S.A.* **76,** 1390–1394.
5. Sager, R., Grabowy, C., and Sano, H. (1981). *Cell* **24,** 41–47.
6. Sano, H., Grabowy, C., and Sager, R. (1981). *Proc. Natl. Acad. Sci. U.S.A.* **78,** 3118–3122.
7. Sager, R., and Kitchin, R. (1975). *Science* **189,** 426–433.
8. Adams, R. L., and Burdon, R. H. (1982). *CRC Crit. Rev. Biochem.* **13,** 349–384.
9. Sager, R., and Kovac, P. (1978). *Somatic Cell Genet.* **4,** 375–392.
10. Taylor, S. M., and Jones, P. A. (1979). *Cell* **17,** 771–779.
11. Sager, R., and Kovac, P. (1982). *Proc. Natl. Acad. Sci.* **79,** 480–484.
12. Harrison, J. J., Anisowicz, A., Gadi, I., Raffeld, M., and Sager, R. (1983). *Proc. Natl. Acad. Sci. U.S.A.* **80,** 6606–6610.
13. Kitchin, R., Gadi, I., Smith, B. L., and Sager, R. (1982). *Somatic Cell Genet.* **8,** 677–689.
14. Smith, B. L., and Sager, R. (1982). *Cancer Res.* **42,** 389–396.
15. Stanbridge, E. J., Der, C. J., Doersen, C., Nishimi, R. Y., Peehl, D. M., Weissman, B. E., and Wilkinson, J. W. (1982). *Science* **215,** 252–259.
16. Klein, G. (1982). "Advances in Viral Oncology." Raven, New York.
17. Smith, B. L., Anisowicz, A., Chodosh, L. A., and Sager, R. (1982). *Proc. Natl. Acad. Sci. U.S.A.* **79,** 1964–1968.
18. Taparowsky, E., Suard, Y., Fasan, N., Ku, K., Goldfarb, M., and Wigler, M. (1982). *Nature (London)* **300,** 762–765; Tabin, C. J., Bradley, S. M., Bargmann, C. I., Weinberg, R. A., Papageorge, A. G., Scolnick, E. M., Dhar, R., Lowy, D. R., and Chang, E. H. (1982). *Nature (London)* **300,** 143–149; Reddy, E. P., Reynolds, R. K., Santos, E., and Barbacid, M. (1982). *Nature (London)* **300,** 149–152.
19. Sager, R., Gadi, I., and Anisowicz, A. (1984). In preparation.
20. We thank Drs. Chiaho Shih and Robert Weinberg for pEJ, and Dr. Richard Mulligan for pSVgpt into which we inserted the EJ gene.
21. Sager, R., Tanaka, K., Anisowicz, A., and Lau, C. (1983). *Fed. Proc. Fed. Am. Soc. Exp. Biol.* **42,** 2189.
22. Sager, R., Tanaka, K., Lau, C., Ebina, Y., and Anisowicz, A. (1984). *Proc. Natl. Acad. Sci. U.S.A.* **80,** 7601–7605.

THE BIOSYNTHESIS OF INSULIN: GENETIC, EVOLUTIONARY, AND PATHOPHYSIOLOGIC ASPECTS*

DONALD F. STEINER

Department of Biochemistry
The University of Chicago
Chicago, Illinois

I. Introduction

IN 1965, when I began studying insulin biosynthesis in slices of a human islet cell adenoma, it was already widely believed that insulin was assembled in the β cell by combination of its separately synthesized constituent B and A chains (Lazarow, 1963; Humbel, 1965). This view seemed to be strongly supported by the success of synthetic chemists in recombining insulin chains with reasonably high yields (Dixon and Wardlaw, 1960; Zahn et al., 1965; Du et al., 1966; Katsoyannis and Tometsko, 1966). The validity of their findings is today underscored by the fact that human insulin is being produced commercially by this method, utilizing as starting material A and B chains synthesized by genetically engineered bacteria (Goeddel et al., 1979; Chance et al., 1981). However, as is often the case in biological systems, there are many reasons why a seemingly simple and direct chemical approach is ignored in favor of a more elaborate and sometimes more esthetically pleasing solution (Fig. 1). Attempting to explain nature's choices is part of the joy of studying natural science, but in doing this we must always try not to allow our preconceptions to shape our interpretations.

While by 1965 several investigators had failed to find evidence for a precursor of insulin in studies on pancreatic tissue slices or extracts (Lazarow, 1963; Taylor et al., 1964; Humbel, 1965; Wang and Carpenter, 1965) it is rather remarkable to note that the possible existence of a zymogenlike form of insulin had been suggested as early as 1916 by Sir Edward Schäfer, some 5 years before the discovery of insulin

*Lecture delivered May 19, 1983.

191

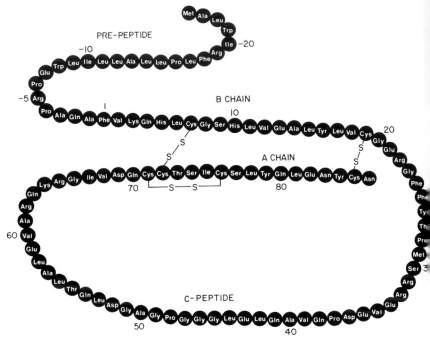

FIG. 1. Covalent structure of rat preproinsulin II.

(Schäfer, 1916) and was also mentioned by MacLeod in 1925 (Campbell and MacLeod, 1925). The premise on which this rather astonishingly prescient observation was based was, of course, incorrect; it was assumed by Schäfer that the reason no one had succeeded in making active preparations of the (putative) blood-sugar lowering principle of the pancreas, which he named "insuline," was that the hormone was present as an inactive zymogenlike "proinsuline." We know now that it is much more difficult to detect proinsulin in the pancreas than insulin (Campbell and MacLeod, 1925; Wang and Carpenter, 1965) and that the success of Banting and Best where others had failed was mainly because they took steps to prevent the proteolytic enzymes of the pancreas from destroying insulin during the preparation of their extracts (Banting and Best, 1922).

Once proinsulin had been isolated and its structure determined (Chance *et al.*, 1968; Steiner *et al.*, 1968, 1969; Nolan *et al.*, 1971) we undertook to understand its role in the biosynthesis of insulin. Here our thinking was influenced by what appeared at the time to be a most compelling explanation for the existence of the prohormone. We were able to show that when proinsulin was fully reduced and unfolded in 8 *M* urea and then returned to a slightly alkaline medium without urea, it regenerated the correct disulfide bridges of insulin much more efficiently than did the separated A and B chains (Steiner and Clark, 1968). Indeed Anfinsen and co-workers had already postulated in 1965 the need for a single-chain precursor of insulin based on the instability of the two-chain insulin molecule in the presence of reducing agents, in sharp contrast to the behavior of several other small single-chain proteins such as ribonuclease (Givol *et al.*, 1965). In this case the reasoning was valid and could be confirmed experimentally, but the conclusion that this property explained the existence of proinsulin was premature for within just a few years it became increasingly obvious that many other small peptide hormones, which either lacked disulfide bridges or did not have stable conformations in solution, were also synthesized as parts of larger precursor polypeptides. We now know that precursors of this kind are very widespread in nature and that they have other important structural features which may relate to the complex demands of the cellular secretory pathway along which they travel. Studies of proinsulin have revealed new aspects of this extremely interesting and important cellular process, many features of which continue to challenge our imagination and experimental ingenuity.

In this article I will attempt to summarize the current status of our knowledge of precursor molecules, as exemplified by proinsulin, and of the nature and subcellular organization of the proteolytic processing mechanisms that act on these to generate a large variety of biologically active products. With the advent of recombinant DNA methodology it has become feasible to study the primary structures of many precursor proteins in much greater detail, to examine the structures of their chromosomal genes and to begin to relate these to pathophysiologic states in man. These new methods also allow us to study the evolution of precursors such as preproinsulin more effectively and concurrently to explore the evolution and generality of the various proteolytic processing mechanisms that have been uncovered as this field has developed over the years since 1965.

II. PROINSULIN STRUCTURE

To understand the structure and chemical properties of proinsulin it is necessary to first become familiar with the molecular topography of insulin. The excellent X-ray crystallographic studies of Hodgkin and co-workers have revealed the native three-dimensional structure of insulin at a resolution of 1.4 Å (Blundell *et al.*, 1972; Chothia *et al.*, 1983). It is a highly organized, compact folded structure which contains many features characteristic of larger more complex globular proteins. Most mammalian insulins exist in solution at high concentrations as dimers or in the presence of metal ions, such as zinc, as spherical metal-coordinated hexamers made up of three slightly asymmetric (isologous) dimers arranged around a three-fold axis of symmetry. Both the A and B chain regions contain helical segments that are packed together to form a central hydrophobic core in the molecule. This core extends across the dimer interface which is made up solely by interactions between hydrophobic regions in the B chain, including an extended region near the C-terminus of the B chain (residues 23–26) that contains three important aromatic residues (Phe-Phe-Tyr). This region forms an antiparallel B strand in the dimer but is also believed to be part of the receptor-binding region of the monomer (Fig. 2). The recent identification of two mutant insulins in man resulting from nucleotide substitutions in the insulin gene, within the region coding for this sequence, emphasizes its importance for the binding of insulin to its receptor (Tager *et al.*, 1979; Shoelson *et al.*, 1983; Kwok *et al.*, 1983; Haneda *et al.*, 1983).

Spectroscopic and chemical evidence indicates that the insulin moiety in proinsulin has essentially the same structure as that seen in insulin crystals (Frank and Veros 1968; Frank *et al.*, 1972) except that the A and B chains are connected together by the large, loosely organized, connecting peptide which extends downward from the C-terminus of the B chain covering that part of the monomer that is on the surface in the hexamer, passing through a loop near its midregion, and then reflecting back upward to partly cover the receptor binding region, and finally joining to the N-terminus of the A chain, as shown schematically in Fig.

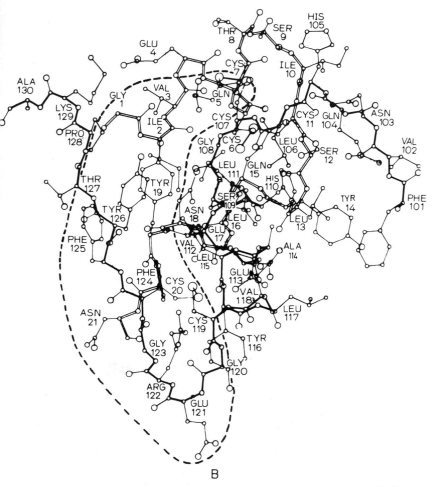

Fig. 2. Porcine insulin monomer indicating the region implicated in receptor binding (enclosed by dashed line). B chain residues are numbered from 101 to 130. (Reproduced with permission of the authors from Wood *et al.*, 1975.)

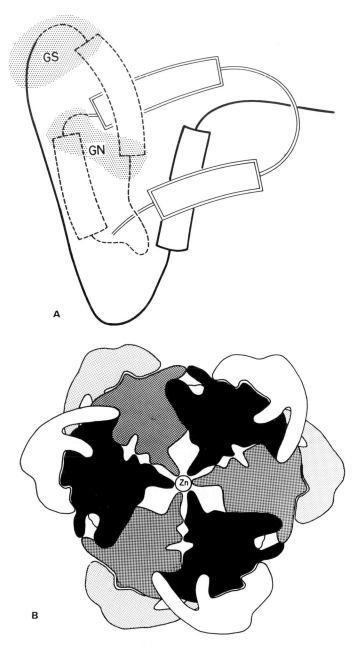

Fig. 3A and B.

3A. This arrangement does not hinder the self-association of proinsulin to form dimers and hexamers (Frank *et al.*, 1972; Steiner, 1973) (Fig. 3B), but it does significantly lower its receptor-binding potency to about 3–5% of that of insulin (Steiner *et al.*, 1972). The central region of the connecting peptide in most higher vertebrates (Fig. 4) is unusually rich in glycine, proline, and other residues which are frequently found in β turns in proteins (Chou and Fasman, 1978). Thus, it seems highly likely that the connecting polypeptide has a hairpinlike conformation in the proinsulin molecule. The Chou–Fasman rules also predict the possible existence of α-helical regions on either side of the central β turns (Snell and Smith, 1975), but these have not been unequivocally demonstrated by optical or X-ray studies. An antiparallel β strand might be an equally plausible structure for these regions. We recently have developed several monoclonal antibodies in rats which are directed against a strong antigenic determinant located in this region of the human C-peptide (Madsen *et al.*, 1983). These antibodies react with both intact proinsulin or free C-peptide and seem to recognize an epitope created by the juxtaposition of subregions of both the N-terminal and C-terminal halves of the C-peptide, as postulated in the hairpin model (Fig. 3A). Another monoclonal antibody prepared in mice reacts only with intact proinsulin or certain of its intermediates (Madsen *et al.*, 1983), and, as shown in Fig. 3A, this antibody appears to recognize another determinant that is made up of the cleavage site (Arg-Arg) and amino acids lying to either side of this basic pair at the B chain–C-peptide junction. Cleavage in this region, as in the conversion to insulin, obliterates this site and so this antibody is potentially useful for studies on proinsulin and its intermediate forms in tissues or in blood.

Fig. 3. (A) Schematic drawing of a proinsulin monomer, illustrating the hypothetical folding of the connecting polypeptide to form a U-shaped structure which covers the binding site (compare with Fig. 2). The binding sites of two monoclonal antibodies to either proinsulin (upper shaded area) or to the C-peptide (lower shaded area) are indicated. (B) Conception of a hexamer of proinsulin, viewed along the three-fold crystallographic axis, indicating the external arrangement of the connecting peptide such that it does not inhibit dimer or hexamer formation. In this projection the solid form at 5 o'clock corresponds to the monomer shown in part A viewed from above. The central darker masses collectively represent the outline of the globular insulin hexamer (see Blundell *et al.*, 1972), and the points of attachment of the C-peptide to the insulin B and A chains are indicated by the fingerlike projections from the outer, lighter colored C-peptide regions.

Amino acid position numbering: 1 2 3 4 5 6 7 8 9 10 11 12 13 14 15 16 17 18 19 20 21 22 23 24 25 26 27 28 29 30 31 32 33 34 35 36 37 38

HUMAN	Glu-Ala-Glu-Asp-Leu-Gln-Val-Gly-Gln-Val-Glu-Leu-Gly-Gly-Gly-Pro-Gly-Ala-Gly-Ser-Leu-Gln-Pro-Leu-Ala-Leu-Glu-Gly-Ser-Leu-Gln
MONKEY	Glu-Ala-Glu-Asp-Pro-Gln-Val-Gly-Gln-Val-Glu-Leu-Gly-Gly-Gly-Pro-Gly-Ala-Gly-Ser-Leu-Gln-Pro-Leu-Ala-Leu-Glu-Gly-Ser-Leu-Gln
HORSE	Glu-Ala-Glu-Asp-Pro-Gln-Val-Gly-Glu-Val-Glu-Leu-Gly-Gly-Gly-Pro-Gly-Leu-Gly-Gly-Leu-Gln-Pro-Leu-Ala-Leu-Ala-Gly-Pro-Gln-Gln
PIG	Glu-Ala-Glu-Asn-Pro-Gln-Ala-Gly-Ala-Val-Glu-Leu-Gly-Gly-Gly-Leu-Gly-Gly-Leu-Gly — Gly — Leu-Gln-Ala-Leu-Ala-Leu-Glu-Gly-Pro-Pro-Gln
COW, LAMB	Glu-Val-Glu-Gly-Pro-Gln-Val-Gly-Ala-Leu-Glu-Leu-Ala-Gly-Gly-Pro-Gly-Ala-Gly-Gly-Leu-Glu — — — Gly-Pro-Pro-Gln
RABBIT	Glu-Val-Glu-Gly-Pro-Gln-Val-Gly-Ala-Leu-Glu-Leu-Ala-Gly-Gly-Pro-Gly-Ala-Gly-Gly-Leu-Gln-Pro-Ser-Ala-Leu-Glu — Ala-Leu-Gln
DOG	Glu-Val-Glu-Asp-Leu-Gln-Val-Arg-Asp-Val-Glu-Leu-Ala-Gly-Ala-Pro-Gly-Glu-Gly-Gly-Leu-Gln-Pro-Leu-Ala-Leu-Glu-Gly-Ala-Leu-Gln
RAT I	Glu-Val-Glu-Asp-Pro-Gln-Val-Pro-Gln-Leu-Glu-Leu-Gly-Gly-Gly-Pro-Glu-Ala-Gly-Asp-Leu-Gln-Thr-Leu-Ala-Leu-Glu-Val-Ala-Arg-Gln
RAT II	Glu-Val-Glu-Asp-Pro-Gln-Val-Ala-Gln-Leu-Glu-Leu-Gly-Gly-Gly-Pro-Gly-Ala-Gly-Asp-Leu-Gln-Thr-Leu-Ala-Leu-Glu-Val-Ala-Arg-Gln
GUINEA PIG	Glu-Leu-Glu-Asp-Pro-Gln-Val-Glu-Gln-Thr-Glu-Leu-Gly-Met-Gly-Leu-Gly-Ala-Gly-Gly-Leu-Gln-Pro-Leu — — Gln-Gly-Ala-Leu-Gln
CHINCHILLA	Glu-Leu-Glu-Asp-Pro-Gln-Val-Gly-Gln-Ala-Asp-Pro-Gly-Val-Val-Pro-Glu-Ala-Gly-Arg-Leu-Gln-Pro-Leu-Ala-Leu-Glu-Met-Thr-Leu-Gln
DUCK	Asp-Val-Glu-Gln-Pro-Leu-Val-Asn-Gly-Pro — Leu-His-Gly-Glu-Val-Gly-Glu — — Leu-Pro-Phe-Gln-His-Glu-Glu — — Tyr-Gln
CHICKEN	Asp-Val-Glu-Gln-Pro-Leu-Val-Ser-Ser-Pro — Leu-Arg-Gly-Glu-Ala-Gly-Val — — Leu-Pro-Phe-Gln-Glu-Glu-Glu-Tyr-Glu-Lys-Val
ANGLERFISH	Asp-Val-Asp-Gln-Leu-Leu-Gly-Phe-Leu-Pro-Pro-Lys-Ser-Gly-Ala-Ala-Ala-Ala-Ala-Gly-Ala-Asp-Asn-Glu-Val-Ala-Glu-Phe-Ala-Phe-Lys-Asp-Gln-Met-Glu-Met-Met-Val
HAGFISH	Asp-Thr-Gly-Ala-Leu-Ala-Ala-Phe-Leu-Pro-Leu-Ala-Tyr-Ala-Glu-Asp-Asn-Glu-Ser-Gln-Asp-Asp-Glu-Ser-Ile-Gly-Ile-Asn-Glu-Val-Leu-Lys-Ser

FIG. 4. Compilation of known amino acid sequences of proinsulin C-peptides. Sources: Steiner, 1976; (dog) Kwok *et al.*, 1983a; (rabbit) R. Chance *et al.*, 1979; (chinchilla) Snell and Smyth, 1975; (chicken) Perler *et al.*, 1980; (anglerfish) Hobart *et al.*, 1980; (hagfish) Chan *et al.*, 1981a.

From the foregoing discussion the role of the C-peptide can easily be visualized as one primarily of structure making, as pointed out in the introductory section. However, several studies with cross-linked insulin derivatives have shown that very short bridge molecules linking the C-terminus of the B chain and the N-terminus of the A chain will suffice for this purpose (Brandenburg and Wollmer, 1973; Busse *et al.*, 1974). Moreover, there is no indication that the excised C-peptide binds to insulin under any conditions, suggesting that it does not precisely "fit" against the insulin structure. Instead it may act to enhance folding primarily by converting the reaction of A and B chains from a bi-molecular reaction to a more efficient and concentration-independent first-order reaction. If this were the only role of the C-peptide then clearly its length would be expected to have gradually decreased as evolution has proceeded. However, this is not the case as is clearly shown in Fig. 4. In most higher vertebrates the C-peptide is 31 residues long (after excision of the paired basic residues linking it to the insulin chains on either side). However, it does vary somewhat in length, being as short as 26 residues in cows and sheep and as long as 38 residues in the anglerfish (Hobart *et al.*, 1980) and 33 in the more primitive hagfish (Chan *et al.*, 1981b). Thus, there has been a slight tendency to shorten-ing of the C-peptide during evolution, but this is not very marked considering its great variability in amino acid sequence and the fact that the conserved length is clearly many times greater than that required to ensure the proper folding and sulfhydril oxidation of proinsulin (Stei-ner, 1978).

We might then inquire, what are the other functions of the C-peptide that require that its length be conserved, but not its amino acid se-quence? Clearly it is not a biologically active peptide hormone even though it is secreted in equimolar amounts with insulin (Rubenstein *et al.*, 1969, 1977). Indeed, no clear-cut functions have yet been found for it. Although it has been postulated to cause a feedback regulation of insulin secretion, such an activity has been difficult to reproduce experi-mentally in many species (Rubenstein *et al.*, 1977). It is our belief that the conservation of length in the C-peptide indicates that it acts as a molecular spacer which serves to enlarge the peptide chain to facilitate its efficient transmembrane segregation in the earliest phases of insulin biosynthesis in the β cell (Patzelt *et al.*, 1978a; Steiner, 1978). This process will be discussed in greater detail in Section III.

In addition, it is possible that the C-peptide also contains some residues which confer appropriate overall properties of charge, solubility, and flexibility to the nascent molecule so as to assist both its folding and structural organization under *in vivo* conditions in the endoplasmic reticulum, as well as its subsequent migration to the Golgi apparatus and its sorting into appropriate secretory granules along with the converting proteases. Recombinant DNA techniques will soon allow mutations to be conveniently introduced into the proinsulin C-peptide region in order to study some of these fascinating questions in greater depth. In nature, however, such "mutations" already exist to a degree in the form of the insulinlike growth factors (IGF I and II). In both cases, proinsulinlike peptides have been isolated which contain insulinlike structures linked by connecting segments that are only about 11 residues long (Rinderknecht and Humbel, 1978). The existence of these molecules clearly indicates that a much shorter connecting peptide segment can indeed function effectively to generate the characteristic insulinlike disulfide bridge structure. However, the IGF peptides maintain their overall length by being elongated elsewhere; thus, some of the peptide material lost from the C-peptide region has been replaced by an extension added to the C-terminus of the A chain. This internal reorganization of the precursor molecule which clearly must be "acceptable" in order to generate the IGF peptide family, would clearly be detrimental to insulin where the C-terminus of the A chain is highly conserved and forms part of the receptor-binding region (Pullen *et al.*, 1976). Thus, we believe that the proinsulin molecule has retained its unique structural organization largely in consequence of constraints against any rearrangements that would have been detrimental to the biological activity of its product.

It should be noted also that the larger size of the proinsulin C-peptide may also be related to the demands for conversion to insulin, a processing event that is not conserved in IGF, which retains its single-chain structure. The longer connecting segment in proinsulin thus may serve to orient the pairs of basic residues optimally for attack by the proinsulin-converting enzyme. As we have suggested elsewhere, it is also possible that mRNA secondary structure may be a conserved feature that imposes constraints on major evolutionary variations in proinsulin organization (Steiner *et al.*, 1980). It should be possible to examine this relatively unexplored area in greater detail as more information on insulin mRNA sequences becomes available.

III. Cellular Organization of the Biosynthetic Process

From the pioneering work of Jamieson, Siekevitz, and Palade (Palade, 1975) the major topographic aspects of secretory protein biosynthesis and transport are now well established. The biosynthesis of most, if not all, secreted proteins takes place in the rough endoplasmic reticulum (RER) where the initial segregation of the secretory product from the general cytoplasm occurs in a process whereby the nascent secretory precursor is translocated across the RER membrane during and/or immediately after its biosynthesis. The discovery of N-terminal extensions on secreted proteins (variously called signal sequences, prepeptides, or leader peptides) has led to many new and exciting developments in this area (Milstein *et al.*, 1972; Kemper *et al.*, 1974; Chan *et al.*, 1976). Elegant studies with reconstituted systems by Blobel and Dobberstein that demonstrate the role of the signal sequence in initiating the binding of ribosomes to microsomal membranes and their formulation of the signal hypothesis represents one of the major advances in this area of the past decade (Blobel and Dobberstein, 1975a,b). More recently Walter and Blobel (1982) have discovered a new ribonucleoprotein particle, which they have called signal recognition particle, or SRP, that interacts with the signal sequence and leads to the formation of the ribosome–membrane junction via the interaction of an SRP–signal peptide–ribosome complex with a receptorlike molecule in the RER membrane, termed the docking protein (Meyer *et al.*, 1982; Gilmore *et al.*, 1982). These events are summarized schematically in Fig. 5.

Following transfer into the luminal spaces of the RER the prepeptide is rapidly cleaved off by the signal peptidase which is located on the inner surface of the RER membrane (Jackson and Blobel, 1977; Kreil, 1981). Wickner and associates (Zwizinski and Wickner, 1980) have isolated and characterized the protease which cleaves the presequences of many secreted proteins in *Escherichia coli* and have also identified its gene. This enzyme appears to be highly conserved both in structure and properties from prokaryotes to higher eukaryotes (W. Wickner, personal communication). It is in the cisternae of the RER, perhaps beginning even before completion of the peptide chain, that folding and structural reorganization of the proinsulin molecule occurs. It is difficult experimentally to measure disulfide bond formation in this compartment. However, in earlier pulse-labeling studies we have been able to extract

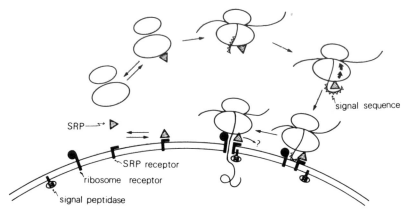

Fig. 5. Schematic representation of the early events in secretory protein biosynthesis leading to the segregation of nascent polypeptides via interaction of the signal sequence with the signal recognition particle, SRP. Reproduced with the permission of the authors from Walter and Blobel (1981).

correctly folded proinsulin from rat islets within 2 minutes after addition of labeled amino acids (unpublished data). Studies on the cell-free synthesis of preproinsulin indicate that the presence of the hydrophobic leader sequence interferes with the correct folding of the proinsulin regions of the chain (Lomedico *et al.*, 1977). We have postulated (Steiner *et al.*, 1980; Docherty and Steiner, 1981) that during insertion the prepeptide forms a transmembrane loop oriented with the N-terminus on the cytosolic side and having the C-terminal region and cleavage site on the luminal side of the membrane (see Fig. 5). Thus, before cleavage occurs the signal sequence may serve as a transmembrane anchor for the newly synthesized proinsulin chain. With the prepeptide buried in the membrane or in some other structure the proinsulin region may be free to fold as it enters the luminal space, even before prepeptide cleavage. Indeed, its folding might even be enhanced by anchorage of the N-terminus in the RER membrane. However, pulse-chase studies on preproinsulin formation and conversion to proinsulin in intact islets indicate that a major fraction of preproinsulin is processed to proinsulin cotranslationally, i.e., before completion of the peptide chain (Patzelt *et al.*, 1978b). Since one of the cysteine residues required to form the disulfide bridge, B19–A20, occurs just before the C-terminal asparagine residue in preproinsulin (Fig. 1), it is unlikely that sulfhydryl oxidation can be completed before the proinsulin chain is freed from its (membrane-bound) signal sequence. Thus, the final stages of the tertiary structural organization of proinsulin probably occur in solution within the cisternae of the RER. The pH and chemical composition of this environment remain to be elucidated for most secretory cells, as does the question as to whether thiol-disulfide exchange enzymes are involved in sulfhydril oxidation of nascent protein chains (Freedman and Hawkins, 1977).

IV. GOLGI/GRANULE PROCESSING OF PROHORMONAL PRODUCTS

After peptide chain completion and folding, newly formed proinsulin is transferred to the Golgi area in the β cell, probably via small microvesicles which bud from smooth regions of the RER nearer the Golgi complex (Palade, 1975; Orci, 1982). This energy dependent process occurs within 10–20 minutes after completion of the peptide chain (Steiner *et al.*, 1970). In addition to its important role in concentrating and packaging secretory products the Golgi complex also serves as a site for sorting and processing a variety of other cellular proteins, such as the precursors of the lysosomal cathepsins (which are then shuttled into their respective storage vesicles) as well as many proteins destined for the plasma membrane (Farquhar and Palade, 1981), including viral glycoproteins (Gumbiner and Kelly, 1982). The Golgi apparatus also is the site where the intracellular proteolysis of prohormones such as proinsulin is initiated (Steiner *et al.*, 1970, 1972; Docherty and Steiner, 1981). As a consequence of the close association of these processing events with other Golgi-associated activities such as lysosome formation (Farquhar and Palade, 1981), it is perhaps not surprising that presently available evidence supports the idea that precursor processing may be accomplished by proteolytic enzymes that are related in structure to some of the lysosomal catheptic proteases. Thus, studies with isolated rat and anglerfish islets have implicated a trypsinlike endoprotease that is inhibited by leupeptin, antipain, and pOH mercuribenzoate sulfonate, all inhibitors of thiol proteases such as cathepsin B (Docherty and Steiner, 1981; Fletcher *et al.*, 1981; Docherty *et al.*, 1982). Moreover, we have shown that rat islet secretion granule fractions, which carry out conversion of endogenously labeled proinsulin *in vitro*, contain a relatively large amount of 31,500 MW cathepsin B, identified by means of a site-specific labeling reagent, ^{125}I-Tyr-Ala-Lys-Arg-CH$_2$Cl (Docherty *et al.*, 1983), but little evidence of cathepsin H, a related thiol protease that appears to be more abundant along with cathepsin B in hepatic lysosomes.

However, it is not yet clear whether the cathepsin B in the islet secretion granule fraction actually is present in the secretion granules per se, as most methods for preparations of insulin granules unfortunately do not exclude lysosomes. Thus, in parallel studies with highly purified chromaffin granules which were not contaminated by lysosomes we were unable to identify significant amounts of cathepsin B (K. Docherty and D. Steiner, unpublished results). Since these granules process precursors of Met and Leu enkephalin, albeit very slowly (Fleminger *et al.*, 1983), the virtual absence of cathepsin B suggests that this enzyme is not, itself, involved in processing. Moreover, model studies on prohormone conversion with isolated cathepsin B have shown that, despite its known facility in cleaving synthetic substrates having paired basic residues, it degrades or inappropriately processes many hormones or their precursors (see McKay *et al.*, 1983; Docherty and Steiner, 1981). It thus seems more plausible to suspect that a more specific cathepsin B-like enzyme may be involved in processing. In islet granule fractions we recently have detected a 38,000 MW peptide that is similar in its labeling characteristics to cathepsin B (Docherty *et al.*, 1983, 1984). This less abundant protease is currently being studied in greater detail. We also have begun studies on the biosynthesis of cathepsin B to investigate the hypothesis that a larger active form of this enzyme might be engaged in Golgi/granule processing. Our preliminary results (see Fig. 6) indicate the existence of a precursor of approximately 43,000 MW (Steiner *et al.*, 1984), and it may be significant that a similar larger form of cathepsin B has been found to be secreted by some cancer cells *in vivo* and *in vitro* (Recklies *et al.*, 1982; Mort *et al.*, 1983).

V. INSULIN GENE STRUCTURE

With the development of systems for the cell-free translation of proteins directed by added specific messenger RNA fractions it became possible to detect the synthesis of many presecretory forms with extended N-termini such as preproinsulin and thus to establish with greater

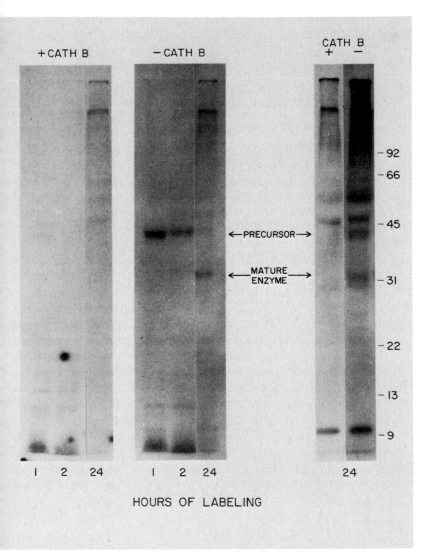

FIG. 6. Labeling of a precursor of cathepsin B in isolated rat islets. Islets were labeled for 1, 2, or 24 hours, sonicated, and immunoprecipitated with an antiserum against rat liver cathepsin B (kindly provided by Dr. H. Kirschke, Halle). Lanes designated + CATH B were samples in which excess unlabeled cathepsin B from rat liver was added with the antiserum. (From Steiner *et al.*, 1984.)

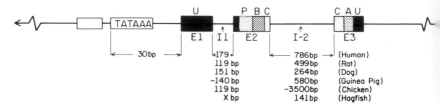

FIG. 7. Diagrammatic representation of the insulin gene in vertebrates. Regions appearing in mature preproinsulin mRNA are shown as bars and the relative size of the 2 introns (I) in various species are tabulated below. U, Untranslated region; P, prepeptide coding region; B, B chain coding region; C, C-peptide coding region; and A, A chain coding region. A typical TATA box signaling transcription initiation is shown approximately 30 base pairs upstream from the messenger start site.

certainty the nature of the initial translation products of their genes. Using such systems we demonstrated that preproinsulin could be initiated *in vitro* by yeast initiator methionine tRNA, thereby establishing with certainty the start point of mRNA translation (Chan *et al.*, 1981a). The subsequent cloning of full-length cDNA copies of the mRNAs for both of the two closely related rat preproinsulins (Chan *et al.*, 1979a) revealed the entire coding sequence of both gene products and provided the necessary final confirmation that preproinsulin is the precursor form encoded within the insulin gene (Chan *et al.*, 1979b).

The availability of rat insulin cDNA probes also opened the way to the isolation and nucleotide sequence analysis of the insulin genes of several species (Fig. 7). Only a single copy of this gene is present in humans (Bell *et al.*, 1980a; Ullrich *et al.*, 1980), dogs (Kwok *et al.*, 1983a), chickens (Perler *et al.*, 1980), and in the Atlantic hagfish, a primitive jawless vertebrate (S. J. Chan and D. F. Steiner, unpublished data). The human insulin gene is located on the short arm of chromosome 11 (Owerbach *et al.*, 1980; Harper *et al.*, 1981). In rats and mice two copies of the insulin gene are present in the chromosomes. The gene coding for insulin I in the rat is altered by the loss of an intervening sequence from the C-peptide coding region, but the rat genes are otherwise closely homologous in nucleotide sequence (> 90%), suggesting that the duplication event leading to their separation occurred relatively recently in evolution (Lomedico *et al.*, 1979).

The presence of a well-conserved intron in the C-peptide region of the insulin gene suggests that in evolution exons containing coding sequences for B chainlike and A chainlike amino acid sequences were brought together. This possible role for intervening sequences, which was first suggested by Gilbert (Gilbert, 1978), will be examined in greater detail in Section VI. In addition to the intron in the coding region of preproinsulin, another intervening sequence is present in the 5' untranslated region just upstream from the initiation site. The arrangement of these intervening sequences is not unusual for eukaryotic genes, but it indicates that processing of nucleotide sequences must occur before mature insulin mRNA is produced. This occurs in the nucleus, probably preceded by capping and polyadenylation of the pre-mRNA (Duguid et al., 1976; Maitra et al., 1982), but little is known about the details of these processes in islet cells. In view of the presence of the second intervening sequence in the C-peptide region in most insulin genes it is conceivable that larger aberrant forms of proinsulinlike material might be generated through translation of incompletely processed pre-mRNA molecules, e.g., perhaps in some islet cell tumors (Duguid and Steiner, 1978). This might not be unexpected since insulinomas often fail to process proinsulin to insulin as completely as normal islet tissue (Rubenstein et al., 1977), a clinically useful observation.

The regions of sequence conservation in the insulin gene are illustrated in Fig. 7. The introns are highly variable in length and sequence, much more so even than the coding sequence for the C-peptide region, which over long evolutionary distances, as between the human and hagfish insulin genes, has become completely randomized (Chan et al., 1981b). It is probably significant that the region of homology among insulin genes extends about 500 base pairs (bp) upstream on the 5' side (Bell et al., 1980a), indicating the likelihood that some controlling elements for the expression of the gene are located in this region. Efforts are currently underway in several laboratories to identify those nucleotide sequences of the gene that are involved in its normal expression in islet tissue (Gruss et al., 1981; Lomedico, 1982; Laub and Rutter, 1983; Nielsen et al., 1983) and to determine whether its transcription is regulated by glucose or other factors. Although it has been shown that glucose affects the incorporation of labeled nucleotides into insulin mRNA (Okamoto, 1981) and its levels (Brunstedt and Chan, 1982; Permutt and Kipnis, 1972), it is not yet clear whether this is a direct effect on transcription or may be due to stabilization of the mRNA. Translation of insulin mRNA is greatly stimulated by glucose, an effect that is independent of RNA synthesis and highly specific for insulin (Steiner *et al.*, 1972; Permutt, 1974; Jahr *et al.*, 1980; Itoh and Okamoto, 1980).

The availability of cDNA clones of the messenger RNAs for pre-proinsulins in several species has prompted attempts to express this protein in various bacterial or animal cells (for a review see Chan *et al.*, 1981c). Thus, it has been possible not only to produce insulin A and B chains in bacteria and combine them (Goeddel *et al.*, 1979; Chance *et al.*, 1981) but also to produce proinsulin either directly (Frank *et al.*, 1981) or via preproinsulin (Talmadge *et al.*, 1980; Chan *et al.*, 1981d). Using a cDNA copy of human preproinsulin (S. J. Chan, unpublished) we have constructed a plasmid in which the distal half of the prepeptide of preproinsulin is fused to the N-terminal half of the leader sequence of the *E. coli* ampicillinase gene giving rise to a perfect hybrid prepeptide (half bacterial and half human) which retains all those structural features which we believe are essential for prepeptide function, including the hydrophobic central region and the more polar and flexible region near the signal peptidase cleavage site (Fig. 8). When this plasmid was expressed in *E. coli*, human proinsulin, correctly cleaved from its pre-peptide, was found mainly in the periplasmic space indicating that the hybrid preprotein had been handled as an exportable product in the bacterial cell. Moreover, the proinsulin appeared to be correctly folded as well. This experiment underscores the universality of the protein export mechanisms of living cells. However, there was no cleavage of proinsulin to insulin suggesting that bacteria may not possess proprotein processing mechanisms. Several other fusions with deletions of important regions of the prepeptide were expressed in the bacterial host cells but were not efficiently segregated (Fig. 8).

VI. Pathophysiologic Aspects of Insulin Biosynthesis

Although it is likely that the complex biosynthetic pathway leading to insulin must be the site of numerous defects, this area is just beginning to be explored more fully. Mutations in the presequences of some bacterial secretory proteins have been shown to prevent their export and/or to interfere in the secretory process more generally, sometimes being lethal (Hall and Silhavy, 1981). Defects of a similar nature in the preproinsulin molecule similarly could prevent its segregation and se-

Human Preproinsulin   Met-Ala-Leu-Trp-Met-Arg-Leu-Leu-Pro-Leu-Leu-Ala-Leu-Leu-Ala-Leu-Trp-Gly-Pro-Asp-Pro-Ala-Ala-Ala-PHE

pJW 1452 -Met-(Res. 2-53)-Ile-Leu-Glu-Ser-Phe-Arg-Pro-Glu-Glu-Arg-Phe-Pro-Ala-Leu-Glu-Ala-Leu-Trp-Gly-Pro-Asp-Pro-Ala-Ala-Ala-PHE

Ampicillinase

pJW 2172   Met-Ser-Ile-Gln-His-Phe-Arg-Val-Ala-Leu-Ala-Leu-Ile-Pro-Ala-Leu-Leu-Ala-Leu-Trp-Gly-Pro-Asp-Pro-Ala-Ala-Ala-PHE

pJW 2243   Met-Ser-Ile-Gln-His-Phe-Arg-Val-Leu-Trp-Gly-Pro-Asp-Pro-Ala-Ala-Ala-PHE

pJW 2324   Met-Ser-Ile-Gln-His-Phe-Arg-Val-Ala-Ala-Ala-PHE

Human Preproins

Ampicillinase   Met-Ser-Ile-Gln-His-Phe-Arg-Val-Ala-Leu-Ile-Pro-Phe-Phe-Ala-Ala-Phe-Cys-Leu-Pro-Val-Phe-Ala-HIS

Plasmid	IRI	% Secreted
pJW 1452	9.4 ng/mg Prot.	87
pJW 2172	2.2 ng/mg Prot.	91
pJW 2243	0.2 ng/mg Prot.	43
pJW 2324	0.2 ng/mg Prot.	11

FIG. 8. Predicted amino acid sequences of several ampicillinase–human preproinsulin hybrids. Resultant hydrophobic prepeptide segments are shown in bold type. The table below the sequences summarizes data on the relative expression levels obtained and the proportion of the immunoreactive proinsulinlike material (IRI) found in the periplasmic space. (See Chan et al., 1981d, for methods of preparation of fusion plasmids and analysis of products.)

cretion from the β cell and perhaps lead to cytosolic accumulations of preproinsulinlike material or other secretory products of a toxic nature. The phenotypic manifestations of this kind of genetic defect might thus include stress-induced cytotoxicity and eventual β cell depletion.

Two families have been identified whose members have inherited alterations in their proinsulin molecules preventing their normal cleavage to insulin (Gabbay *et al.*, 1979; Kanazawa *et al.*, 1979). These defects can be rationalized in terms of the almost universal use of paired basic residues to mark cleavage sites in proproteins as discussed earlier. It seems highly probable that the trypsinlike converting enzyme(s) specifically require paired basic residues for their activity. Studies of one family with hyperproinsulinemia of this kind revealed the presence in the blood of an intermediate cleavage form of proinsulin. It was proposed that this defect is due to the replacement of one of the basic residues in the cleavage site at the C-peptide–A-chain junction with a neutral amino acid (Robbins *et al.*, 1981). Similarly, in a New Zealand family with proalbuminemia, amino acid sequence analysis revealed that one of the paired arginine residues within the basic hexapeptide sequence at the N-terminus of the proprotein had been replaced by a glutamine residue (Brennan and Carrell, 1978). These molecular defects appear to shed some further light on the properties of the cleavage system but do not give any indication as to whether the same or individually specialized enzymes are involved in the cleavage of the various proproteins in their respective tissues of origin.

The demonstration of heritable defects in cleavage of prohormones, due to point mutations at cleavage sites, appears to be opening the way to the discovery of other disorders in endocrine or neural regulation due to the faulty processing of precursors. The defects described above seem to be rather benign. Thus, failure to cleave proinsulin at the B–C junction would still allow material having considerable biological activity to circulate. However, members of one of the families with proinsulinemia associated with a cleavage defect at the C–A junction (Robbins *et al.*, 1981) exhibit a mild diabetes, which is consistent with evidence that cleavage at this position is required to raise the biological activity of proinsulin from a low level of 3–4% into a more normal range (Steiner *et al.*, 1972). Similar considerations regarding biological activity, or spectrum of actions, may well apply to the conversion of many other prohormones and neurosecretory peptide precursors, e.g., the ACTH–endorphin precursor and others. Thus, further exploration for cleavage defects may reveal new endocrine or neurological disorders.

Going beyond proinsulin, it has long been suspected that defects within the insulin molecule might give rise to diabetes or related metabolic disorders (Steiner *et al.*, 1970). Such a possibility has now been realized in the discovery of a patient with an unusual diabetes associated with hyperinsulinemia (Tager *et al.*, 1979). This syndrome was shown to be due to an abnormal insulin which had a leucine residue substituting for one of the two phenylalanine residues in the C-terminal region of the B chain (Given *et al.*, 1980). These residues lie within the receptor-binding region of the hormone and make important contributions to binding enhancement (see Fig. 2). By a semisynthetic procedure Tager and his associates (Tager *et al.*, 1980) synthesized both of the two possible structures for this mutant insulin and tested these in various systems, including a high-pressure liquid chromatographic system capable of resolving insulins with single amino acid substititions (Shoelson *et al.*, 1983). It was thus possible to unequivocally demonstrate that this abnormal insulin was Leu B^{25} insulin. In our laboratory Dr. S. Kwok confirmed the above findings by restriction enzyme cleavage analysis of DNA from circulating leukocytes of this patient (Kwok *et al.*, 1981). In the normal human insulin gene the nucleotide sequence TTC-TTC codes for the two phenylalanine residues at positions B_{24} and B_{25}. The sequence complementary to TCTTC has been shown to be the recognition site for cleavage by the restriction enzyme *Mbo* II. Thus, replacement of nucleotides coding for either of the two phenylalanine residues with those coding for a leucine residue would be expected (in 11 of the 12 possible leucine codon substitutions at this site) to destroy this recognition sequence (Fig. 9). Southern blot analysis of the patient's DNA after cleavage with *Mbo*II demonstrated the presence of a new band of DNA which hybridized to a human insulin cDNA probe. This single band of 0.9 kilobases had the size expected for the sum of the two fragments normally produced by *Mbo*II cleavage in this region of the gene. Subsequent cloning and nucleotide sequence analysis of the mutant allele revealed a single nucleotide transversion in the codon for phenylalanine B^{25} changing it to a codon specifying leucine (Kwok *et al.*, 1983b).

More recently we have studied a second patient with an abnormal

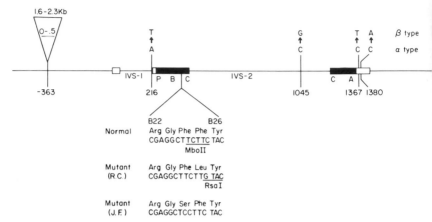

FIG. 9. Structures of two mutant insulin alleles from subjects with mild hyperin-sulinemic diabetes. Both mutations result in the loss of a normal Mbo II cleavage site in the B chain coding region, while one (R.C.) results in the creation of a new site for RsaI cleavage. α and β refer to four known allelic differences in the human insulin gene, which are presumably not of functional significance (Ullrich *et al.*, 1980). The mutant genes in both patients appeared to be of the α-type.

insulin associated with mild maturity-onset diabetes. Other family members in several generations also exhibited the same abnormality in association with varying degrees of glucose intolerance (Haneda *et al.*, 1983). Its mode of inheritance was as an autosomal dominant. Studies of plasma insulin from the proband by HPLC showed this to be a more hydrophilic insulin (Shoelson *et al.*, 1983). Nonetheless, MBO cleavage studies of leukocyte DNA demonstrated a cleavage defect in the same recognition site as in the patient having Leu B[25] insulin. Cloning and nucleotide sequence analysis of the alleles of the insulin gene in this patient was carried out and revealed this defect to be due to a different single-point mutation occurring in the important $B_{24,25}$ (Phe-Phe) region of the B chain leading to Ser[1324] insulin. These results are summarized in Fig. 9. These findings represent the first documented instances of point mutations in the insulin genes giving rise to defective hormone molecules (insulinopathies).

Further exploration of the genetic bases for diabetes is now feasible thanks to the development of new and more efficient techniques for cloning genes coupled with the ingenious methods that now exist for rapidly and conveniently sequencing them. It should soon be possible to apply these approaches equally effectively to studies of insulin receptors and receptor defects as well as to the search for the complex genetic alterations that predispose individuals to the more severe juvenile-onset varieties of diabetes. These defects appear to involve multisubunit membrane-associated proteins (receptors, antigens, and/or viral recognition sites), and these will, of course, be more difficult to successfully clone and analyze than the simple one-gene systems that have been studied thus far. However, the rapid progress of the last 5 years seems to presage even more remarkable developments in the years immediately ahead. We appear to be entering an exciting era in which rapid advances will be possible in our understanding and treatment of diabetes and other poorly understood disorders with strong genetic components, such as malignancy and arteriosclerosis.

VII. Evolutionary Aspects of Insulin Biosynthesis

The evolution of insulin is an interesting and potentially important problem. Insulin plays a major metabolic role in all vertebrates, and probably in many invertebrates as well, regulating the metabolism of carbohydrates, lipids, and proteins and integrating nutrition with growth, either directly through its own intrinsic growth promoting activity, or indirectly through receptors for the structurally related insulinlike growth factors of which two have been identified and sequenced (IGF I and II) (Rinderknecht and Humbel, 1978). Recent reports of the possible presence of insulin or related peptides in unicellular organisms based on radioimmunoassay emphasize the interest that this area is beginning to generate (Roth et al., 1982).

At the present time, however, definitive structural information is available on only about 25 insulins—all from vertebrates. These samples range across the major vertebrate orders including some mammals, birds, reptiles, and teleost fishes. The most primitive organism from which insulin has been isolated and studied in detail is the Atlantic hagfish (*Myxine glutinosa*), a jawless vertebrate (*Agnatha*) that lives on the bottom of the sea, feeding largely on detritus that settles to the ocean floor. The hagfishes are, of course, not really fish at all, but exhibit many primitive features including a notochord, a lack of osmoregulation, and very little cephalization (Brodal and Fänge, 1963). They are thus more similar to *Amphioxus* and other protochordates.

In *Amphioxus,* cells identifiable by immunocytochemical techniques as islet cells are present in the epithelium of the gut and are often of the so-called "open" type (Van Noorden and Falkmer, 1980). In the hagfish the insulin-producing B cells, as well as the somatostatin-producing D cells, appear to have migrated from the mucosal epithelium to form a small, compact islet organ weighing 1–2 mg, which is located near the point of entry of the bile duct into the duodenom (Van Noorden and Falkmer, 1980). This arrangement seems to represent an intermediate stage in the morphogenesis of the higher vertebrate pancreas. However, in the hagfish the zymogen-producing acinar cells remain in the gut mucosa and there is no pancreatic parenchyma aside from the small islet organ. The exocrine pancreas first appears in the cartilaginous fishes (for a review, see Van Noorden and Falkmer, 1980).

This sequence of evolutionary stages seems to be recapitulated in normal gnathostomian development. Thus, in the early embryo, pancreatic rudiments arise as buds from the duodenal portion of the endodermal tube, and very early in this process a few epithelial cells that have immunocytochemical features of islet cells migrate out of the epithelial layer into the adjacent mesenchyme where they continue to develop as islet cells, giving rise to the characteristic duct-associated islets of the mammalian pancreas (Pictet and Rutter, 1972). Several studies have now shown conclusively that these islet cells are truly of endodermal origin and do not arise from migratory cells of neural origin (Pictet *et al.*, 1976; Fontaine *et al.*, 1977). All these observations imply the existence of a close evolutionary relationship between the islet cells, particularly the B cells, and the exocrine pancreatic cells. This relationship is further strengthened by the findings that under some circumstances, i.e., after B cell loss or injury, pancreatic duct cells can apparently give rise to new B cells and even of new islets (Bonner-Weir *et al.*, 1981). However, insulin-producing B cells rarely, if ever, appear elsewhere in the intestinal tract, and evidence for the production of insulin by various extrapancreatic tissues, including brain (Havrankova *et al.*, 1978) and pituitary (Hatfield *et al.*, 1981) remain to be fully substantiated (Eng and Yalow, 1981), e.g., by direct biosynthetic studies or by demonstration of the presence of true insulin gene-derived mRNA in these sites. We will return to this close association between the endocrine and exocrine pancreas in Section VIII when we discuss the possible evolutionary origin of the insulin gene.

Studies on the amino acid sequence (Peterson *et al.*, 1975) and three-dimensional structure (Cutfield *et al.*, 1979) of hagfish insulin have revealed that despite the replacement of about 40% of the amino acids at various positions along the chains with residues that differ from those seen in mammalian insulin, the main course of the peptide chains in the hagfish insulin monomer has remained essentially identical to that seen in crystalline pork insulin (Fig. 10). These findings are consistent with other studies on protein evolution, which have shown that the tertiary structure of functionally related proteins is more highly conserved than the amino acid sequence, especially over long evolutionary distances (Grütter *et al.*, 1983).

A further implication of this finding is that the basic structure of insulin was already well defined early in vertebrate evolution and has undergone relatively little change during the subsequent stages leading to man, a period of divergence of about 500 million years. This is consistent with the idea that insulin is a considerably more ancient and widespread hormone in phylogeny and implies that we must look to much more primitive organisms (Chan *et al.*, 1981c) to learn more about its evolutionary origins. But before doing so we might first ask about the evolution of insulin's precursor. What structural changes has it undergone during vertebrate evolution, and are there significant differences in insulin biosynthetic mechanisms between higher and lower vertebrates?

By applying recombinant DNA technology to this problem we were able to clone a cDNA copy of the mRNA of hagfish insulin (Chan *et al.*, 1981b) and from this to predict the complete structure of hagfish preproinsulin. These results, illustrated in Fig. 11, show that hagfish preproinsulin is remarkably similar in structure to the preproinsulins of higher vertebrates (compare Figs. 11 and 1). The prepeptide is similar in size and in those structural features necessary for its function as a signal sequence. The cleavage site is a threonine residue rather than alanine, a substitution that would surely be compatible with signal peptidase action. The hagfish C-peptide is 33 amino acids long, rather than 31 as in man, but it shows essentially no significant amino acid sequence homology to any other C-peptide except that of the anglerfish (see Fig. 4). This finding underscores the high rate of mutation acceptance in the C-peptide which makes it an excellent indicator of short-range evolutionary relationships among proinsulins (Markussen and Vølund, 1974).

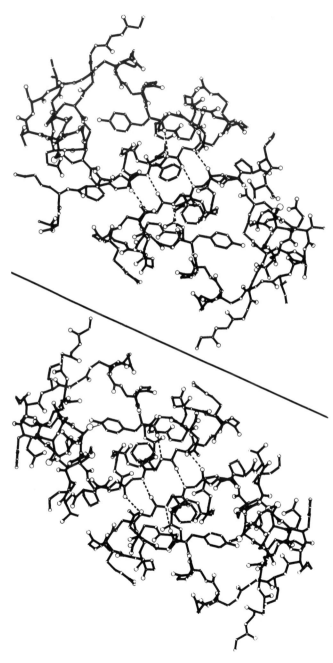

FIG. 10. Comparison of the three-dimensional structure of the human insulin dimer (right) (viewed along the two-fold dimer axis) with the corresponding dimer of hagfish insulin (left). (Reproduced courtesy of Prof. Guy Dodson, York, England, unpublished data.)

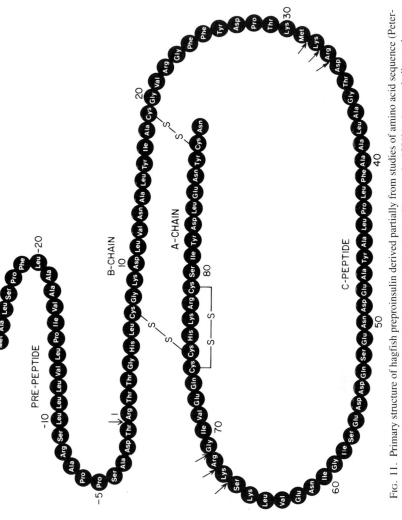

FIG. 11. Primary structure of hagfish preproinsulin derived partially from studies of amino acid sequence (Peterson et al., 1975) and from the nucleotide sequence of the mRNA (Chan et al., 1981b). Arrows indicate cleavage sites for conversion of the precursor to insulin.

It is of interest to note that the characteristic pairs of basic residues are present on either side of the C-peptide in hagfish proinsulin (Fig. 11), indicating that the precursor processing mechanism for prohormones discussed earlier was evolutionarily "old" at the time of divergence of the hagfish from the main line of vertebrate evolution. Recent studies with endocrine precursor peptides from aplysia (Schueller *et al.*, 1982) as well as from yeast (Kurjan and Herskowitz, 1982) confirm that proprotein processing mechanisms are of ancient evolutionary origin. Presecretory proteins similar to those of eukaryotes have been found in many prokaryotes as well (Kreil, 1981; Hall and Silhavy, 1981), suggesting that the basic segregation mechanism for secretory protein synthesis is very ancient and essentially universal. On the other hand, proprotein processing may be a more characteristic feature of eukaryotic cells, particularly the use of paired basic residues to mark sites of processing. The origins of this mechanism may in some respects be viewed as parallel with the development of DNA splicing in eukaryotes.

VIII. Evolutionary Origins of the Insulin Gene

Insulin is a member of a superfamily of related proinsulinlike peptides which includes IGF I and II (Rinderknecht and Humbel, 1978) and relaxin, a two-chain ovarian hormone that is involved in parturition (Isaacs *et al.*, 1978). It has been proposed that the submaxillary gland nerve growth factor (NGF) is also related to proinsulin (Frazier *et al.*, 1972), although in this case the disulfide arrangement differs from that characteristic of insulin, the IGFs, and relaxin, and the amino acid homology is less marked. It is likely that these proteins arose from an ancestral proinsulinlike protein. The structures of these proteins are illustrated schematically in Fig. 12 along with their precursor peptides (Haley *et al.*, 1982). This comparison points up the extreme variability in connecting peptide length that is compatible with the simply defined role of structure making or folding enhancing. It seems more likely that this variability, coupled with the presence of the intron in this region of both the insulin and relaxin genes (Hudson *et al.*, 1983) provides clues to the evolutionary origins and interrelationships of this protein superfamily. Of particular interest in this connection is an old observation that insulin might be related to some of the exocrine pancreatic pro-

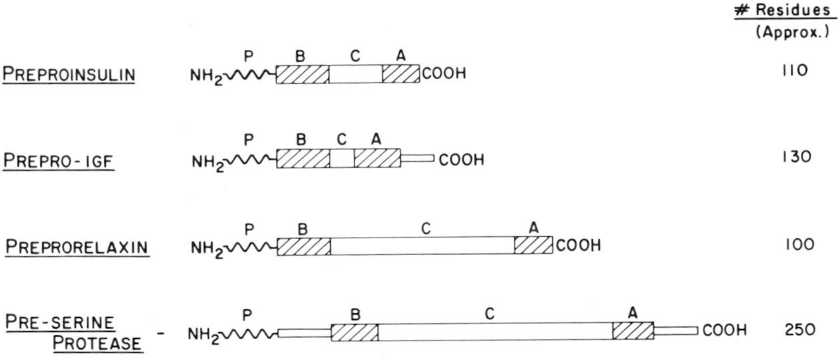

FIG. 12. Schematic representation of the insulin superfamily of hormones and growth factors, P, Prepeptide; B, B chainlike; C, connecting peptide segment; A, A chainlike; IGF, insulinlike growth factor.

teases. When I first noted some homology between the insulin chains and certain regions of the pancreatic serine proteases by direct observation in 1966 (D. F. Steiner, unpublished) the structure of proinsulin had not yet been determined. The region of apparent homology to the B chain was near the N-terminus of the trypsin sequence while the A chainlike region was near the C-terminus. The "connecting segment" lying between these chains was approximately 140 amino acids in length. Subsequent structural analysis of proinsulin confirmed that, indeed, the B chain preceded the A chain (Chance *et al.*, 1968; Steiner *et al.*, 1969), but when the C-peptide sequence was obtained it was much shorter, and it bore no resemblance to the intervening peptide region of the serine proteases. This fact discouraged me from pursuing the idea of homology further until more information on ancestral forms might become available. In the meantime others have pointed out this homology independently, particularly de Haen in a careful and thorough study (De Haen *et al.*, 1976) and also Adelson (Adelson, 1971) who drew attention to numerous suggestive homologies between the digestive proteases and various hormones including insulin.

With the advent of recombinent DNA technology it has become feasible to reexamine this question by direct comparison of the gene structures for these hormones and those of the serine proteases. The results are indeed promising but by no means conclusive. Both the insulin and relaxin genes contain introns within their C-peptide coding

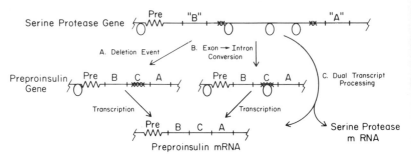

Fig. 13. General scheme for the derivation of new genes and products from preexisting genes. The specific example shown is the possible derivation of the insulin superfamily of proteins from a larger primordial serine proteaselike gene. Three possible mechanisms could have acted to produce the smaller new gene structure, as follows: (A) A classical duplication of the parental gene followed by a deletion of the region between the double-X marks to produce an internally shortened peptide product (proinsulin); (B) gene duplication followed by conversion of the exons between the X marks into introns; (C) a more attractive possibility based on present-day knowledge of mRNA splicing would be that alternative splicing of the initial mRNA transcript of the serine protease gene produced small amounts of preproinsulin mRNA as a side product prior to duplication and mutational stabilization of the new version.

regions suggesting a possible mechanism for the generation of a proinsulinlike peptide from a putative ancestral serine protease gene essentially by processing out the intervening coding region during transcription as though it were part of an intron, perhaps due to an error in RNA processing leading to the use of alternative splicing sites as outlined in Fig. 13 (Chan *et al.*, 1981c). Additional evidence supports this idea as follows:

1. The amino acid sequence of the rat relaxin connecting segment shows limited but significant homology with the corresponding central regions of serine proteases (Fig. 14), as expected if prorelaxin is an intermediate stage in the evolution of the serine gene product toward a proinsulinlike or IGF-like molecule.

2. The insulin gene's C-peptide intron is evolutionarily highly stable and is present in essentially the same position even in the hagfish gene (S. J. Chan and D. F. Steiner, unpublished).

3. The serine protease gene (Craik *et al.*, 1983) is made up of several exons arranged such that the insulin B-like and A-like sequences are

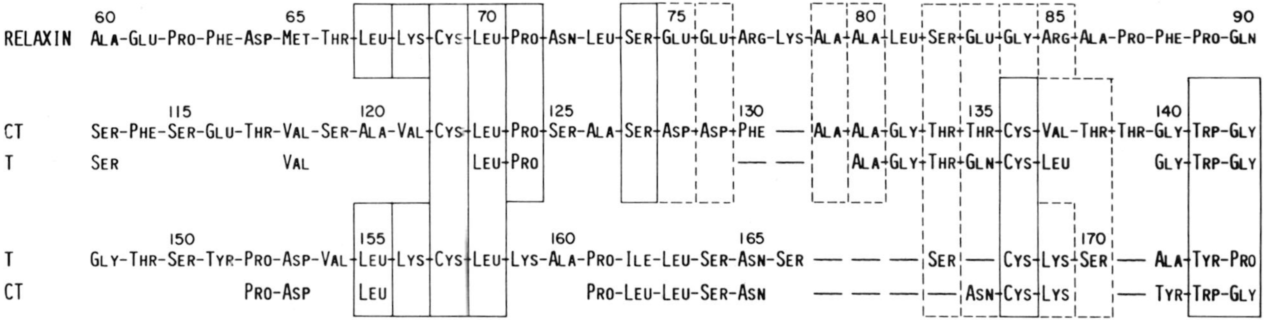

Fig. 14. Homologies in the central region of the connecting peptide segment of (rat) relaxin with the (bovine) serine proteases chymotrypsin (CT) or trypsin (T). Numbers refer to respective alignments within the prorelaxin or chymotrypsinogen sequences. Solid boxes enclose identical residues, dashed boxes enclose similar residues, blanks represent deletions necessary for the alignment. It should be noted that these relaxin sequences are not well conserved. Both human and porcine prorelaxins lack the cysteine residue (position 69), which is the key residue for this comparison. Thus, the apparent homology will need to be reexamined when the sequences of more primitive prorelaxins become available.

each on separate exons separated by a long nucleotide sequence containing several introns and exons as illustrated diagramatically in Fig. 13. It is not yet known whether the genes for the IGF peptides have introns in or near their C-peptide-like regions, as would be predicted by this theory.

According to this hypothesis the origin of the insulin superfamily might have occurred originally through alterations in the processing of the messenger RNA of an ancestral serine protease gene, thereby giving rise as a coincidental event to small amounts of preproinsulinlike mRNA. Similar alternative splicing mechanisms have been found in several other endocrine systems in which they lead to the production of novel or altered homonal products (Miller and Eberhardt, 1983; Amara *et al.*, 1982). The cosecretion of this insuline-like peptide along with these digestive enzymes in some primitive gut (or neuroregulatory?) cell may have been selectively advantageous in several ways, as discussed in greater detail elsewhere (Steiner *et al.*, 1969, 1972; Chan *et al.*, 1981c). If this occurred then the gene encoding this particular RNA processing variant might be preserved via gene duplication followed by mutational changes in the copy gene leading to the predominant expression of insulinlike rather than serine proteaselike material under altered genetic control. Ultimately a ''new'' cell type could arise with the exclusive task of elaborating and regulating the release of this important product. In this manner a cycle of evolution would have been completed, beginning with the generation of a new gene product cut from older genetic ''cloth'' and culminating in the development of a new endocrine/regulatory cell type—the β cell. (For further discussion of various theories regarding peptide hormone evolution see Steiner *et al.*, 1984.)

ACKNOWLEDGMENTS

I wish to dedicate this manuscript to the memory of Dr. Robert H. Williams (Seattle), who first stimulated and fostered my interest in insulin research and also to the late Professor Fred Carpenter (Berkeley) whose pioneering work on insulin structure and proteolytic susceptibility provided guidance in the early phases of my research on proinsulin. I am also greatly endebted to Professor Dorothy C. Hodgkin and to Drs. Sture Falkmer, Arthur H. Rubenstein, Shu Jin Chan, Simon C. M. Kwok, Kevin Docherty, Ole Madsen, David Nielsen, Howard S. Tager, Åke Lernmark, Stefan Emdin, Guy Dodson, Susan Terris, John Cutfield, and Susan Cutfield who have all participated in and/or contributed ideas in various aspects of the work described herein. Studies from the author's laboratory have been supported by grants from the NIH (AM 13914 and AM 20595), the Novo Research Institute, the Kroc Foundation, the Lolly Coustan Memorial Fund, and Cetus Corporation.

REFERENCES

Adelson, J. W. (1971). *Nature (London)* **229**, 321–325.

Amara, S. G., Jonas, V., Rosenfeld, M. G., Ong, E. S., and Evans, R. M. (1982). *Nature (London)* **298**, 240–244.

Banting, F. G., and Best, C. H. (1922). *J. Lab. Clin. Med.* **7**, 251.

Bell, G. I., Pictet, R., and Rutter, W. J. (1980a). *Nucleic Acids Res.* **8**, 4091–4109.

Bell, G. I., Pictet, R. L., Rutter, W. J., Cordell, B., Tischer, E., and Goodman, H. M. (1980b). *Nature (London)* **284**, 26–32.

Blobel, G., and Dobberstein, B. (1975a). *J. Cell Biol.* **67**, 835–851.

Blobel, G., and Dobberstein, B. (1975b). *J. Cell Biol.* **67**, 852–862.

Blundell, T., Dodson, G., Hodgkin, D., and Mercola, D. (1972). *Adv. Protein Chem.* **26**, 279–402.

Bonner-Weir, S., Trent, D. F., Honey, R. N., and Weir, G. C. (1981). *Diabetes* **30**, 64–69.

Brandenburg, D., and Wollmer, A. (1973). *Hoppe-Seyler's Z. Physiol. Chem.* **354**, 613–627.

Brennan, S. O., and Carrell, R. W. (1978). *Nature (London)* **274**, 908–909.

Brodal, A., and Fänge, R. (1963). "The Biology of Myxine." Universitetsforlaget, Oslo,

Brunstedt, J., and Chan, S. J. (1982). *Biochem. Biophys. Res. Commun.* **106**, 1383–1389.

Busse, W. D., Hansen, S. R., and Carpenter, F. H. (1974). *J. Am. Chem. Soc.* **96**, 5949–5950.

Campbell, W. K., and MacLeod, J. J. R. (1925). *In* "Medicine Monographs," Vol. VI, p. 18. Williams & Wilkins, Baltimore, Maryland.

Chan, S. J., Keim, P., and Steiner, D. F. (1976). *Proc. Natl. Acad. Sci. U.S.A.* **73**, 1964–1968.

Chan, S. J., Noyes, B. E., Agarwal, K. L., and Steiner, D. F. (1979a). *Proc. Natl. Acad. Sci. U.S.A.* **76**, 5036–5040.

Chan, S. J., Noyes, B. E., Agarwal, K. L., Ackerman, E., Quinn, P. S., Keim, P. S., Sigler, P. B., Henrikson, R. L., and Steiner, D. F. (1979b). *Proc. IDF Congr. 10th,* 113–118. Excerpta Medica, Amsterdam.

Chan, S. J., Ackerman, E. J., Quinn, P. S., Sigler, P. B., and Steiner, D. F. (1981a). *J. Biol. Chem.* **256**, 3271–3275.

Chan, S. J., Emdin, S. O., Kwok, S. C. M., Kramer, J. M., Falkmer, S., and Steiner, D. F. (1981b). *J. Biol. Chem.* **256**, 7595–7602.

Chan, S. J., Kwok, S. C. M., and Steiner, D. F. (1981c). *Diabetes Care* **4**, 41–10.

Chan, S. J., Weiss, J., Konrad, M., White, T., Bahl, C., Yu, S-D., Marks, D., and Steiner, D. F. (1981d). *Proc. Natl. Acad. Sci. U.S.A.* **78**, 5401–5405.

Chance, R. E., Ellis, R. M., and Bromer, W. W. (1968). *Science* **161**, 165–167.

Chance, R. E., Hoffmann, J. A., Johnson, M. G., Wolfe, T. M., Blix, P. M., and Rubenstein, A. H. (1979). "Studies on Rabbit C-peptide in Proinsulin, Insulin and C-peptide" (S. Baba, T. Kaneko, and N. Yanaihara, eds.), pp. 99–105. Excerpta Medica, Amsterdam.

Chance, R. E., Kroeff, E. P., and Hoffman, J. A. (1981). In "Insulins, Growth Hormone and Recombinant DNA Technology" (J. L. Guerigian, ed.), pp. 71–86. Raven, New York.

Chothia, C., Lesk, A. M., Dodson, G. G., and Hodgkin, D. C. (1983). Nature (London) 302, 500–505.

Chou, P. Y., and Fasman, G. D. (1978). Annu. Rev. Biochem. 47, 251.

Craik, C. S., Rutter, W. J., and Fletterick, R. (1983). Science 220, 1125–1129.

Cutfield, J. F., Cutfield, S. M., Dodson, E. J., Dodson, G. G., Emdin, S. F., and Reynolds, C. D. (1979). J. Mol. Biol. 132, 85–100.

De Haen, C., Swanson, E., and Teller, D. C. (1976). J. Mol. Biol. 106., 639–661.

Dixon, G. H., and Wardlaw, A. C. (1960). Nature (London) 188, 721–724.

Docherty, K., and Steiner, D. F. (1981). Annu. Rev. Physiol. 44, 625–638.

Docherty, K., Carroll, R. J., and Steiner, D. F. (1982). Proc. Natl. Acad. Sci. U.S.A. 79, 4613–4617.

Docherty, K., Carroll, R. J., and Steiner, D. F. (1983). Proc. Natl. Acad. Sci. U.S.A. 80, 3245–3249.

Du, Y. C. et al. (1966). Kexue Tongbau 17, 241–277.

Duguid, J. R., and Steiner, D. F. (1978). Proc. Natl. Acad. Sci. U.S.A. 75, 3249–3253.

Duguid, J. R., Chan, S. J., Keim, P., Heinrikson, R., Hortin, G., Hofmann, C., Labrecque, A., and Steiner, D. F. (1976). Int. Congr. Ser. 413, 9–17. Excerpta Medica, Amsterdam.

Eng, J., and Yalow, R. (1981). Proc. Natl. Acad. Sci. U.S.A. 78, 4576–4578.

Farquhar, M. G., and Palade, G. E. (1981). J. Cell Biol. 91, 77s–103s.

Fleminger, G., Ezra, E., Kilpatrick, D. L., and Udenfriend, S. (1983). Proc. Natl. Acad. Sci. U.S.A. 80, 6418–6421.

Fletcher, D. J., Quigley, J. P., Bauer, G. E., and Noe, B. D. (1981). J. Cell Biol. 90, 312–322.

Fontaine, J., Le Lievre, C., and Le Douarin, N. M. (1977). Gen. Comp. Endocrinol. 33, 394–404.

Frank, B. H., and Veros, A. J. (1968). Biochem. Biophys. Res. Commun. 32, 155–160.

Frank, B. H., Veros, A. J., and Pekar, A. H. (1972). Biochemistry 11, 4926–4931.

Frank, B. H., Pettee, J. M., Zimmerman, R. E., and Burck, P. J. (1981). In "Peptide Structure and Biological Function" (D. H. Rich and E. Gross, eds.), pp. 729–738. Pierce Chem. Co., Rockford, Illinois.

Frazier, W. A., Angeletti, R. H., and Bradshaw, R. A. (1972). Science 176, 482–488.

Freedman, R. B., and Hawkins, H. C. (1977). Biochem. Soc. Trans. 5, 348–357.

Gabbay, K. H., Bergenstal, R. M., Wolff, J., Mako, M. E., and Rubenstein A. H. (1979). Proc. Natl. Acad. Sci. U.S.A., 76, 2881–2885.

Gilbert, W. (1978). Nature (London) 271, 501.

Gilmore, R., Walter, P., and Blobel, G. (1982). J. Cell Biol. 95, 470–477.

Given, B. D., Mako, M. E., Tager, H. S., Baldwin, D., Markese, J., Rubenstein, A. H., Olefsky, J., Kobayashi, M., Kolterman, O., and Poucher, R. (1980). *N. Engl. J. Med.* **302**, 129–135.

Givol, D., Delorenzo, F., Goldberger, R. F., and Anfinsen, C. B. (1965). *Proc. Natl. Acad. Sci. U.S.A.* **53**, 676–684.

Goeddel, D. V., Kleid, D. G., Bolivar, F., Heyneker, H. L., Yansura, D. G., Crea, R., Hirose, T., Kraszewski, A., Itakura, K., and Riggs, A. D. (1979). *Proc. Natl. Acad. Sci. U.S.A.* **76**, 106–110.

Gruss, P., Efstratiadis, A., Karathanasis, S., Konig, M., and Khoury, G. (1981). *Proc. Natl. Acad. Sci. U.S.A.* **78**, 6091–6095.

Grütter, M. G., Weaver, L. H., and Matthews, B. W. (1983). *Nature (London)* **303**, 828–830.

Gumbiner, B., and Kelly, R. B. (1982). *Cell* **28**, 51–59.

Haley, J., Hudson, P., Scanlon, D., John, M., Cronk, M., Shine, J., Tregear, G., and Niall, H. (**1982**). *DNA* **1**, 155–162.

Hall, M. N., and Silhavy, T. J. (1981) *Annu. Rev. Genet.* **15**, 91–142.

Haneda, M., Chan, S. J., Kwok, S. C. M., Rubenstein, A. H., and Steiner, D. F. (1983). *Proc. Natl. Acad. Sci. U.S.A.* **80**, 6366–6370.

Harper, M. E., Ullrich, A., and Saunders, G. F. (1981). *Proc. Natl. Acad. Sci. U.S.A.* **78**, 4458–4460.

Hatfield, J. S., Pansky, B., Waller, H. J., and Budd, G. C. (1981). *Micron* **12**, 205–206.

Havrankova, J., Schmechel, D., Roth, J., and Brownstein, M. (1978). *Proc. Natl. Acad. Sci. U.S.A.* **75**, 5737–5741.

Hobart, P. M., Shen, L-P., Crawford, R., Pictet, R. L., and Rutter, W. J. (1980). *Science* **210**, 1360–1363.

Hudson, P., Haley, J., John, M., Cronk, M., Crawford, R., Haralambidis, J., Tregear, G., Shine, J., and Niall, H. (1983). *Nature (London)* **301**, 628–631.

Humbel, R. E. (1965). *Proc. Natl. Acad. Sci. U.S.A.* **53**, 853–859.

Isaacs, N., James, R., Niall, Hu, Bryant-Greenwood, G., Dodson, G., Evans, A., and North, A. C. T. (1978). *Nature (London)* **271**, 478–281.

Itoh, N., and Okamoto, H. (1980). *Nature (London)* **283**, 100–102.

Jackson, R. C., and Blobel, G. (1977). *Proc. Natl. Acad. Sci. U.S.A.* **74**, 5598–5602.

Jahr, H., Schroder, D., Ziegler, B., Ziegler, M., and Zuhlke, H. (1980). *Eur. J. Biochem.* **110**, 499–505.

Kanazawa, Y., Hayashi, M., Ikeuchi, M., Kasuga, M., Oka, Y., Sato, H., Kiramatsu, K., and Kosaka, K. (1979). *In* "Proinsulin, Insulin, C-Peptide: Proceedings of the Symposium on Proinsulin, Insulin and C-Peptide" (S. Baba, T. Kaneko, and N. Yanihara, eds.), p. 262. Excerpta Medica, Amsterdam.

Katsoyannis, P. G., and Tometsko, A. (1966). *Proc. Natl. Acad. Sci. U.S.A.* **55**, 1554–1561.

Kemper, B., Habener, J. F., Mulligan, R. C., Potts, J. T., Jr., and Rich, A. (1974). *Proc. Natl. Acad. Sci. U.S.A.* **71**, 3731–3735.

Kreil, G. (1981). *Annu. Rev. Biochem.* **50**, 317–348.

Kurjan, J., and Herskowitz, I. (1982). *Cell* **30**, 933.

Kwok, S. C. M., Chan, S. J., Rubenstein, A. H., Poucher, R., and Steiner, D. F. (1981). *Biochem. Biophys. Res. Commun.* **98**, 844–849.

Kwok, S. C. M., Chan, S. J., and Steiner, D. F. (1983). *J. Biol. Chem.* **258**, 2357–2363.

Kwok, S. C. M., Steiner, D. F., Rubenstein, A. H., and Tager, H. S. (1983b). *Diabetes* **32**, 872–875.

Laub, O., and Rutter, W. J. (1983). *J. Biol. Chem.* **258**, 6043–6050.

Lazarow, A. (1963). *Recent Prog. Horm. Res.* **19**, 489–540.

Lomedico, P. T. (1982). *Proc. Natl. Acad. Sci. U.S.A.* **79**, 5798–5802.

Lomedico, P. T., Chan, S. J., Steiner, D. F., and Saunders, G. F. (1977). *J. Biol. Chem.* **252**, 7971–7978.

Lomedico, P., Rosenthal, N., Efstratiadis, A., Gilbert, W., Kolodner, R., and Tizard, R. (1979). *Cell* **18**, 545–558.

Madsen, O. D., Cohen, R. M., Fitch, F. W., Rubenstein, A. W., and Steiner, D. F. (1983). *Endocrinology* in press.

Maitra, U., Stringer, E. A., and Chaudhuri, A. (1982). *Annu. Rev. Biochem.* **51**, 869–900.

Markussen, J., and Vølund, A. (1974). *Int. J. Peptide Protein Res.* **6**, 79–86.

Meyer, D. I., Krause, E., and Dobberstein, B. (1982). *Nature (London)* **297**, 647–650.

Miller, W. M., and Eberhardt, N. L. (1983). *Endocr. Rev.* **4**, 97–130.

Milstein, C., Brownlee, G. G., Harrison, T. M., and Mathews, M. B. (1972). *Nature (London) New Biol.* **239**, 117–120.

Mort, J. S., Leduc, M. S., and Recklies, A. D. (1983). *Biochim. Biophys. Acta* **755**, 369–375.

Nielsen, D. A., Chou, J., MacKrell, A. J., Casadaban, M. J., and Steiner, D. F. (1983). *Proc. Natl. Acad. Sci. U.S.A.* **80**, 5198–5202

Nolan, C., Margoliash, E., Peterson, J. D., and Steiner, D. F. (1971). *J. Biol. Chem.* **246** 2780–2795.

Okamoto, H. (1981). *Mol. Cell. Biochem.* **37**, 43–61.

Orci, L. (1982). *Diabetes* **31**, 538–565.

Owerbach, D., Bell, G. I., Rutter, W. J., and Shows, T. B. (1980). *Nature (London)* **286**, 82–84.

Palade, G. (1975). *Science* **189**, 347–358.

Patzelt, C., Chan, S. J., Duguid, J., Hortin, G., Keim, P., Heinrikson, R. L., and Steiner, D. F. (1978a). *FEBS Meet. 11th Copenhagen,* **47**, 69–78. Pergamon, Oxford.

Patzelt, C., Labrecque, A. D., Duguid, J. R., Carroll, R. J., Keim, P., Heinrikson, R. L., and Steiner, D. F. (1978b). *Proc. Natl. Acad. Sci. (U.S.A.* **75**, 1260–1264.

Perler, F., Efstratiadis, A., Lomedico, P., Gilbert, W., Kolodner, R., and Dodgson, J. (1980). *Cell* **20**, 555–566.

Permutt, M. A. (1974). *J. Biol. Chem.* **249**, 2738–2742.

Permutt, M. A., and Kipnis, D. M. (1972). *J. Biol. Chem.* **247**, 1200–1207.

Peterson, J. D., Steiner, D. F., Emdin, S. O., and Falkmer, S. (1975). *J. Biol. Chem.* **250**, 5183–5191.

Pictet, R., and Rutter, W. J. (1972). *Handb. Physiol. Endocrinol.* **I**, 25–66.

Pictet, R. L., Rall, L. B., Phelps, P., and Rutter, W. J. (1976). *Science* **191**, 191–192.

Pullen, R. A., Lindsay, D. G., Wood, S. P., Tickle, I. J., Blundell, T. L., Wollmer, A., Krail, G., Brandenburg, D., Zahn, H., Gliemann, J., and Gammeltoft, S. (1976). *Nature (London)* **259**, 369–373.

Recklies, A. D., Poole, A. R., and Mort, J. S. (1982). *Biochem. J.* **207**, 633–636.

Rinderknecht, E., and Humbel, R. E. (1978). *FEBS Lett.* **89**, 283–286.

Robbins, D. C., Blix, P. M., Rubenstein, A. H., Kanazawa, Y., Kosaka, K., and Tager, H. S. (1981). *Nature (London)* **291**, 679–681.

Roth, J., LeRoith, D., Shiloach, J., Rosenzweig, J. L., Lesniak, M. A., and Havrankova, J. (1982). *New Eng. J. Med.* **306**, 523–527.

Rubenstein, A. H., Clark, J. L., Melani, F., and Steiner, D. F. (1969). *Nature (London)* **224**, 697–699.

Rubenstein, A. H., Steiner, D. F., Horwitz, D. L., Mako, M. E., Block, M. B., Starr, J. I., Kuzuya, H., and Melani, F. (1977). *Recent Prog. Horm. Res.* **33**, 435–475.

Schäfer, E. A. (1916). *In* "The Endocrine Organs, An Introduction to the Study of Internal Secretion," p. 128. Longmans, London.

Schueller, R. H., Jackson, J. F., McAllister, L., Schwartz, J., Kandel, E. R., and Axel, R. (1982). *Cell* **28** 707–719.

Shoelson, S., Haneda, M., Blix, P., Nanjo, A., Sanke, T., Inouye, K., Steiner, D. F., Rubenstein, A. H., and Tager, H. S. (1983). *Nature (London)* **302**, 540–543.

Snell, C. R., and Smyth, D. G. (1975). *J. Biol. Chem.* **250**, 6291–6295.

Steiner, D. F. (1973). *Nature (London)* **243**, 528–530.

Steiner, D. F. (1976). *Handb. Biochem. Mol. Biol.* **III**, 381.

Steiner, D. F. (1978). *Diabetes* **27**, (Suppl. 1), 161–169.

Steiner, D. F., and Clark, J. L. (1968). *Proc. Natl. Acad. Sci. U.S.A.* **60**, 622–629.

Steiner, D. F., and Oyer, P. C. (1967). *Proc. Natl. Acad. Sci. U.S.A.* **57**, 473–480.

Steiner, D. F., Hallund, W., Rubenstein, A. H., Cho, S., and Bayliss, C. (1968). *Diabetes* **17**, 725–736.

Steiner, D. F., Clark, J. L., Nolan, C., Rubenstein, A. H., Margoliash, E., Aten, B., and Oyer, P. E. (1969). *Rec. Prog. Horm. Res.* **25**, 207–268.

Steiner, D. F., Clark, J. L., Nolan, C., Rubenstein, A. H., Margoliash, E., Melani, F., and Oyer, P. E. (1970). *In* "Nobel Symposium 13, on the Pathogenesis of Diabetes mellitus" (E. Cerasi and R. Luft, eds.), pp. 57–80. Almqvist and Wiksell, Stockholm.

Steiner, D. F., Kemmler, W., Clark, J. L., Oyer, P. E., and Rubenstein, A. H. (1972). *Handb. Physiol. Endocrinol.* **I**, 175–198.

Steiner, D. F., Quinn, P. S., Patzelt, C., Chan, S. J., Marsh, J., and Tager, H. S. (1980). *In* "Cell Biology: A Comprehensive Treatise" (L. Goldstein and D. M. Prescott, eds.), Vol. IV, pp. 175–201. Academic Press, New York.

Steiner, D. F., Chan, S. J., Docherty, K., Emdin, S., Dodson, G., and Falkmer, S. (1984). *In* "Evolution and Tumour Pathology of the Neuroendocrine System" (S. Falkmer and R. Hakanson, eds.). Elsevier, Amsterdam, in press.

Steiner, D. F., Docherty, K., and Carroll, R. (1984). *J. Cell Biochem.* **24**, 121–130.

Tager, H. S., Given, B., Baldwin, D., Mako, M., Markese, J., Rubenstein, A. H., Olefsky, J., Kobayashi, M., Kolterman, O., and Poucher, R. (1979). *Nature (London)* **281**, 122–125.

Tager, H. S., Thomas, N., Assoian, R., Rubenstein, A. H., Saekow, M., Olefsky, J., and Kaiser, E. T. (1980). *Proc. Natl. Acad. Sci. U.S.A.* **77,** 3181–3185.

Talmadge, K., Stahl, S., and Gilbert, W. (1980). *Proc. Natl. Acad. Sci. U.S.A.* **77,** 3369–3373.

Taylor, K. W., Parry, D. G., and Howard Smith, G. (1964). *Nature (London)* **203,** 1144–1146.

Ullrich, A., Dull, T. J., Gray, A., Brosius, J., and Sures, I. (1980). *Science* **209,** 612–615.

Ullrich, A., Dull, T. J., Gray, A., Philips, J. A., III, and Peter, S. (1982). *Nucleic Acids Res.* **10,** 2225–2240.

Van Noorden, S., and Falkmer, S. (1980). *Invest. Cell Pathol.* **3,** 21–35.

Walter, P., and Blobel, G. (1981). *J. Cell Biol.* **91,** 551–556.

Walter, P., and Blobel, G. (1982). *Nature (London),* **399,** 691–698.

Wang, S. S., and Carpenter, F. H. (1965). *J. Biol. Chem.* **240,** 1619–1625.

Wood, S. P., Blundell, T. L., Wollmer, A., Lazarus, N. R., and Neville, R. W. J. (1975). *Eur. J. Biochem.* **55,** 531–542.

Zahn, H., Gutte, B., and Brinkhoff, O. (1965). *Angew. Chem.* **77,** 509.

Zwizinski, C., and Wickner, W. (1980). *J. Biol. Chem.* **255,** 7973–7977.

FORMER OFFICERS OF THE HARVEY SOCIETY

1905–1906

President: GRAHAM LUSK
Vice-President: SIMON FLEXNER
Treasurer: FREDERIC S. LEE
Secretary: GEORGE B. WALLACE

Council:
   C. A. HERTER
   S. J. MELTZER
   EDWARD K. DUNHAM

1906–1907

President: GRAHAM LUSK
Vice-President: SIMON FLEXNER
Treasurer: FREDERIC S. LEE
Secretary: GEORGE B. WALLACE

Council:
   C. A. HERTER
   S. J. MELTZER
   JAMES EWING

1907–1908

President: GRAHAM LUSK
Vice-President: JAMES EWING
Treasurer: EDWARD K. DUNHAM
Secretary: GEORGE B. WALLACE

Council:
   SIMON FLEXNER
   THEO. C. JANEWAY
   PHILIP H. HISS, JR.

1908–1909

President: JAMES EWING
Vice-President: SIMON FLEXNER
Treasurer: EDWARD K. DUNHAM
Secretary: FRANCIS C. WOOD

Council:
   GRAHAM LUSK
   S. J. MELTZER
   ADOLPH MEYER

1909–1910*

President: JAMES EWING
Vice-President: THEO. C. JANEWAY
Treasurer: EDWARD K. DUNHAM
Secretary: FRANCIS C. WOOD

Council:
   GRAHAM LUSK
   S. J. MELTZER
   W. J. GIES

1910–1911

President: SIMON FLEXNER
Vice-President: JOHN HOWLAND
Treasurer: EDWARD K. DUNHAM
Secretary: HAVEN EMERSON

Council:
   GRAHAM LUSK
   S. J. MELTZER
   JAMES EWING

---

* At the Annual Meeting of May 18, 1909, these officers were elected. In publishing the 1909–1910 volume their names were omitted, possibly because in that volume the custom of publishing the names of the incumbents of the current year was changed to publishing the names of the officers selected for the ensuing year.

1911–1912

President: S. J. MELTZER
Vice-President: FREDERIC S. LEE
Treasurer: EDWARD K. DUNHAM
Secretary: HAVEN EMERSON

Council:
  GRAHAM LUSK
  JAMES EWING
  SIMON FLEXNER

1912–1913

President: FREDERIC S. LEE
Vice-President: WM. H. PARK
Treasurer: EDWARD K. DUNHAM
Secretary: HAVEN EMERSON

Council:
  GRAHAM LUSK
  S. J. MELTZER
  WM. G. MACCALLUM

1913–1914

President: FREDERIC S. LEE
Vice-President: WM. G. MACCALLUM
Treasurer: EDWARD K. DUNHAM
Secretary: AUGUSTUS B. WADSWORTH

Council:
  GRAHAM LUSK
  WM. H. PARK
  GEORGE B. WALLACE

1914–1915

President: WM. G. MACCALLUM
Vice-President: RUFUS I. COLE
Treasurer: EDWARD K. DUNHAM
Secretary: JOHN A. MANDEL

Council:
  GRAHAM LUSK
  FREDERIC S. LEE
  W. T. LONGCOPE

1915–1916

President: GEORGE B. WALLACE*
Treasurer: EDWARD K. DUNHAM
Secretary: ROBERT A. LAMBERT

Council:
  GRAHAM LUSK
  RUFUS I. COLE
  NELLIS B. FOSTER

1916–1917

President: GEORGE B. WALLACE
Vice-President: RUFUS I. COLE
Treasurer: EDWARD K. DUNHAM
Secretary: ROBERT A. LAMBERT

Council:
  GRAHAM LUSK†
  W. T. LONGCOPE
  S. R. BENEDICT
  HANS ZINSSER

1917–1918

President: EDWARD K. DUNHAM
Vice-President: RUFUS I. COLE
Treasurer: F. H. PIKE
Secretary: A. M. PAPPENHEIMER

Council:
  GRAHAM LUSK
  GEORGE B. WALLACE
  FREDERIC S. LEE
  PEYTON ROUS

---

* Dr. William G. MacCallum resigned after election. On Doctor Lusk's motion Doctor George B. Wallace was made President—no Vice-President was appointed.

† Doctor Lusk was made Honorary permanent Counsellor.

1918–1919

President: GRAHAM LUSK   *Council:*
Vice-President: RUFUS I. COLE   GRAHAM LUSK
Treasurer: F. H. PIKE   JAMES W. JOBLING
Secretary: K. M. VOGEL   FREDERIC S. LEE
                                         JOHN AUER

1919–1920

President: WARFIELD T. LONGCOPE   *Council:*
Vice-President: S. R. BENEDICT   GRAHAM LUSK
Treasurer: F. H. PIKE   HANS ZINSSER
Secretary: K. M. VOGEL   FREDERIC S. LEE
                                         GEORGE B. WALLACE

1920–1921*

President: WARFIELD T. LONGCOPE   *Council:*
Vice-President: S. R. BENEDICT   GRAHAM LUSK
Treasurer: A. M. PAPPENHEIMER   FREDERIC S. LEE
Secretary: HOMER F. SWIFT   HANS ZINSSER
                                         GEORGE B. WALLACE

1921–1922

President: RUFUS I. COLE   *Council:*
Vice-President: S. R. BENEDICT   GRAHAM LUSK
Treasurer: A. M. PAPPENHEIMER   HANS ZINSSER
Secretary: HOMER F. SWIFT   H. C. JACKSON
                                         W. T. LONGCOPE

1922–1923

President: RUFUS I. COLE   *Council:*
Vice-President: HANS ZINSSER   GRAHAM LUSK
Treasurer: CHARLES C. LIEB   W. T. LONGCOPE
Secretary: HOMER F. SWIFT   H. C. JACKSON
                                         S. R. BENEDICT

1923–1924

President: EUGENE F. DUBOIS   *Council:*
Vice-President: HOMER F. SWIFT   GRAHAM LUSK
Treasurer: CHARLES C. LIEB   ALPHONSE R. DOCHEZ
Secretary: GEORGE M. MACKENZIE   DAVID MARINE
                                         PEYTON ROUS

---

* These officers were elected at the Annual Meeting of May 21, 1920 but were omitted in the publication of the 1919–1920 volume.

1924–1925

President: EUGENE F. DuBOIS
Vice-President: PEYTON ROUS
Treasurer: CHARLES C. LIEB
Secretary: GEORGE M. MACKENZIE

Council:
GRAHAM LUSK
RUFUS COLE
HAVEN EMERSON
WM. H. PARK

1925–1926

President: HOMER F. SWIFT
Vice-President: H. B. WILLIAMS
Treasurer: HAVEN EMERSON
Secretary: GEORGE M. MACKENZIE

Council:
GRAHAM LUSK
EUGENE F. DuBOIS
WALTER W. PALMER
H. D. SENIOR

1926–1927

President: WALTER W. PALMER
Vice-President: WM. H. PARK
Treasurer: HAVEN EMERSON
Secretary: GEORGE M. MACKENZIE

Council:
GRAHAM LUSK
HOMER F. SWIFT
A. R. DOCHEZ
ROBERT CHAMBERS

1927–1928

President: DONALD D. VAN SLYKE
Vice-President: JAMES W. JOBLING
Treasurer: HAVEN EMERSON
Secretary: CARL A. L. BINGER

Council:
GRAHAM LUSK
RUSSEL L. CECIL
WARD J. MACNEAL
DAVID MARINE

1928–1929

President: PEYTON ROUS
Vice-President: HORATIO B. WILLIAMS
Treasurer: HAVEN EMERSON
Secretary: PHILIP D. MCMASTER

Council:
GRAHAM LUSK
ROBERT CHAMBERS
ALFRED F. HESS
H. D. SENIOR

1929–1930

President: G. CANBY ROBINSON
Vice-President: ALFRED F. HESS
Treasurer: HAVEN EMERSON
Secretary: DAYTON J. EDWARDS

Council:
GRAHAM LUSK
ALFRED E. COHN
A. M. PAPPENHEIMER
H. D. SENIOR

1930–1931

President: ALFRED E. COHN
Vice-President: J. G. HOPKINS
Treasurer: HAVEN EMERSON
Secretary: DAYTON J. EDWARDS

Council
GRAHAM LUSK
O. T. AVERY
A. M. PAPPENHEIMER
S. R. DEIWILER

1931–1932

President: J. W. JOBLING
Vice-President: HOMER W. SMITH
Treasurer: HAVEN EMERSON
Secretary: DAYTON J. EDWARDS

Council:
GRAHAM LUSK
S. R. DETWILER
THOMAS M. RIVERS
RANDOLPH WEST

1932–1933

President: ALFRED F. HESS
Vice-President: HAVEN EMERSON
Treasurer: THOMAS M. RIVERS
Secretary: EDGAR STILLMAN

Council:
GRAHAM LUSK
HANS T. CLARKE
WALTER W. PALMER
HOMER W. SMITH

1933–1934

President: ALFRED HESS*
Vice-President: ROBERT K. CANNAN
Treasurer: THOMAS M. RIVERS
Secretary: EDGAR STILLMAN

Council:
STANLEY R. BENEDICT
ROBERT F. LOEB
WADE H. BROWN

1934–1935

President: ROBERT K. CANNAN
Vice-President: EUGENE L. OPIE
Treasurer: THOMAS M. RIVERS
Secretary: RANDOLPH H. WEST

Council:
HERBERT S. GASSER
B. S. OPPENHEIMER
PHILIP E. SMITH

1935–1936

President: ROBERT K. CANNAN
Vice-President: EUGENE L. OPIE
Treasurer: THOMAS M. RIVERS
Secretary: RANDOLPH H. WEST

Council:
ROBERT F. LOEB
HOMER W. SMITH
DAVID MARINE

1936–1937

President: EUGENE L. OPIE
Vice-President: PHILIP E. SMITH
Treasurer: THOMAS M. RIVERS
Secretary: McKEEN CATTELL

Council:
GEORGE B. WALLACE
MARTIN H. DAWSON
JAMES B. MURPHY

1937–1938

President: EUGENE L. OPIE
Vice-President: PHILIP E. SMITH
Treasurer: THOMAS M. RIVERS
Secretary: McKEEN CATTELL

Council:
GEORGE B. WALLACE
MARTIN H. DAWSON
HERBERT S. GASSER

---

*Dr. Hess died December 5, 1933.

1938–1939

President: PHILIP E. SMITH
Vice-President: HERBERT S. GASSER
Treasurer: KENNETH GOODNER
Secretary: MCKEEN CATTELL

Council:
  HANS T. CLARKE
  JAMES D. HARDY
  WILLIAM S. TILLETT

1939–1940

President: PHILIP E. SMITH
Vice-President: HERBERT S. GASSER
Treasurer: KENNETH GOODNER
Secretary: THOMAS FRANCIS, JR.

Council:
  HANS T. CLARKE
  N. CHANDLER FOOT
  WILLIAM S. TILLETT

1940–1941

President: HERBERT S. GASSER
Vice-President: HOMER W. SMITH
Treasurer: KENNETH GOODNER
Secretary: THOMAS FRANCIS, JR.

Council:
  N. CHANDLER FOOT
  VINCENT DU VIGNEAUD
  MICHAEL HEIDELBERGER

1941–1942

President: HERBERT S. GASSER
Vice-President: HOMER W. SMITH
Treasurer: KENNETH GOODNER
Secretary: JOSEPH C. HINSEY

Council:
  HARRY S. MUSTARD
  HAROLD G. WOLFF
  MICHAEL HEIDELBERGER

1942–1943

President: HANS T. CLARKE
Vice-President: THOMAS M. RIVERS
Treasurer: KENNETH GOODNER
Secretary: JOSEPH C. HINSEY

Council:
  ROBERT F. LOEB
  HAROLD G. WOLFF
  WILLIAM C. VON GLAHN

1943–1944

President: HANS T. CLARKE
Vice-President: THOMAS M. RIVERS
Treasurer: COLIN M. MACLEOD
Secretary: JOSEPH C. HINSEY

Council:
  ROBERT F. LOEB
  WILLIAM C. VON GLAHN
  WADE W. OLIVER

1944–1945

President: ROBERT CHAMBERS
Vice-President: VINCENT DU VIGNEAUD
Treasurer: COLIN M. MACLEOD
Secretary: JOSEPH C. HINSEY

Council:
  WADE W. OLIVER
  MICHAEL HEIDELBERGER
  PHILIP D. MCMASTER

1945–1946

President: ROBERT CHAMBERS
Vice-President: VINCENT DU VIGNEAUD
Treasurer: COLIN M. MACLEOD
Secretary: EDGAR G. MILLER, JR.

Council:
  PHILIP D. MCMASTER
  EARL T. ENGLE
  FRED W. STEWART

1946–1947

President: VINCENT DU VIGNEAUD
Vice-President: WADE W. OLIVER
Treasurer: COLIN M. MACLEOD
Secretary: EDGAR G. MILLER, JR.

Council:
    EARL T. ENGLE
    HAROLD G. WOLFF
    L. EMMETT HOLT, JR.

1947–1948

President: VINCENT DU VIGNEAUD
Vice-President: WADE W. OLIVER
Treasurer: HARRY B. VAN DYKE
Secretary: MACLYN MCCARTY

Council:
    PAUL KLEMPERER
    L. EMMETT HOLT, JR.
    HAROLD G. WOLFF

1948–1949

President: WADE W. OLIVER
Vice-President: ROBERT F. LOEB
Treasurer: HARRY B. VAN DYKE
Secretary: MACLYN MCCARTY

Council:
    PAUL KLEMPERER
    SEVERO OCHOA
    HAROLD L. TEMPLE

1949–1950

President: WADE W. OLIVER
Vice-President: ROBERT F. LOEB
Treasurer: JAMES B. HAMILTON
Secretary: MACLYN MCCARTY

Council:
    WILLIAM S. TILLETT
    SEVERO OCHOA
    HAROLD L. TEMPLE

1950–1951

President: ROBERT F. LOEB
Vice-President: MICHAEL HEIDELBERGER
Treasurer: JAMES B. HAMILTON
Secretary: LUDWIG W. EICHNA

Council:
    WILLIAM S. TILLETT
    A. M. PAPPENHEIMER, JR.
    DAVID P. BARR

1951–1952

President: RENÉ J. DUBOS
Vice-President: MICHAEL HEIDELBERGER
Treasurer: JAMES B. HAMILTON
Secretary: LUDWIG W. EICHNA

Council:
    DAVID P. BARR
    ROBERT F. PITTS
    A. M. PAPPENHEIMER, JR.

1952–1953

President: MICHAEL HEIDELBERGER
Vice-President: SEVERO OCHOA
Treasurer: CHANDLER McC. BROOKS
Secretary: HENRY D. LAUSON

Council:
    ROBERT F. PITTS
    JEAN OLIVER
    ALEXANDER B. GUTMAN

1953–1954

President: SEVERO OCHOA
Vice-President: DAVID P. BARR
Treasurer: CHANDLER McC. BROOKS
Secretary: HENRY D. LAUSON

Council:
    JEAN OLIVER
    ALEXANDER B. GUTMAN
    ROLLIN D. HOTCHKISS

1954–1955

President: DAVID P. BARR
Vice-President: COLIN M. MACLEOD
Treasurer: CHANDLER McC. BROOKS
Secretary: HENRY D. LAUSON

Council:
  ALEXANDER B. GUTMAN
  ROLLIN D. HOTCHKISS
  DAVID SHEMIN

1955–1956

President: COLIN M. MACLEOD
Vice-President: FRANK L. HORSFALL, JR.
Treasurer: CHANDLER McC. BROOKS
Secretary: RULON W. RAWSON

Council:
  ROLLIN D. HOTCHKISS
  DAVID SHEMIN
  ROBERT F. WATSON

1956–1957

President: Frank L. HORSFALL, JR.
Vice-President: WILLIAM S. TILLETT
Treasurer: CHANDLER McC. BROOKS
Secretary: RULON W. RAWSON

Council:
  DAVID SHEMIN
  ROBERT F. WATSON
  ABRAHAM WHITE

1957–1958

President: WILLIAM S. TILLETT
Vice-President: ROLLIN D. HOTCHKISS
Treasurer: CHANDLER McC. BROOKS
Secretary: H. SHERWOOD LAWRENCE

Council:
  ROBERT F. WATSON
  ABRAHAM WHITE
  JOHN V. TAGGART

1958–1959

President: ROLLIN D. HOTCHKISS
Vice-President: ANDRE COURNAND
Treasurer: CHANDLER McC. BROOKS
Secretary: H. SHERWOOD LAWRENCE

Council:
  ABRAHAM WHITE
  JOHN V. TAGGART
  WALSH McDERMOTT

1959–1960

President: ANDRE COURNAND
Vice-President: ROBERT F. PITTS
Treasurer: EDWARD J. HEHRE
Secretary: H. SHERWOOD LAWRENCE

Council:
  JOHN V. TAGGART
  WALSH McDERMOTT
  ROBERT F. FURCHGOTT

1960–1961

President: ROBERT F. PITTS
Vice-President: DICKINSON W. RICHARDS
Treasurer: EDWARD J. HEHRE
Secretary: ALEXANDER G. BEARN

Council:
  WALSH McDERMOTT
  ROBERT F. FURCHGOTT
  LUDWIG W. EICHNA

1961–1962

President: DICKINSON W. RICHARDS
Vice-President: PAUL WEISS
Treasurer: I. HERBERT SCHEINBERG
Secretary: ALEXANDER G. BEARN

Council:
  ROBERT F. FURCHGOTT
  LUDWIG W. EICHNA
  EFRAIM RACKER

1962–1963

President: PAUL WEISS
Vice-President: ALEXANDER B. GUTMAN
Treasurer: I. HERBERT SCHEINBERG
Secretary: ALEXANDER G. BEARN

Council:
LUDWIG W. EICHNA
EFRAIM RACKER
ROGER L. GREIF

1963–1964

President: ALEXANDER B. GUTMAN
Vice-President: EDWARD L. TATUM
Treasurer: SAUL J. FARBER
Secretary: ALEXANDER G. BEARN

Council:
EFRAIM RACKER
ROGER L. GREIF
IRVING M. LONDON

1964–1965

President: EDWARD TATUM
Vice-President: CHANDLER McC. BROOKS
Treasurer: SAUL J. FARBER
Secretary: RALPH L. ENGLE, JR.

Council:
ROGER L. GREIF
LEWIS THOMAS
IRVING M. LONDON

1965–1966

President: CHANDLER McC. BROOKS
Vice-President: ABRAHAM WHITE
Treasurer: SAUL J. FARBER
Secretary: RALPH L. ENGLE, JR.

Council:
IRVING M. LONDON
LEWIS THOMAS
GEORGE K. HIRST

1966–1967

President: ABRAHAM WHITE
Vice-President: RACHMIEL LEVINE
Treasurer: SAUL J. FARBER
Secretary: RALPH L. ENGLE. JR.

Council:
LEWIS THOMAS
GEORGE K. HIRST
DAVID NACHMANSOHN

1967–1968

President: RACHMIEL LEVINE
Vice-President: SAUL J. FARBER
Treasurer: PAUL A. MARKS
Secretary: RALPH L. ENGLE, JR.

Council:
GEORGE K. HIRST
DAVID NACHMANSOHN
MARTIN SONENBERG

1968–1969

President: SAUL J. FARBER
Vice-President: JOHN V. TAGGART
Treasurer: PAUL A. MARKS
Secretary: ELLIOTT F. OSSERMAN

Council:
DAVID NACHMANSOHN
MARTIN SONENBERG
HOWARD A. EDER

1969–1970

President: JOHN V. TAGGART
Vice-President: BERNARD L. HORECKER
Treasurer: PAUL A. MARKS
Secretary: ELLIOTT F. OSSERMAN

Council:
MARTIN SONENBERG
HOWARD A. EDER
SAUL J. FARBER

1970–1971

President: BERNARD L. HORECKER
Vice-President: MACLYN McCARTY
Treasurer: EDWARD C. FRANKLIN
Secretary: ELLIOTT F. OSSERMAN

Council:
HOWARD A. EDER
SAUL J. FARBER
SOLOMON A. BERSON

1971–1972

President: MACLYN McCARTY
Vice-President: ALEXANDER G. BEARN
Treasurer: EDWARD C. FRANKLIN
Secretary: ELLIOTT F. OSSERMAN

Council:
SAUL J. FARBER
SOLOMON A. BERSON
HARRY EAGLE

1972–1973

President: ALEXANDER G. BEARN
Vice-President: PAUL A. MARKS
Treasurer: EDWARD C. FRANKLIN
Secretary: JOHN ZABRISKIE

Council:
HARRY EAGLE
JERARD HURWITZ

1973–1974

President: PAUL A. MARKS
Vice-President: IGOR TAMM
Treasurer: EDWARD C. FRANKLIN
Secretary: JOHN B. ZABRISKIE

Council:
HARRY EAGLE
CHARLOTTE FRIEND
JERARD HURWITZ

1974–1975

President: IGOR TAMM
Vice-President: GERALD M. EDELMAN
Treasurer: STEPHEN I. MORSE
Secretary: JOHN B. ZABRISKIE

Council:
JERARD HURWITZ
H. SHERWOOD LAWRENCE
CHARLOTTE FRIEND

1975–1976

President: GERALD M. EDELMAN
Vice-President: ELVIN A. KABAT
Treasurer: STEPHEN I. MORSE
Secretary: JOHN B. ZABRISKIE

Council:
PAUL A. MARKS
H. SHERWOOD LAWRENCE
CHARLOTTE FRIEND

1976–1977

President: ELVIN A. KABAT
Vice-President: FRED PLUM
Treasurer: STEPHEN I. MORSE
Secretary: DONALD M. MARCUS

Council:
H. SHERWOOD LAWRENCE
PAUL A. MARKS
BRUCE CUNNINGHAM

1977–1978

President: FRED PLUM
Vice-President: CHARLOTTE FRIEND
Treasurer: STEPHEN I. MORSE
Secretary: DONALD M. MARCUS

Council:
  PAUL A. MARKS
  BRUCE CUNNINGHAM
  VITTORIO DEFENDI

1978–1979

President: CHARLOTTE FRIEND
Vice-President: MARTIN SONENBERG
Treasurer: ALFRED STRACHER
Secretary: DONALD M. MARCUS

Council:
  BRUCE CUNNINGHAM
  VITTORIO DEFENDI
  DEWITT S. GOODMAN

1979–1980

President: MARTIN SONENBERG
Vice-President: KURT HIRSCHHORN
Treasurer: ALFRED STRACHER
Secretary: EMIL C. GOTSCHLICH

Council:
  VITTORIO DEFENDI
  DEWITT S. GOODMAN
  ORA ROSEN

1980–1981

President: KURT HIRSCHHORN
Vice President: GERALD WEISSMANN
Treasurer: ALFRED STRACHER
Secretary: EMIL C. GOTSCHLICH

Council:
  RALPH NACHMAN
  DEWITT S. GOODMAN
  ORA ROSEN

1982–1983

President: DEWITT S. GOODMAN
Vice President: MATTHEW D. SCHARFF
Treasurer: ALFRED STRACHER
Secretary: EMIL C. GOTSCHLICH

Council:
  KURT HIRSCHHORN
  RALPH L. NACHMAN
  GERALD WEISSMANN

CUMULATIVE AUTHOR INDEX*

Dr. John J. Abel, 1923–24 (d)
Prof. J. D. Adami, 1906–07 (d)
Dr. Roger Adams, 1941–42 (d)
Dr. Thomas Addis, 1927–28 (d)
Dr. Julius Adler, 1976–77 (h)
Dr. E. D. Adrian, 1931–32 (h)
Dr. Fuller Albright, 1942–43 (h)
Dr. Franz Alexander, 1930–31 (h)
Dr. Frederick Allen, 1916–17 (a)
Dr. John F. Anderson, 1908–09 (d)
Dr. R. J. Anderson, 1939–40 (d)
Dr. Christopher H. Andrews, 1961–62 (h)
Dr. Christian B. Anfinsen, 1965–66 (h)
Prof. G. V. Anrep, 1934–35 (h)
Dr. Charles Armstrong, 1940–41 (d)
Dr. Ludwig Aschoff, 1923–24 (d)
Dr. Leon Asher, 1922–23 (h)
Dr. W. T. Astbury, 1950–51 (h)
Dr. Edwin Astwood, 1944–45 (h)
Dr. Joseph C. Aub, 1928–29 (d)
Dr. K. Frank Austen, 1977–78 (h)
Dr. Julius Axelrod, 1971–72 (h)
Dr. E. R. Baldwin, 1914–15 (d)
Dr. David Baltimore, 1974–75 (h)
Prof. Joseph Barcroft, 1921–22 (d)
Dr. Philip Bard, 1921–22 (h)
Dr. H. A. Barker, 1949–50 (h)
Prof. Lewellys Barker, 1905–06 (d)
Dr. Julius Bauer, 1932–33 (d)
Prof. William M. Bayliss, 1921–22 (d)
Dr. Frank Beach, 1947–48 (h)
Dr. George W. Beadle, 1944–45 (h)
Dr. Alexander G. Bearn, 1974–75 (a)
Dr. Albert Behnke, 1941–42 (h)
Dr. Baruj Benacerraf, 1971–72 (a)
Prof. F. G. Benedict, 1906–07 (d)

Dr. Stanley Benedict, 1915–16 (d)
Dr. D. Bennett, 1978–79 (a)
Dr. M. V. L. Bennett, 1982–83 (a)
Prof. R. R. Bensley, 1914–15 (d)
Dr. Seymour Benzer, 1960–61 (h)
Dr. Paul Berg, 1971–72 (h)
Dr. Max Bergmann, 1935–36 (d)
Dr. Sune Bergström, 1974–75 (h)
Dr. Robert W. Berliner, 1958–59 (h)
Dr. Solomon A. Berson, 1966–67 (a)
Dr. Marcel C. Bessis, 1962–63 (h)
Dr. C. H. Best, 1940–41 (h)
Dr. A. Biedl, 1923–24 (h)
Dr. Rupert E. Billingham, 1966–67 (h)
Dr. Richard J. Bing, 1954–55 (a)
Dr. J. Michael Bishop, 1982–83 (a)
Dr. John J. Bittner, 1946–47 (d)
Prof. Francis G. Blake, 1934–35 (d)
Dr. Alfred Blalock, 1945–46 (d)
Dr. Günter Blobel, 1980–81 (a)
Dr. Konrad Bloch, 1952–53 (a)
Dr. Walter R. Bloor, 1923–24 (d)
Dr. David Bodian, 1956–57 (h)
Dr. Walter F. Bodmer, 1976–77 (h)
Dr. James Bonner, 1952–53 (h)
Dr. Jules Bordet, 1920–21 (h)
Dr. William T. Bovie, 1922–23 (d)
Dr. Edward A. Boyse, 1971–72, 1975–76 (h)
Dr. Stanley E. Bradley, 1959–60 (a)
Dr. Daniel Branton, 1981–82 (a)
Dr. Armin C. Braun, 1960–61 (h)
Dr. Eugene Braunwald, 1975–76 (h)
Prof. F. Bremer, (h)†
Prof. T. G. Brodie, 1909–10 (d)
Dr. Detlev W. Bronk, 1933–34 (d)
Dr. B. Brouwer, 1925–26 (d)

---

*(h), honorary; (a), active; (d) deceased.
†Did not present lecture because of World War II.

Dr. Donald D. Brown, 1980–81 (a)
Dr. Michael S. Brown, 1977–78 (h)
Dr. Wade H. Brown, 1928–29 (d)
Dr. John M. Buchanan, 1959–60 (h)
Dr. John Cairns, 1970–1971 (h)
Prof. A. Calmette, 1908–09 (d)
Dr. Melvin Calvin, 1950–51 (h)
Prof. Walter B. Cannon, 1911–12 (d)
Prof. A. J. Carlson, 1915–16 (d)
Dr. William B. Castle, 1934–35 (h)
Prof. W. E. Castle, 1910–11 (d)
Dr. I. L. Chaikoff, 1951–52 (d)
Dr. Robert Chambers, 1926–27 (d)
Dr. B. Chance, 1953–54 (h)
Dr. Jean-Pierre Changeux, 1979–80 (a)
Dr. Charles V. Chapin, 1913–14 (d)
Dr. Erwin Chargaff, 1956–57 (h)
Dr. Merrill W. Chase, 1965–66 (a)
Dr. Alan M. Chesney, 1929–30 (d)
Prof. Hans Chiari, 1910–11 (d)
Dr. C.M. Child 1928–29 (d)
Prof. Russell H. Chittenden, 1911–12 (d)
Prof. Henry A. Christian, 1915–16 (d)
Dr. W. Mansfield Clark; 1933–34 (d)
Dr. Albert Claude, 1947–48 (a)
Dr. Samuel W. Clausen, 1942–43 (d)
Dr. Zanvil A. Cohn, 1981–82 (a)
Dr. Phillip P. Cohen, 1964–65 (h)
Dr. Stanley N. Cohen, 1978–79 (a)
Dr. Alfred E. Cohn, 1927–28 (d)
Dr. Edwin F. Cohn, 1927–28, 1938–39 (d)
Prof. Otto Cohnheim, 1909–10 (d)
Dr. Rufus Cole, 1913–14, 1929–30 (d)
Dr. J. B. Collip, 1925–26 (h).
Dr. Edgar L. Collis, 1926–27 (d)
Dr. Julius H. Comroe, Jr., 1952–53 (h)
Dr. James B. Conant, 1932–33 (h)
Prof. Edwin G. Conklin, 1912–13 (d)

Dr. Jerome W. Conn, 1966–67 (h)
Dr. Albert H. Coons, 1957–58 (d)
Dr. Carl F. Cori, 1927–28, 1945–46 (h)
Dr. Gerty T. Cori, 1952–53 (d)
Dr. George W. Corner, 1932–33 (h)
Dr. George C. Cotzias, 1972–73 (d)
Prof. W. T. Councilman, 1906–07 (d)
Dr. Andre Cournand, 1950–51 (a)
Dr. E. V. Cowdry, 1922–23 (d)
Dr. Lyman C. Craig, 1949–50 (d)
Dr. George Crile, 1907–08 (d)
Dr. S. J. Crowe, 1931–32 (d)
Dr. Harvey Cushing, 1910–11, 1932–33 (d)
Prof. Arthur R. Cushny, 1910–11 (d)
Sir Henry Dale, 1919–20, 1936–37 (h)
Dr. I. deBurgh Daly, 1935–36 (d)
Dr. C. H. Danforth, 1938–39 (d)
Dr. James F. Danielli, 1962–63 (h)
Dr. James E. Darnell, Jr., 1973–74 (a)
Dr. C. B. Davenport, 1908–09 (d)
Dr. Earl W. Davie, 1981–82 (a)
Dr. Bernard D. Davis, 1954–55 (a)
Dr. Christian deDuve, 1963–64 (h)
Dr. Max Delbruck, 1945–46 (h)
Dr. Hector F. DeLuca, 1979–80 (a)
Dr. F. D'Herelle, 1928–29 (d)
Dr. John H. Dingle, 1956–57 (d)
Dr. Frank J. Dixon, 1962–63 (h)
Dr. A. R. Dochez, 1924–25 (d)
Dr. E. C. Dodds, 1934–35 (h)
Dr. E. A. Doisy, 1933–34 (d)
Dr. Vincent P. Dole, 1971–72 (h)
Prof. Henry H. Donaldson, 1916–17 (d)
Dr. Paul Doty, 1958–59 (h)
Prof. Georges Dreyer, 1919–20 (d)
Dr. Cecil K. Drinker, 1937–38 (d)
Dr. J. C. Drummond, 1932–33 (d)
Lewis I. Dublin, 1922–23 (h)

Dr. Eugene F. DuBois, 1915–16, 1938–39, 1946–47 (d)

Dr. René J. Dubos, 1939–40 (a)

Dr. Renato Dulbecco, 1967–68 (h)

Dr. E. K. Dunham, 1917–19 (d)

Dr. L. C. Dunn, 1939–40 (d)

Dr. Vincent du Vigneaud, 1942–43, 1954–55 (a)

Dr. R. E. Dyer, 1933–34 (h)

Dr. Harry Eagle, 1959–60 (a)

Dr. E. M. East, 1930–31 (d)

Dr. J. C. Eccles, 1955–56 (h)

Dr. Gerald M. Edelman, 1972–73 (a)

Prof. R. S. Edgar, 1967–68 (h)

Dr. David L. Edsall, 1907–08 (d)

Dr. John T. Edsall, 1966–67 (h)

Dr. William Einthoven, 1924–25 (d)

Dr. Herman N. Eisen, 1964–65 (h)

Dr. Joel Elkes, 1961–62 (h)

Dr. C. A. Elvehjem, 1939–40 (d)

Dr. Haven Emerson, 1954–55 (d)

Dr. John F. Enders, 1947–48, 1963–64 (h)

Dr. Boris Ephrussi, 1950–51 (h)

Dr. Joseph Erlanger, 1912–13, 1926–27 (h)

Dr. Earl A. Evans, Jr., 1943–44 (h)

Dr. Herbert M. Evans, 1923–24 (h)

Dr. James Ewing, 1907–08 (d)

Dr. Knud Faber, 1925–26 (d)

Dr. W. Falta, 1908–09 (d)

Dr. W. O. Fenn, 1927–28 (d)

Dr. Frank Fenner, 1956–57 (h)

Dr. H. O. L. Fischer, 1944–45 (d)

Dr. L. B. Flexner, 1951–52 (h)

Dr. Simon Flexner, 1911–12 (d)

Dr. Otto Folin, 1907–08, 1919–20 (d)

Prof. John A. Fordyce, 1914–15 (d)

Dr. Nellis B. Foster, 1920–21 (d)

Dr. Edward Francis, 1927–28 (d)

Dr. Thomas Francis, Jr., 1941–42 (d)

Dr. H. Fraenkel-Conrat, 1956–57 (h)

Dr. Robert T. Frank, 1930–31 (d)

Dr. Edward C. Franklin, 1981–82 (d)

Dr. Donald S. Fredrickson, 1972–73 (h)

Dr. Charlotte Friend, 1976–77 (a)

Dr. C. Fromageot, 1953–54 (h)

Dr. Joseph S. Fruton, 1955–56 (a)

Dr. John F. Fulton, 1935–36 (d)

Dr. E. J. Furshpan, 1980–81 (a)

Dr. Jacob Furth, 1967–68 (a)

Dr. D. Carleton Gadjusek, 1976–77 (h)

Dr. Ernest F. Gale, 1955–56 (h)

Dr. Joseph G. Gall, 1975–76 (h)

Dr. T. F. Gallagher, 1956–57 (a)

Dr. James L Gamble, 1946–47 (d)

Dr. Herbert S. Gasser, 1936–37 (d)

Dr. Frederick P. Gay, 1914–15, 1930–31 (d)

Dr. Eugene M. K. Geiling, 1941–42 (d)

Dr. Isidore Gersh, 1949–50 (h)

Dr. George O. Gey, 1954–55 (d)

Dr. John H. Gibbon, 1957–58 (d)

Dr. Harry Goldblatt, 1937–38 (h)

Dr. Joseph L. Goldstein, 1977–78 (h)

Dr. Robert A. Good, 1971–72 (a)

Dr. Earnest W. Goodpasture, 1929–30 (d)

Dr. Carl W. Gottschalk, 1962–63 (h)

Dr. J. Gough, 1957–58 (h)

Prof. J. I. Gowans, 1968–69 (h)

Dr. Evarts A. Graham, 1923–24, 1933–34 (d)

Dr. S. Granick, 1948–49 (h)

Dr. David E. Green, 1956–57 (h)

Dr. Howard Green, 1978–79 (a)

Dr. Paul Greengard, 1979–80 (a)

Prof. R. A. Gregory, 1968–69 (h)

Dr. Donald R. Griffin, 1975–76 (h)

Dr. Jerome Gross, 1972–73 (h)

Dr. Roger Guillemin, 1975–76 (h)

Dr. I. C. Gunsalus, 1949–50 (h)

Dr. John B. Gurdon, 1973–74 (h)

Dr. Alexander B. Gutman, 1964–65 (a)

Dr. J. S. Haldane, 1916–17 (d)
Dr. William S. Halsted, 1913–14 (d)
Dr. H. J. Hamburger, 1922–23 (d)
Dr. Hidesaburo Hanafusa, 1979–80 (a)
Dr. J. D. Hardy, 1953–54 (a)
Sir William Hardy, 1930–31 (d)
Dr. Harry Harris, 1980–81 (a)
Prof. Henry Harris, 1969–70 (h)
Dr. Ross G. Harrison, 1907–08, 1933–34 (d)
Dr. H. K. Hartline, 1941–42 (h)
Dr. E. Newton Harvey, 1944–45 (h)
Dr. A. Baird Hastings, 1940–41 (a)
Dr. Selig Hecht, 1937–38 (d)
Prof. Sven H. Hedin, 1913–14 (d)
Dr. Michael Heidelberger, 1932–33 (a)
Prof. Ludvig Hektoen, 1909–10 (d)
Prof. L. J. Henderson, 1914–15 (d)
Dr. Yandell Henderson, 1917–19 (d)
Dr. James B. Herrick, 1930–31 (d)
Dr. A. D. Hershey, 1955–56 (h)
Prof. Christian Herter, 1906–07 (d)
Dr. Alfred F. Hess, 1920–21 (d)
Dr. A. V. Hill, 1924–25 (h)
Dr. George Hirst, 1948–49 (a)
Dr. Philip H. Hiss, 1908–09 (d)
Dr. Dorothy C. Hodgkin, 1965–66 (h)
Dr. Alan F. Hofmann, 1978–79 (a)
Dr. Klaus Hofmann, 1963–64 (h)
Prof. F. Gowland Hopkins, 1920–21 (d)
Dr. Bernard L. Horecker, 1961–62 (a)
Dr. Frank Horsfall, Jr., 1952–53 (d)
Dr. R. D. Hotchkiss, 1953–54 (a)
Dr. B. A. Houssay, 1935–36 (h)
Prof. W. H. Howell, 1905–06, 1916–17 (d)
Dr. John Howland, 1912–13, 1922–23 (d)
Dr. David H. Hubel, 1976–77 (h)
Prof. G. Carl Huber, 1909–10 (d)

Dr. Robert J. Huebner, 1960–61 (h)
Dr. Charles Huggins, 1946–47 (h)
Dr. David M. Hume, 1968–69 (d)
Prof. George Huntington, 1906–07 (d)
Dr. Jerard Hurwitz, 1968–69 (a)
Dr. Hugh Huxley, 1964–65 (h)
Dr. Vernon M. Ingram, 1965–66 (h)
Dr. Kurt J. Isselbacher, 1973–74 (h)
Dr. A. C. Ivy, 1931–32 (d)
Dr. Francois Jacob, 1959–60 (h)
Dr. Merkel Jacobs, 1926–27 (d)
Dr. Walter A. Jacobs, 1923–24 (a)
Prof. Theodore C. Janeway, 1912–13 (d)
Dr. Joseph Jastro, 1907–08 (d)
Prof. H. S. Jennings, 1911–12 (d)
Dr. Niels K. Jerne, 1974–75 (h)
Dr. J. W. Jobling, 1916–17 (d)
Dr. Edwin O. Jordan, 1907–08 (d)
Prof. Elliott P. Joslin, 1914–15 (d)
Dr. Alfred Jost, 1958–59 (h)
Dr. Elvin A. Kabat, 1950–51 (a)
Prof. Herman M. Kalckar, 1949–50 (h)
Dr. Yuet Wai Kan, 1980–81 (a)
Dr. Eric R. Kandel, 1977–78 (a)
Dr. Henry S. Kaplan, 1968–69 (h)
Dr. Nathan O. Kaplan, 1970–71 (h)
Dr. Ephraim Katchalski, 1963–64 (h)
Prof. E. C. Kendall, 1919–20 (h)
Dr. Eugene P. Kennedy, 1961–62 (h)
Dr. Seymour S. Kety, 1975–76 (h)
Dr. H. Gobind Khorana, 1966–67 (h)
Dr. Edwin D. Kilbourne, 1977–78 (a)
Dr. A Klug, 1978–79 (a)
Dr. George Klein, 1973–74 (h)
Dr. P. Klemperer, 1953–54 (d)
Dr. B. C. J. G. Knight, 1947–48 (h)
Prof. Franz Knoop, 1912–13 (d)
Dr. F. C. Koch, 1937–38 (d)
Prof. W. Kolle, 1924–25 (d)
Dr. Hilary Koprowski, 1964–65 (h)

Dr. Arthur Kornberg, 1957–58 (a)
Dr. Daniel E. Koshland, Jr., 1969–70 (h)
Prof. Albrecht Kossel, 1911–12 (d)
Dr. Allen K. Krause, 1921–22 (d)
Dr. H. A. Krebs, 1948–49 (h)
Dr. August Krogh, 1922–23 (d)
Dr. Stephen W. Kuffler, 1959–60 (h)
Dr. Henry G. Kunkel, 1963–64 (a)
Dr. L. O. Kunkel, 1932–33 (d)
Dr. Rebecca C. Lancefield, 1940–41 (a)
Dr. Eugene M. Landis, 1936–37 (h)
Dr. Ernst Laquer, 1945–46 (d)
Dr. Henry A. Lardy, 1964–65 (h)
Dr. K. S. Lashley, 1930–31 (d)
Dr. H. Sherwood Lawrence, 1972–73 (a)
Dr. H. A. Lawson, 1927–28 (h)
Dr. J. B. Leathes, 1908–09 (d)
Dr. Philip Leder, 1978–79 (a)
Dr. Joshua Lederberg, 1957–58 (h)
Dr. Frederic S. Lee, 1905–06, 1917–19 (d)
Dr. W. E. LeGros Clark, 1962–63 (h)
Dr. A. L. Lehninger, 1953–54 (h)
Dr. Luis F. Leloir, 1960–61 (h)
Dr. C. Levaditi, 1928–29 (d)
Dr. P. A. Levene, 1905–06 (d)
Dr. Rita Levi-Montalcini, 1964–65 (h)
Dr. Sam Z. Levine, 1946–47 (d)
Dr. Howard B. Lewis, 1940–41 (d)
Dr. Paul A. Lewis, 1916–17 (d)
Prof. Thomas Lewis, 1914–15 (d)
Dr. Warren H. Lewis, 1925–26, 1935–36 (d)
Dr. Richard C. Lewontin, 1974–75 (h)
Dr. Choh Hao Li, 1950–51 (h)
Dr. K. Kindstrom-Lang, 1938–39 (d)
Dr. Karl P. Link, 1943–44 (h)
Dr. Fritz Lipmann, 1948–49 (a)
Dr. C. C. Little, 1921–22 (d)
Prof. Jacques Loeb, 1910–11, 1920–21 (d)
Dr. Leo Loeb, 1940–41 (d)
Dr. Robert F. Loeb, 1941–42 (a)
Prof. A. S. Loevenhart, 1914–15 (d)
Dr. Otto Loewi, 1932–33 (d)
Dr. E. S. London, 1927–28 (h)
Dr. Irving M. London, 1960–61 (a)
Dr. C. N. H. Long, 1936–37 (h)
Dr. Esmond R. Long, 1929–30 (h)
Prof. Warfield T. Longcope, 1915–16 (d)
Dr. Rafael Lorente de Nó, 1946–47 (a)
Prof. Konrad Lorenz, 1959–60 (h)
Dr. William D. Lotspeich, 1960–61 (d)
Dr. Oliver H. Lowry, 1962–63 (a)
Dr. Einar Lundsgaard, 1937–38 (d)
Dr. S. E. Luria, 1964–65 (h)
Dr. Graham Lusk, 1908–09, 1929–30 (d)
Dr. Andre Lwoff, 1954–55 (h)
Dr. Feodor Lynen, 1952–53 (h)
Dr. A. B. Macallum, 1908–09 (d)
Dr. W. G. MacCallum, 1908–09 (d)
Prof. J. J. R. MacLeod, 1913–14 (d)
Dr. William deB. MacNider, 1928–29 (d)
Dr. Thorvald Madsen, 1924–25, 1936–37 (d)
Dr. E. Margoliash, 1970–71 (h)
Prof. A. Magnus-Levy, 1909–10 (d)
Dr. H. W. Magoun, 1951–52 (h)
Dr. F. B. Mallory, 1912–13 (d)
Dr. Frank C. Mann, 1927–28 (d)
Dr. David Marine, 1923–24 (d)
Dr. Clement L. Markert, 1963–64 (h)
Dr. Paul A. Marks, 1970–71 (a)
Dr. Guy Marrian, 1938–39 (h)
Prof. W. McKim Marriott, 1919–20 (d)
Dr. E. K. Marshall, Jr., 1929–30 (d)
Dr. Manfred M. Mayer, 1976–77 (h)

246   CUMULATIVE AUTHOR INDEX

DR. DANIEL MAZIA, 1957–58 (h)
DR. MACLYN MCCARTY, 1969–70 (a)
PROF. E. V. MCCOLLUM, 1916–17 (d)
DR. WALSH MCDERMOTT, 1967–68 (a)
DR. HARDEN M. MCDONNELL (h)
DR. W. D. MCELROY, 1955–56 (h)
DR. PHILIP D. MCMASTER, 1941–42 (a)
DR. P. B. MEDAWAR, 1956–57 (h)
DR. WALTER J. MEEK, 1940–41 (d)
PROF. ALTON MEISTER, 1967–68 (h)
DR. S. J. MELTZER, 1906–07 (d)
PROF. LAFAYETTE B. MENDEL, 1905–06, 1914–15 (d)
DR. R. BRUCE MERRIFIELD, 1971–72 (h)
PROF. ADOLPH MEYER, 1909–10 (d)
PROF. HANS MEYER, 1905–06 (d)
DR. KARL MEYER, 1955–56 (a)
DR. K. F. MEYER, 1939–40 (d)
DR. OTTO MEYERHOF, 1922–23 (d)
DR. LEONOR MICHAELIS, 1926–27 (d)
DR. WILLIAM S. MILLER, 1924–25 (d)
PROF. CHARLES S. MINOT, 1905–06 (d)
DR. GEORGE R. MINOT, 1927–28 (d)
DR. BEATRICE MINTZ, 1975–76 (h)
DR. A. E. MIRSKY, 1950–51 (a)
DR. JACQUES MONOD, 1961–62 (h)
DR. CARL V. MOORE, 1958–59 (h)
DR. FRANCIS D. MOORE, 1956–57 (h)
DR. STANFORD MOORE, 1956–57 (h)
PROF. T. H. MORGAN, 1905–06 (d)
DR. GIUSEPPE MORUZZI, 1962–63 (h)
DR. J. HOWARD MUELLER, 1943–44 (d)
PROF. FRIEDRICH MULLER, 1906–07 (d)
DR. H. J. MULLER, 1947–48 (d)
DR. HANS MÜLLER-EBERHARD, 1970–71 (a)
PROF. JOHN R. MURLIN, 1916–17 (d)
DR. W. P. MURPHY, 1927–28 (d)
DR. DAVID NACHMANSOHN, 1953–54 (a)
DR. F. R. NAGER, 1925–26 (d)
DR. DANIEL NATHANS, 1974–75 (h)
DR. JAMES V. NEEL, 1960–61 (h)
DR. ELIZABETH F. NEUFELD, 1979–80 (a)

DR. FRED NEUFELD, 1926–27 (d)
SIR ARTHUR NEWSHOLME, 1920–21 (d)
DR. MARSHALL W. NIRENBERG, 1963–64 (h)
DR. HIDEYO NOGUVHI, 1915–16 (d)
DR. JOHN H. NORTHROP, 1925–26, 1934–35 (d)
DR. G. J. V. NOSSAL, 1967–68 (h)
PROF. FREDERICK G. NOVY, 1934–35 (d)
DR. RUTH S. NUSSENZWEIG, 1982–83 (a)
DR. VICTOR NUSSENZWEIG, 1982–83 (a)
PROF. GEORGE H. F. NUTTALL, 1912–13 (d)
DR. SEVERO OCHOA, 1950–51 (a)
DR. LLOYD J. OLD, 1971–72, 1975–76 (h)
DR. JOHN OLIPHANT, 1943–44 (d)
DR. JEAN OLIVER, 1944–45 (h)
DR. BERT W. O'MALLEY, 1976–77 (h)
DR. J. L. ONCLEY, 1954–55 (h)
DR. EUGENE L. OPIE, 1909–10, 1928–29, 1954–55 (d)
PROF. HENRY F. OSBORN, 1911–12 (d)
DR. MARY JANE OSBORN, 1982–83 (a)
DR. THOMAS B. OSBORNE, 1910–11 (d)
DR. WINTHROP J. V. OSTERHOUT, 1921–22, 1929–30 (h)
DR. GEORGE E. PALADE, 1961–62 (a)
DR. A. M. PAPPENHEIMER, JR., 1956–57, 1980–81 (a)
DR. JOHN R. PAPPENHEIMER, 1965–66 (a)
PROF. ARTHUR B. PARDEE, 1969–70 (h)
DR. EDWARDS A. PARK, 1938–39 (d)
PROF. W. H. PARK, 1905–06 (d)
PROF. G. H. PARKER, 1913–14 (d)
DR. STEWART PATON, 1917–19 (d)
DR. JOHN R. PAUL, 1942–43 (d)
DR. L. PAULING, 1953–54 (h)
DR. FRANCIS W. PEABODY, 1916–17 (d)
PROF. RICHARD M. PEARCE, 1909–10 (d)
DR. RAYMOND PEARL, 1921–22 (d)
DR. WILLIAM STANLEY PEART, 1977–78 (h)
DR. WILDER PENFIELD, 1936–37 (d)

Dr. M. F. Perutz, 1967–68 (h)
Dr. John P. Peters, 1937–38 (d)
Dr. W. H. Peterson, 1946–47 (d)
Dr. David C. Phillips, 1970–71 (h)
Dr. Ernst P. Pick, 1929–30 (h)
Dr. Ludwig Pick, 1931–32 (d)
Dr. Gregory Pincus, 1966–67 (d)
Dr. Clemens Pirquet, 1921–22 (d)
Dr. Colin Pitendrigh, 1960–61 (h)
Dr. Robert Pitts, 1952–53 (d)
Dr. A. Policard, 1931–32 (h)
Prof. George J. Popjak, 1969–70 (h)
Dr. Keith R. Porter, 1955–56 (a)
Prof. Rodney R. Porter, 1969–70 (h)
Dr. W. T. Porter, 1906–07, 1917–19 (d)
Dr. Mark Ptashne, 1973–74 (h)
Dr. T. T. Puck, 1958–59 (h)
Dr. J. J. Putnam, 1911–12 (d)
Dr. Efraim Racker, 1955–56 (a)
Dr. Hermann Rahn, 1958–59 (h)
Dr. Charles H. Rammelkamp, Jr., 1955–56 (h)
Dr. S. Walter Ranson, 1936–37 (d)
Dr. Kenneth B. Raper, 1961–62 (h)
Dr. Alexander Rich, 1982–83 (a)
Dr. Arnold R. Rich, 1946–47 (d)
Prof. Alfred N. Richards, 1920–21, 1934–35 (a)
Dr. Dickinson W. Richards, 1943–44 (a)
Prof. Theodore W. Richards, 1911–12 (d)
Dr. Curt P. Richter, 1942–43 (h)
Dr. D. Rittenberg, 1948–49 (d)
Dr. Thomas M. Rivers, 1933–34 (d)
Dr. William Robbins, 1942–43 (h)
Dr. O. H. Robertson, 1942–43 (d)
Prof. William C. Rose, 1934–35 (h)
Dr. M. J. Rosenau, 1908–09 (d)
Dr. Russell Ross, 1981–82 (a)
Dr. Jesse Roth, 1981–82 (a)
Dr. F. J. W. Roughton, 1943–44 (h)
Dr. Peyton Rous, 1935–36 (d)
Dr. Wallace P. Rowe, 1975–76 (h)
Dr. Harry Rubin, 1965–66 (h)
Prof. Max Rubner, 1912–13 (d)

Dr. Frank H. Ruddle, 1973–74 (h)
Dr. John Runnstrom, 1950–51 (h)
Major Frederick F. Russell, 1912–13 (d)
Dr. F. R. Sabin, 1915–16 (d)
Dr. Leo Sachs, 1972–73 (h)
Dr. Ruth Sager, 1982–83 (a)
Dr. Bengt Samuelsson, 1979–80 (a)
Dr. Wilbur A. Sawyer, 1934–35 (d)
Dr. Howard Schachman, 1972–73 (h)
Prof. E. A. Schafer, 1907–08 (d)
Dr. Robert T. Schimke, 1980–81 (a)
Dr. Matthew D. Scharff, 1973–74 (a)
Dr. Harold A. Scheraga, 1967–68 (h)
Dr. Bela Schick, 1922–23 (h)
Dr. Oscar Schloss, 1924–25 (d)
Prof. Adolph Schmidt, 1913–14 (d)
Dr. Carl F. Schmidt, 1948–49 (h)
Dr. Knut Schmidt-Neilsen, 1962–63 (h)
Dr. Francis O. Schmitt, 1944–45 (h)
Dr. R. Schoeneheimer, 1936–37 (d)
Dr. P. F. Scholander, 1961–62 (h)
Dr. Nevin S. Scrimshaw, 1962–63 (h)
Dr. William H. Sebrell, 1943–44 (h)
Prof. W. T. Sedgwick, 1911–12 (d)
Dr. Walter Seegers, 1951–52 (h)
Dr. J. Edwin Seegmiller, 1969–70 (h)
Dr. Michael Sela, 1971–72 (h)
Dr. Philip A. Shaffer, 1922–23 (d)
Dr. James A. Shannon, 1945–46 (a)
Dr. David Shemin, 1954–55 (a)
Dr. Henry C. Sherman, 1917–19 (d)
Dr. Richard Shope, 1935–36 (d)
Dr. Ephraim Shorr, 1954–55 (d)
Dr. Robert L. Sinsheimer, 1968–69 (h)
Dr. E. C. Slater, 1970–71 (h)
Dr. G. Elliot Smith, 1930–31 (d)
Dr. Emil L. Smith, 1966–67 (h)
Dr. Homer W. Smith, 1939–40 (d)
Dr. Philip E. Smith, 1929–30 (d)
Prof. Theobald Smith, 1905–06 (d)

Dr. George D. Snell, 1978–79 (a)
Dr. Solomon H. Snyder, 1977–78 (h)
Dr. T. M. Sonneborn, 1948–49 (h)
Dr. S. P. L. Sorenson, 1924–25 (d)
Dr. Carl C. Speidel, 1940–41 (h)
Dr. Sol Spiegelman, 1968–69 (a)
Dr. Roger W. Sperry, 1966–67 (h)
Dr. William C. Stadie, 1941–42 (d)
Dr. Earl R. Stadtman, 1969–70 (h)
Dr. Roger Stanier, 1959–60 (h)
Dr. Wendell Stanley, 1937–38 (d)
Dr. Earnest H. Starling, 1907–08 (d)
Dr. Donald F. Steiner, 1982–83 (a)
Dr. Isaac Starr, 1946–47 (h)
Dr. William H. Stein, 1956–57 (a)
Dr. P. Stetson, 1927–28
Prof. George Stewart, 1912–13 (d)
Prof. Ch. Wardell Stiles, 1915–16 (d)
Dr. C. R. Stockard, 1921–22 (d)
Dr. Walter Straub, 1928–29 (h)
Dr. George L. Streeter, 1933–34 (h)
Dr. Jack L. Strominger, 1968–69 (h)
Dr. R. P. Strong, 1913–14 (d)
Prof. Earl W. Sutherland, Jr., 1961–62 (d)
Prof. Homer F. Swift, 1919–20 (d)
Dr. W. W. Swingle, 1931–32 (d)
Dr. V. P. Sydenstricker, 1942–43 (h)
Dr. Albert Szent-Gyorgyi, 1938–39 (h)
Dr. W. H. Taliaferro, 1931–32 (d)
Prof. Alonzo E. Taylor, 1907–08 (d)
Dr. Howard M. Temin, 1973–74 (h)
Prof. W. S. Thayer, 1911–12 (d)
Dr. Hugo Theorell, 1965–66 (h)
Dr. Lewis Thomas, 1967–68 (a)
Dr. William S. Tillett, 1949–50 (a)
Dr. Arne Tiselius, 1939–40 (h)
Dr. A. R. Todd, 1951–52 (h)
Dr. Gordon M. Tomkins, 1972–73 (h)
Dr. Susumu Tonegawa, 1979–80 (a)
Dr. Sidney Udenfriend, 1964–65 (a)
Colonel F. P. Underhill, 1917–19 (d)

Dr. Hans Ussing, 1963–64 (h)
Dr. P. Roy Vagelos, 1974–75 (h)
Dr. Donald D. Van Slyke, 1915–16 (d)
Dr. Martha Vaughan, 1981–82 (a)
Prof. Victor C. Vaughn, 1913–14 (d)
Prof. Max Verworn, 1911–12 (d)
Prof. Carl Voegtlin, 1919–20 (d)
Dr. U.S. von Euler, 1958–59 (h)
Dr. Alexander von Muralt, 1947–48 (h)
Prof. Carl von Noorden, 1905–06 (d)
Dr. Selman A. Waksman, 1944–45 (d)
Dr. George Wald, 1945–46 (h)
Dr. Jan Waldenstrom, 1960–61 (h)
Prof. Augustus D. Waller, 1913–14 (d)
Dr. Josef Warkany, 1952–53 (h)
Colonel Stafford L. Warren, 1945–46 (h)
Dr. Alfred S. Warthin, 1917–19 (d)
Dr. C. J. Watson, 1948–49 (h)
Dr. Joseph T. Wearn, 1939–40 (h)
Dr. H. H. Weber, 1953–54 (d)
Prof. J. Clarence Webster, 1905–06 (d)
Dr. L. T. Webster, 1931–32 (d)
Dr. A. Ashley Weech, 1938–39 (h)
Dr. Silvio Weidmann, 1965–66 (h)
Dr. Paul Weiss, 1958–59 (a)
Dr. Charles Weissmann, 1981–82 (a)
Dr. William H. Welch, 1915–16 (d)
Dr. Thomas H. Weller, 1956–57 (h)
Prof. H. Gideon Wells, 1910–11 (d)
Dr. K. F. Wenckebach, 1922–23 (d)
Dr. George H. Whipple, 1921–22 (h)
Dr. Abraham White, 1947–48 (a)
Dr. Carl J. Wiggers, 1920–21, 1956–57 (d)
Dr. V. B. Wigglesworth, 1959–60 (h)
Dr. Carroll M. Williams, 1951–52 (h)

Dr. Linsley R. Williams, 1917–19 (d)

Dr. Richard Willstatter, 1926–27 (d)

Dr. Edmund B. Wilson, 1906–07 (d)

Dr. Edwin B. Wilson, 1925–26 (d)

Prof. J. Gordon Wilson, 1917–19 (h)

Dr. William F. Windle, 1944–45 (h)

Dr. F. R. Winton, 1951–52 (h)

Dr. Maxwell M. Wintrobe, 1949–50 (h)

Prof. S. B. Wolbach, 1920–21 (d)

Dr. Harold G. Wolff, 1943–44 (d)

Dr. Harland G. Wood, 1949–50 (h)

Dr. W. Barry Wood, Jr., 1951–52 (d)

Dr. William B. Wood, 1977–78 (h)

Prof. Sir Michael F. A. Woodruff, 1970–71 (h)

Dr. Robert B. Woodward, 1963–64 (h)

Dr. R. T. Woodyatt, 1915–16 (d)

Dr. D. W. Woolley, 1945–46 (d)

Sir Almroth E. Wright, 1906–07 (d)

Dr. Rosalyn S. Yalow, 1966–67 (h)

Prof. Robert M. Yerkes, 1917–19, 1935–36 (d)

Dr. Paul C. Zamecnik, 1959–60 (h)

Dr. L. Zechmeister, 1951–52 (h)

Dr. Norton D. Zinder, 1966–67 (a)

Prof. Hans Zinsser, 1914–15 (d)

ACTIVE MEMBERS

Dr. Bent Aasted
Dr. Ruth Gail Abramson
Dr. Steven B. Abramson
Dr. S. A. Acharya
Dr. Frederic J. Agate
Dr. Edward H. Ahrens
Dr. Agop Aintablian
Dr. Philip Aisen
Dr. Salah Al-Askari
Dr. Qais Al-Awqati
Dr. Anthony A. Albanese
Dr. Michael Harris Alderman
Dr. Robert Alexander
Dr. Emma Gates Allen
Dr. Fred H. Allen, Jr.
Dr. Jona Allerhand
Dr. Fred Allison, Jr.
Dr. Robert D. Allison
Dr. Norman R. Alpert
Dr. Blanche F. Alter
Dr. Norman Altszuler
Dr. Burton M. Altura
Dr. Richard P. Ames
Dr. A. F. Anderson*
Dr. Charles Anderson*
Dr. Helen M. Anderson
Dr. Karl E. Anderson
Dr. Giuseppe A. Andres
Dr. Muriel M. Andrews
Dr. Alfred Angrist*
Dr. Reginald M. Archibald*
Dr. Francis P. Arena
Dr. Diana C. Argyros
Dr. Irwin M. Arias
Dr. Donald Armstrong
Dr. Aaron Arnold
Dr. Robert B. Aronson
Dr. Hiroshi Asanuma
Dr. Paul W. Aschnér*
Dr. Amir Askari
Dr. Muvaffak A. Atamer

Dr. Dana W. Atchley*
Dr. Kimball Chase Atwood
Dr. Arleen D. Auerbach
Dr. Arthur H. Aufses, Jr.
Dr. Joseph T. August
Dr. Peter A. M. Auld
Dr. Felice B. Aull
Dr. Robert Austrian
Dr. Avram Avramides
Dr. Theodore W. Av Ruskin
Dr. D. Robert Axelrod
Dr. Stephen M. Ayres
Dr. L. Fred Ayvazian
Dr. Henry A. Azar
Dr. Efrain C. Azmitia
Dr. Rostom Bablanian
Dr. Radoslav Bachvaroff
Dr. Mortimer E. Bader
Dr. Richard A. Bader
Dr. George Baehr*
Dr. Leslie Baer
Dr. Silvio Baez
Dr. John C. Baiardi
Dr. Robert D. Baird*
Mrs. Katherine J. Baker
Dr. Sulamita Balagura
Dr. John C. Balardi*
Dr. David S. Baldwin
Dr. Horace S. Baldwin*
Dr. M. Earl Balis
Dr. Amiya K. Banerjee
Dr. S. Banerjee*
Dr. Arthur Bank
Dr. Norman Bank
Dr. Alvan L. Barach*
Dr. W. H. Barber*
Dr. Jose Luis Barbosa-Saldivar
Dr. Marion Barclay
Dr. S. B. Barker*
Dr. Lane Barksdale
Dr. W. A. Barnes

*Life member.

Dr. Harry Baron
Dr. Howard Baron
Dr. Jeremiah A. Barondess
Dr. David P. Barr*
Dr. Bruce A. Barron
Dr. Guy T. Barry
Dr. Claudio Basilico
Dr. C. Andrew L. Bassett
Dr. Jeanne Bateman*
Dr. Jack R. Battisto
Dr. Stephen G. Baum
Dr. Leona Baumgartner*
Dr. Eliot F. Beach*
Dr. Joseph W. Beard*
Dr. Alexander G. Bearn
Dr. Carl Becker
Dr. E. Lovell Becker
Dr. Joseph W. Becker
Dr. William H. Becker
Dr. Paul B. Beeson*
Dr. Richard E. Behrman
Dr. Brian Beiman
Dr. Julius Belford
Dr. Bertrand Bell
Dr. Fritz Karl Beller
Dr. Baruj Benacerraf
Dr. Morris Bender*
Dr. Aaron Bendich
Dr. Bernard Benjamin*
Dr. Bry Benjamin
Dr. Ivan L. Bennett
Dr. Thomas P. Bennett
Dr. Harvey L. Benovitz
Dr. Gordon Benson
Dr. Richard Beresford
Dr. Benjamin N. Berg*
Dr. Kare Berg
Dr. Stanley S. Bergen
Dr. Adolph Berger
Dr. Lawrence Berger
Dr. Ingemar Berggard
Dr. James Berkman
Dr. Alice R. Bernheim*

Dr. Alan W. Bernheimer
Dr. Harriet Bernheimer
Dr. Leslie Bernstein
Dr. Car A. Berntsen
Dr. George Packer Berry*
Dr. John F. Bertles
Dr. Otto A. Bessey*
Dr. Joseph J. Betheil
Dr. Margaret Bevans
Dr. Sherman Beychok
Dr. Rajesh M. Bhatnagar
Dr. Celso Bianco
Dr. John T. Bigger, Jr.
Dr. R. J. Bing*
Dr. Carl A. L. Binger*
Dr. Francis Binkley
Dr. Mark W. Bitensky
Dr. Ira Black
Dr. William A. Blanc
Dr. Kenneth C. Blanchard*
Dr. David H. Blankenhorn
Dr. Sheldon P. Blau
Dr. Richard W. Blide
Dr. Andrew Blitzer
Dr. Gunter Blobel
Dr. Konrad E. Bloch
Dr. Arthur D. Bloom
Dr. Barry Bloom
Dr. Richard S. Bockman
Dr. Oscar Bodansky*
Dr. Diethelm Boehme
Dr. Bruce I. Bogart
Dr. Morton D. Bogdonoff
Dp. Alfred J. Bollet
Dr. Richard J. Bonforte
Dr. Roy W. Bonsnes*
Dr. Robert M. Bookchin
Dr. Ellen Borenfreund
Dr. Frank Boschenstein
Dr. Adele L. Boskey
Dr. Barbara H. Bowman
Dr. Linn J. Boyd*
Dr. Robert J. Boylan

*Life member.

Dr. Richard C. Bozian
Dr. Robert Brackenbury
Dr. Stanley Bradley*
Dr. Thomas B. Bradley
Dr. Leon Bradlow
Dr. J. Leonard Brandt
Dr. Lawrence J. Brandt
Dr. Daniel Branton
Dr. Jo Anne Brasel
Dr. Thomas A. Brastitus
Dr. Goodwin Breinin
Dr. Esther Breslow
Dr. Jan L. Breslow
Dr. Robin Briehl
Dr. Stanley A. Briller
Dr. Anne E. Briscoe
Dr. Susan Broder
Dr. Felix Bronner
Dr. Chandler McC. Brooks
Dr. Dana C. Brooks
Dr. Clinton D. Brown
Dr. D. E. S. Brown*
Dr. John Lyman Brown
Dr. Ted Brown
Dr. Howard C. Bruenn*
Dr. Elmer Brummer
Dr. J. Marion Bryant
Dr. J. Robert Buchanan
Dr. Nancy M. Buckley
Dr. Joseph A. Buda
Dr. Elmer D. Bueker
Dr. George E. Burch*
Dr. Joseph H. Burchenal
Dr. Richard Burger
Dr. Dean Burk*
Dr. Edward R. Burka
Dr. E. A. Burkhardt*
Dr. John J. Burns
Dr. Earl O. Butcher*
Dr. Vincent P. Butler, Jr.
Dr. Joel N. Buxbaum
Dr. Abbie Knowlton Calder
Dr. Peter T. B. Caldwell

Dr. Lawrence A. Caliguiri
Dr. Berry Campbell*
Dr. Robert E. Canfield
Dr. Paul Jude Cannon
Dr. Guilio L. Cantoni
Dr. Charles R. Cantor
Dr. Eric T. Carlson
Dr. Peter Wagner Carmel
Dr. Fred Carpenter
Dr. Malcolm B. Carpenter
Dr. Hugh J. Carroll
Dr. Steven Carson
Dr. Anne C. Carter
Dr. Sidney Carter
Dr. J. Casals-Ariet*
Dr. David B. Case
Dr. Robert B. Case
Dr. Albert E. Casey*
Dr. Joan I. Casey
Dr. William D. Cash
Dr. McKeen Cattell*
Dr. William Caveness*
Dr. Peter P. Cervoni
Dr. Raju S. K. Chaganti
Dr. R. W. Chambers
Dr. Philip C. Chan
Dr. W. Y. Chan
Dr. J. P. Chandler*
Dr. Merrill W. Chase*
Dr. Norman E. Chase
Dr. Herbert Chasis*
Dr. Kirk C. S. Chen
Dr. Tehodore Chenkin
Dr. David S. Chi
Dr. Marie T. Chiao
Dr. Shiu Chien
Dr. C. Gardner Child*
Dr. Francis P. Chinard
Dr. Herman Chmel
Dr. Yong Sung Choi
Dr. Purnell W. Choppin
Dr. Charles L. Christian
Dr. Ronald V. Christie*

*Life member.

Dr. Judith K. Christman
Dr. Nicholas P. Christy
Dr. Jacob Churg
Dr. Duncan W. Clark*
Dr. Frank H. Clarke
Dr. Albert Claude*
Dr. Hartwig Cleve
Dr. Leighton E. Cluff
Dr. Jaime B. Coelho
Dr. Bernard Cohen
Dr. Cal K. Cohn
Dr. Mildred Cohn*
Dr. Zanvil A. Cohn
Dr. Henry Colcher
Dr. Randolph P. Cole
Dr. Morton Coleman
Dr. Neville Colman
Dr. Spencer L. Commerford
Dr. Richard M. Compans
Dr. Neal J. Conan, Jr.
Dr. Lawrence A. Cone
Dr. Stephen C. Connolly
Dr. James H. Conover
Dr. Jean L. Cook
Dr. John S. Cook
Dr. Stuart D. Cook
Dr. George Cooper
Dr. Norman S. Cooper
Dr. Jack M. Cooperman
Dr. W. M. Copenhaver*
Dr. George N. Cornell
Dr. James S. Cornell
Dr. George Corner*
Dr. Armand F. Cortese
Dr. Daniel L. Costa
Dr. Thomas Costantino
Dr. Richard Costello
Dr. Lucien J. Cote
Dr. Andre Cournand*
Dr. David Cowen
Dr. Herold R. Cox*
Dr. George Craft
Dr. John P. Craig

Dr. B. B. Crohn*
Dr. Richard J. Cross
Dr. Mary K. Crow
Dr. Bruce Cunningham
Dr. Dorothy J. Cunningham
Dr. Edward C. Curnen*
Dr. Mary G. McCrea Curnen
Dr. T. J. Curphey*
Dr. Samuel W. Cushman
Dr. Samuel Dales
Dr. Marie Maynard Daly
Dr. Joseph Dancis
Dr. John A. Dancus
Dr. Betty S. Danes
Dr. Farrington Daniels, Jr.
Dr. R. C. Darling*
Dr. James E. Darnell, Jr.
Dr. Fredric Daum
Dr. Fred M. Davenport
Dr. Charles M. David
Dr. John David
Dr. Leo M. Davidoff*
Dr. Murray Davidson
Dr. Nicholas O. Davidson
Dr. Earl W. Davie
Dr. Jean Davignon
Dr. Bernard D. Davis
Dr. Robert P. Davis
Dr. Emerson Day
Dr. Noorbibi K. Day
Dr. Stacey B. Day
Dr. Peter G. Dayton
Dr. Norman Deane
Dr. Robert H. De Bellis
Dr. Vittorio Defendi
Dr. Paul F. de Gara*
Dr. Thomas J. Degnan
Dr. A. C. DeGraff*
Dr. John E. Deitrick*
Dr. C. E. de la Chapelle*
Dr. Nicholas Delhias
Dr. R. J. Dellenback
Dr. Felix E. Demartini

*Life member.

Dr. Quentin B. Deming
Dr. Felix de Narvaez
Dr. Robert Desnick
Dr. Dickson D. Despommier
Dr. Ralph A. Deterling, Jr.
Dr. Wolf-Dietrich Dettbarn
Dr. Ingrith J. Deyrup
Dr. Elaine Diacumakos
Dr. Herbert S. Diamond
Dr. Leroy S. Dietrich
Dr. George W. Dietz, Jr.
Dr. Mario Di Girolamo
Dr. Alexander B. Dimich
Dr. Peter Dineen
Dr. J. R. Di Palma
Dr. P. A. Di Sant'Agnese
Dr. Zacharias Dische
Dr. Ann M. Dnistrian
Dr. Charles A. Doan*
Dr. William Dock*
Dr. Alvin M. Donnenfeld
Dr. David Donner
Dr. Philip J. Dorman
Dr. Louis B. Dotti*
Dr. Gordon W. Douglas
Dr. R. Gordon Douglas, Jr.
Dr. Steven D. Douglas
Dr. Charles V. Dowling
Dr. Peter C. Dowling
Dr. Alan W. Downie*
Dr. Cora Downs*
Dr. Arnold Drapkin
Dr. David A. Dreiling
Dr. Paul Driezen
Dr. David T. Dresdale
Dr. Lewis M. Drusin
Dr. Ronald E. Drusin
Dr. René J. Dubos*
Dr. Allan Dumont
Dr. Bo Dupont
Dr. Vincent Du Vigneaud*
Dr. Murray Dworetzky
Dr. D. Dziewiatkowski

Dr. Harry Eagle
Dr. Lila W. Easley
Dr. John C. Eccles*
Dr. Gerald M. Edelman
Dr. Norman Edelman
Dr. Howard A. Eder
Dr. Adrian L. E. Edwards
Dr. Richard M. Effros
Dr. Hans J. Eggers
Dr. Kathryn H. Ehlers
Dr. Klaus Eichmann
Dr. Ludwig W. Eichna*
Dr. Max Eisenberg
Dr. Moises Eisenberg
Dr. William J. Eisenmenger
Dr. Robert P. Eisinger
Dr. Stuart D. Elliott
Dr. John T. Ellis
Dr. Rose-Ruth Tarr Ellison
Dr. Peter Elsbach
Dr. Samuel K. Elster
Dr. Charles A. Ely*
Dr. Kendall Emerson, Jr.*
Dr. Morris Engelman
Dr. Mary Allen Engle
Dr. Ralph L. Engle, Jr.
Dr. Leonard Epifano
Dr. Bernard F. Erlanger
Dr. Solomon Estren
Dr. Hugh E. Evans
Dr. Henry E. Evert
Dr. Ronald B. Faanes
Dr. Stanley Fahn
Dr. Gordon F. Fairclough, Jr.
Dr. Saul J. Farber
Dr. Mehdi Farhangi
Dr. Peter B. Farnsworth
Dr. John W. Farquhar
Dr. Lee E. Farr*
Dr. Aaron Feder*
Dr. Martha E. Fedorko
Dr. Muriel F. Feigelson
Dr. Philip Feigelson

*Life member.

Dr. Maurice Feinstein
Dr. Daniel Feldman
Dr. Colin Fell
Dr. Soldano Ferrone
Dr. Bernard N. Fields
Dr. Ronald R. Fieve
Dr. Arthur M. Figur
Dr. Howard Fillit
Dr. Laurence Finberg
Dr. Louis M. Fink
Dr. Stanley R. Finke
Dr. John T. Finkenstaedt
Dr. Edward E. Fischel
Dr. Saul H. Fischer*
Dr. Vincent A. Fischetti
Dr. Arthur Fishberg*
Dr. Paul B. Fisher
Dr. Patrick J. Fitzgerald
Dr. Martin FitzPatrick
Dr. Raul Fleischmajer
Dr. Alan R. Fleischman
Dr. Howard Fleit
Dr. Charles Flood*
Dr. Alfred L. Florman*
Dr. Kathleen M. Foley
Dr. Conrad T. O. Fong
Dr. Joseph Fortner
Dr. Arthur C. Fox
Dr. Lewis M. Fraad*
Dr. Tova Francus
Dr. Blas Frangione
Dr. Harry Meyer Frankel
Dr. John E. Franklin, Jr.
Dr. Richard C. Franson
Dr. Andrew G. Frantz
Dr. Carl E. Frasch
Dr. Blair A. Fraser
Dr. Irwin M. Freedberg
Dr. Aaron D. Freedman
Dr. Michael L. Freedman
Dr. Alvin Freiman
Dr. Matthew Jay Freund
Dr. Richard H. Freyburg*

Dr. Henry Clay Frick, II
Dr. Arnold J. Friedhof
Dr. Ralph Friedlander*
Dr. Eli A. Friedman
Dr. Ronald Friedman
Dr. Charlotte Friend
Dr. George W. Frimpter
Dr. William Frisell
Dr. Joseph S. Fruton*
Dr. Fritz F. Fuchs
Dr. Mildred Fulop
Dr. Robert F. Furchgott*
Dr. Palmer H. Futcher*
Dr. Jacques L. Gabrilove
Dr. Morton Galdston
Dr. W. Einar Gall
Dr. G. Gail Garnder
Dr. William A. Gardner*
Dr. Martin Gardy
Dr. Owen W. Garrigan
Dr. Lawrence Gartner
Dr. Nancy E. Gary
Dr. Jerald D. Gass
Dr. Frederick T. Gates, III
Dr. Sabastiano Gattoni
Dr. Mario Gaudino
Dr. Gerald E. Gaull
Dr. Malcolm Gefter
Dr. Walton B. Geiger
Dr. Lester M. Geller
Dr. Jeremiah M. Gelles
Dr. Donald Gerber
Dr. James L. German, III
Dr. Edward L. Gershey
Dr. E. C. Gerst
Dr. Menard Gertler
Dr. Melvin Gertner
Dr. Norman R. Gevirtz
Dr. Nimai Ghosh
Dr. Stanley Giannelli, Jr.
Dr. Allan Gibofsky
Dr. Irma Gigli
Dr. Fred Gilbert

*Life member.

Dr. Harriet S. Gilbert
Dr. Helena Gilder
Dr. Alfred Gilman
Dr. Sid Gilman
Dr. Charles Gilvarg
Dr. H. Earl Ginn
Dr. James Z. Ginos
Dr. Harold S. Ginsberg
Dr. Isaac F. Gittleman
Dr. Sheldon Glabman
Dr. Philip R. Glade
Dr. Herman Gladstone
Dr. Warren Glaser
Dr. George B. Jerzy Glass
Dr. Ephraim Glassmann*
Dr. Vincent V. Glaviano
Dr. Frank Glenn*
Dr. Marvin L. Gliedman
Dr. David L. Globus
Dr. Martin J. Glynn, Jr.*
Dr. David J. Gocke
Dr. Henry P. Godfrey
Dr. Gabriel C. Godman
Dr. G. Nigel Godson
Dr. Walther F. Goebel*
Dr. Edmond A. Goidl
Dr. Robert B. Golbey
Dr. Allen M. Gold
Dr. Leslie I. Gold
Dr. Jonathan W. M. Gold
Dr. Allan R. Goldberg
Dr. Burton Goldberg
Dr. Anna Goldfeder
Dr. Roberta M. Goldring
Dr. William Goldring*
Dr. Edward I. Goldsmith
Dr. Eli D. Goldsmith*
Dr. David A. Goldstein
Dr. Gideon Goldstein
Dr. Jack Goldstein
Dr. Marvin H. Goldstein
Dr. Robert Goldstein
Dr. Julius Golubow

Dr. Robert A. Good
Dr. Robert Goodhart*
Dr. DeWitt S. Goodman
Dr. Laurance D. Goodwin
Dr. Norman L. Gootman
Dr. Albert S. Gordon*
Dr. Alvin J. Gordon
Dr. Gary G. Gordon
Dr. Harry H. Gordon*
Dr. Irving Gordon*
Dr. Emil Claus Gotschlich
Dr. Eugene Gottfried
Dr. Otto Götze
Dr. Dicran Goulian, Jr.
Dr. Arthur W. Grace*
Dr. R. F. Grady
Dr. Irving Graef*
Dr. William R. Grafe
Dr. Samuel Graff*
Dr. Frank A. Graig
Dr. Lester Grant
Dr. Arthur I. Grayzel
Dr. Jack Peter Green
Dr. Peter H. R. Green
Dr. Robert H. Green
Dr. Saul Green
Dr. Lowell M. Greenbaum
Dr. Elias L. Greene
Dr. Lewis J. Greene
Dr. Olga Greengard
Dr. Ezra M. Greenspan
Dr. Isidor Greenwald*
Dr. Robert A. Greenwald
Dr. Mary R. Greenwood
Dr. Gregory Gregariadis
Dr. Anastasia Gregoriades
Dr. John D. Gregory
Dr. Roger I. Greif
Dr. Ira Greifer
Dr. Giancarlo Guideri
Dr. Joel Grinker
Dr. Arthur Grishman
Dr. David Grob

*Life member.

Dr. Howard S. Grob
Dr. Arthur P. Grollman
Dr. Lionel Grossbard
Dr. Melvin Grumbach
Dr. Dezider Grunberger
Dr. Harry Grundfest*
Dr. Alan B. Gruskin
Dr. Alexandra D. Gruss
Dr. Joseph J. Guarneri
Dr. Ruth M. Gibits
Dr. Richard S. Gubner
Dr. Peter Guida
Dr. Anthony J. Grieco
Dr. Guido Guidotti
Dr. Connie M. Guion*
Dr. Stephen J. Gulotta
Dr. Sidney Gutstein
Dr. Gail S. Habicht
Dr. David V. Habif
Dr. John W. Hadden
Dr. Susan Jane Hadley
Dr. Hanspaul Hagenmaier
Dr. Jack W. C. Hagstrom
Dr. Kathleen A. Haines
Dr. David P. Hajjer
Dr. Seymour P. Halbert
Dr. Bernard H. Hall*
Dr. Robert I. Hamby
Dr. James B. Hamilton*
Dr. John Hamilton
Dr. Leonard Hamilton
Dr. Paul B. Hamilton*
Dr. Warner S. Hammond*
Dr. Chester W. Hampel*
Dr. H. Hanafusa
Dr. Eugene S. Handler
Dr. Evelyn E. Handler
Dr. Leonard C. Harber
Dr. James D. Hardy*
Dr. Ken Harewood
Dr. Peter Cahners Harpel
Dr. Albert H. Harris*
Dr. Michael B. Harris

Dr. Ruth C. Harris
Dr. Benjamin Harrow*
Dr. Una Hart
Dr. ReJane Harvey
Dr. Rudy Haschemeyer
Dr. George A. Hashim
Dr. Sam A. Hashim
Dr. George M. Hass*
Dr. William K. Hass
Dr. A. Baird Hastings*
Dr. Victor Hatcher
Dr. A. Daniel Hauser
Dr. Richard Hawkins
Dr. Arthur M. Hayes
Dr. John M. Hefton
Dr. Richard M. Hayes
Dr. Michael Heidelberger*
Dr. William Carroll Heird
Dr. Leon Hellman
Dr. Lawrence Helson
Dr. Walter L. Henley
Dr. Philip H. Henneman
Dr. Victor Herbert
Dr. Robert M. Hearbst*
Dr. Michael Herman
Dr. Morris Herman*
Dr. Frederic P. Herter
Dr. Robert B. Hiatt
Dr. Paul J. Higgins
Dr. Margaret Hilgartner
Dr. Charles H. Hill
Dr. Lawrence E. Hinkle, Jr.
Dr. Joseph C. Hinsey*
Dr. Christophe H. W. Hirs
Dr. Jacob Hirsch
Dr. James G. Hirsch
Dr. Jules Hirsch
Dr. Robert L. Hirsch
Dr. Kurt Hirschhorn
Dr. George K. Hirst*
Dr. Paul Hochstein
Dr. Paul F. A. Hoefer*
Dr. Thomas I. Hoen*

*Life member.

Dr. Alan F. Hofmann
Dr. Duncan A. Holiday
Dr. Raymond F. Holden*
Dr. Mary Jean C. Holland
Dr. Charles S. Hollander
Dr. Vincent Hollander
Dr. J. H. Holmes*
Dr. Peter R. Holt
Dr. Donald A. Holub
Dr. Robert S. Holzman
Dr. Edward W. Hook
Dr. Bernard L. Horecker
Dr. William H. Horner
Dr. Marshall S. Horwitz
Dr. Verne D. Hospelhorn
Dr. Rollin D. Hotchkiss*
Dr. S. D. Hotta
Dr. Michael Luray Howe
Dr. Howard H. T. Hsu
Dr. Konrad Chang Hsu
Dr. Ming-Ta Hsu
Dr. William N. Hubbard, Jr.
Dr. Lisa C. Hudgins
Dr. L. E. Hummel*
Dr. George H. Humphreys*
Dr. Jerard Hurwitz
Dr. Dorris Hutchinson
Dr. Thomas H. Hutteroth
Dr. Michael Iacobellis
Dr. Genevieve S. Incefy
Dr. Laura Inselman
Dr. Harry L. Ioachim
Dr. Henry D. Isenberg
Dr. Harold D. Itskovitz
Dr. Richard W. Jackson*
Dr. Jerry C. Jacobs
Dr. Eric A. Jaffe
Dr. Ernst R. Jaffe
Dr. Herbert Jaffe
Dr. S. Jakowska
Dr. George James
Dr. James D. Jamieson
Dr. Aaron Janoff

Dr. Alfonso H. Janoski
Dr. Henry D. Janowitz
Dr. Saul Jarcho*
Dr. Charles I. Jaworski
Dr. Jamshid Javid
Dr. Norman B. Javitt
Dr. S. Michel Jazwinski
Dr. Graham H. Jeffries
Dr. Alan J. Johnson
Dr. Dorothy D. Johnson
Dr. Walter D. Johnson, Jr.
Dr. Barbara Johnston
Dr. Kenneth H. Johnston
Dr. Thomas Jones
Dr. Alan S. Josephson
Dr. A. Jost*
Dr. Austin L. Joyner*
Dr. Ronald Kaback
Dr. Elvin A. Kabat*
Dr. Lawrence J. Kagen
Dr. Martin Kahn
Dr. Melvin Kahn
Dr. Thomas Kahn
Dr. Eric R. Kandel
Dr. Sungzong Kang
Dr. Stephen M. Kaplan
Dr. Alfred J. Kaltman
Dr. Mikio Kamiyama
Dr. William Kammerer
Dr. Sandra Kammerman
Dr. Yoshinobu Kanno
Dr. Thomas G. Kantor
Dr. F. F. Kao
Dr. Barry H. Kaplan
Dr. Attallah Kappas
Dr. S. J. Karakashian
Dr. Arthur Karanas
Dr. Arthur Karlin
Dr. Maxwell Karshan*
Dr. Stuart S. Kassan
Dr. Arnold M. Katz
Dr. Michael Katz
Dr. Mitchell A. Katz

*Life member.

Dr. George L. Kauer, Jr.*
Dr. David M. Kaufman
Dr. Hans Kaunitz
Dr. Herbert J. Kayden
Dr. Donald Kaye
Dr. D. Gordon I. Kaye
Dr. B. H. Kean
Dr. Aaron Kellner
Dr. Stephen Kent
Dr. Alan J. Kenyon
Dr. Muriel Kerr
Dr. Lee Kesner
Dr. Richard H. Kessler
Dr. Gerald T. Keusch
Dr. Andre C. Kibrick*
Dr. John G. Kidd*
Dr. Edwin D. Kilbourne
Dr. Margaret Kilcoyne
Dr. Diana C. Killip
Dr. Thomas Killip
Dr. Yoon Berm Kim
Dr. Young Tai Kim
Dr. Thomas J. Kindt
Dr. Barry G. King*
Dr. Donald West King
Dr. Glenn C. King*
Dr. Lawrence C. Kingsland, Jr.
Dr. David W. Kinne
Dr. John M. Kinney
Dr. R. A. Kinsella*
Dr. Esben Kirk
Dr. D. M. Kirschenbaum
Dr. David Klapper
Dr. Arthur A. Klein
Dr. Bernard Klein
Dr. Herbert Klein
Dr. Robert S. Klein
Dr. David L. Kleinberg
Dr. Abraham M. Kleinman
Dr. A. K. Kleinschmidt
Dr. Percy Klingenstein
Dr. Jerome L. Knittle

Dr. W. Eugene Knox
Dr. Joseph A. Kochen
Dr. Shaul Kochwa
Dr. Samuel Saburo Koide
Dr. Kiyomi Koizumi
Dr. M. J. Kopac*
Dr. Levy Kopelovich
Dr. Arthur Kornberg
Dr. Peter Kornfeld
Dr. Leonard Korngold
Dr. Irvin M. Korr*
Dr. Charles E. Kossmann*
Dr. Ione A. Kourides
Dr. Arthur Kowalsky
Dr. O. Dhodanand Kowlessar
Dr. Philip Kozinn
Dr. Irwin H. Krakoff
Dr. Lawrence R. Krakoff
Dr. Alvan Krasna
Dr. Richard M. Krause
Dr. Richard Kravath
Dr. Norman Kretchmer
Dr. Howard P. Krieger
Dr. Robert A. Kritzler
Dr. Robert Schild Krooth
Dr. Stephen Krop*
Dr. Saul Krugman
Dr. Edward J. Kuchinskas
Dr. Friedrich Kueppers
Dr. I. Newton Kugelmass*
Dr. Ashok B. Kulkarni
Dr. Henry G. Kunkel
Dr. Sherman Kupfer
Dr. Herbert S. Kupperman
Dr. Marvin Kuschner
Dr. Henn Kutt
Dr. Sau-Ping Kwan
Dr. David M. Kydd
Dr. Chun-Yen Lai
Dr. Robert G. Lahita
Dr. Michael Lake*
Dr. Michael Lamm

*Life member.

Dr. Robert Landesman
Dr. Frank R. Landsberger
Dr. M. Daniel Lane
Dr. William B. Langan
Dr. Gertrude Lange
Dr. Kurt Lange
Dr. Louis Langman*
Dr. Philip Lanzkowsky
Dr. John H. Laragh
Dr. Nicholas F. LaRusso
Dr. Etienne Y. Lasfargues
Dr. Sigmund E. Lasker
Dr. Leonard Laster
Dr. Raffaelle Lattes
Dr. John Lattimer
Dr. Henry D. Lauson
Dr. Beverly Lavietes
Dr. Leroy S. Lavine
Dr. Christine Lawrence
Dr. H. S. Lawrence
Dr. Walter Lawrence, Jr.
Dr. Richard W. Lawton
Dr. Robert W. Leader
Dr. Stanley L. Lee
Dr. Sylvia Lee-Huang
Dr. Robert S. Lees
Dr. Albert M. Lefkovits
Dr. David Lehr*
Dr. Gerard M. Lehrer
Miss Grace Leidy
Dr. Edgar Leifer
Dr. Louis Leiter*
Dr. John Lenard
Dr. Edwin H. Lennette*
Dr. E. Carwile LeRoy
Dr. Stephen H. Leslie
Dr. Gerson J. Lesnick
Dr. Gerson T. Lesser
Dr. Harry Le Veen
Dr. Stanley M. Levenson
Dr. Arthur H. Levere
Dr. Ricahrd D. Levere

Dr. Harold A. Levey
Dr. Robert Levi
Dr. Aaron R. Levin
Dr. Louis Levin*
Dr. Philip Levine*
Dr. Rachmiel Levine
Dr. Robert A. Levine
Dr. Cyrus Levinthal
Dr. Marvin F. Levitt
Dr. Barnet M. Levy
Dr. David E. Levy
Dr. Harvey M. Levy
Dr. Lester Levy
Dr. Milton Levy*
Dr. Sharon Lewin
Dr. Arthur Lewis
Dr. James L. Lewis
Dr. N. D. C. Lewis*
Dr. Marjorie Lewisohn *
Dr. Allyn B. Ley
Dr. Herbert C. Lichtman
Dr. Charles S. Lieber
Dr. Kenneth Lieberman
Dr. Seymour Lieberman
Dr. Frederick M. Liebman
Dr. Martin R. Liebowitz
Dr. Fannie Liebson
Dr. Frank Lilly
Dr. Edith M. Lincoln*
Dr. Alfred S. C. Ling
Dr. George Lipkin
Dr. Martin Lipkin
Dr. Fritz Lipmann*
Dr. M. B. Lipsett
Dr. Julius Littman*
Dr. George Liu
Dr. Darrell T. Liu
Dr. Arthur Livermore
Dr. Rodolfo Llinas
Dr. David P. C. Lloyd*
Dr. Joseph LoBue
Dr. Michael D. Lockshin

*Life member.

Dr. John N. Loeb
Dr. Robert F. Loeb*
Dr. Werner R. Loewenstein
Dr. Irving M. London
Dr. R. Lorente de Nó*
Dr. Barbara W. Low
Dr. Jerome Lowenstein
Dr. Oliver H. Lowry*
Dr. Fred V. Lucas
Dr. Jean M. Lucas-Lenard
Dr. E. Hugh Luckey
Dr. A. Leonard Luhby
Dr. Daniel S. Lukas
Dr. Carol Lusty
Dr. Clara J. Lynch*
Dr. Harold Lyons
Dr. Michael Lyons
Dr. George I. Lythcott
Dr. Kenneth McAlpin*
Dr. Marsh McCall
Dr. W. S. McCann*
Dr. Kenneth S. McCarty
Dr. Maclyn McCarty
Dr. Robert McClusky
Dr. David J. McConnell
Dr. Donovan J. McCune*
Dr. Walsh McDermott
Dr. Fletcher McDowell
Dr. Robert C. McEvoy
Dr. Currier McEwen*
Dr John C. McGiff
Dr. Eleanor McGowan
Dr. Paul R. McHugh
Dr. Rustin McIntosh*
Dr. Cosmo G. MacKenzie*
Dr. Robert G. McKittrick
Dr. John Macleod*
Dr. Donald J. McNamara
Dr. James J. McSharry
Dr. Charles K. McSherry
Dr. Robert M. McVie
Dr. Thomas Maack

Dr. Nicholas T. Macris
Dr. Melville G. Magida*
Dr. T. P. Magill*
Dr. Jacob V. Maizel, Jr.
Dr. Ole J. W. Malm
Dr. William M. Manger
Dr. Belur N. Manjula
Dr. Mart Mannik
Dr. James M. Manning
Dr. Wladyslaw Manski
Dr. Karl Maramorosch
Dr. Aaron J. Marcus
Dr. Donald M. Marcus
Dr. Philip I. Marcus
Dr. Norman Marine
Dr. Morri Markowitz
Dr. Morton Marks
Dr. Paul A. Marks
Dr. Robin Marks-Kaufman
Dr. Douglas A. Marsland*
Dr. Daniel S. Martin
Dr. Richard L. Masland
Dr. Bento Mascarenhas
Dr. Richard C. Mason*
Dr. Arthur M. Master*
Dr. Edmund B. Masurovsky
Dr. Leonard M. Mattes
Dr. Robert Matz
Dr. Paul H. Mauer
Dr. Evelyn A. Mauss
Dr. Morton H. Maxwell
Dr. Klaus Mayer
Dr. Aubre de L. Maynard
Dr E. W. Maynert
Dr. Rajarshi Mazumder
Dr. Abraham Mazur
Dr. Valentino Mazzia
Dr. John G. Mears
Dr. Edward Meilman
Dr. Harriet K. Meiss
Dr. Gilbert W. Mellin
Dr. Robert B. Mellins

*Life member.

Dr. Ismael Mena
Dr. Milton Mendlowitz*
Dr. Walter L. Mersheimer
Dr. Edward J. Messina
Dr. William Metcalf
Dr. Karl Meyer*
Dr. Leo M. Meyer*
Dr. Alexander J. Michie
Dr. Joseph Michl
Dr. Go Burroughs Mider*
Dr. Yves B. Mikol
Dr. Peter O. Milch
Dr. Donna Mildvan
Dr. A. T. Milhorat*
Dr. David K. Miller*
Dr. Frederick Miller
Dr. John A. P. Millett*
Dr. C. Richard Minick
Dr. George S. Mirick*
Dr. Ormond G. Mitchell
Dr. Peter Model
Dr. Walter Modell*
Dr. Carl Monder
Dr. Charles Moody
Dr. Dan H. Moore*
Dr. Stanford Moore
Dr. Brian L. G. Morgan
Dr. Anatol G. Morrell
Dr. Augusto Moreno
Dr. Gilda Morillo-Cucci
Dr. Akiro Morishima
Dr. Thomas Quinlan Morris
Dr. Kevin P. Morrissey
Dr. Alan N. Morrison
Dr. John Morrisson
Dr. Stephen I. Morse
Dr. Norman Moscowitz
Dr. Michael W. Mosesson
Dr. Melvin L. Moss
Dr. Harry Most*
Dr. Isabel M. Mountain*
Dr. Arden W. Moyer

Dr. Richard W. Moyer
Dr. Stuart Mudd*
Dr. G. H. Mudge
Dr. Meredith Mudgett
Dr. John V. Mueller
Dr. M. G. Mulinos*
Dr. Otto H. Muller*
Dr. Hans J. Müller-Eberhard
Dr. Ursula Müller-Eberhard
Dr. George E. Murphy
Dr. James S. Murphy
Dr. M. Lois Murphy
Dr. Carl Muschenheim*
Dr. W. P. Laird Myers
Dr. Martin S. Nachbar
Dr. Ralph L. Nachman
Dr. David D. Nachmansohn*
Dr. Ronald L. Nagel
Dr. Gabriel G. Nahas
Dr. Tatsuji Namba
Dr. William Nastuk
Dr. Benjamin H. Natelson
Dr. Samuel Natelson
Dr. Gerald Nathenson
Dr. M. Nathenson
Dr. Stanley G. Nathenson
Dr. Clayton L. Natta
Dr. Brian A. Naughton
Dr. Enid A. Neidle
Dr. Norton Nelson
Dr. Harold C. Neu
Dr. Maria M. New
Dr. Walter Newman
Miss Eleanor B. Newton*
Dr. Shih-hsun Ngai
Dr. Chi Nguyen-Huu
Dr. Warren W. Nichols
Dr. John F. Nicholson
Dr. John L. Nickerson*
Dr. Giorgio L. Nicolis
Dr. Julian Niemetz

*Life member.

Dr. Ross Nigrelli*
Dr. Jerome Nisselbaum
Dr. Charles Noback*
Dr. W. C. Noble*
Dr. M. R. Nocenti
Dr. Angelika Noegel
Dr. Robert Nolan
Dr. John H. Northrop
Dr. Robert A. Norum
Dr. Hymie L. Nossel
Dr. Richard Novick
Dr. Alex B. Novikoff
Dr. Abraham Novogrodsky
Dr. Ruth Nussenzweig
Dr. Victor Nussenzweig
Dr. Irwin Nydick
Dr. William B. Ober
Dr. Manuel Ochoa, Jr.
Dr. Severo Ochoa*
Dr. Herbert F. Oettgen
Dr. Michiko Okamoto
Dr. Arthur J. Okinaka
Dr. William M. O'Leary
Dr. Allen I. Oliff
Dr. Carl A. Olsson
Dr. Eng Bee Ong
Dr. Peter Orahovats
Dr. Irwin Oreskes
Dr. Marian Orlowski
Dr. Ernest V. Orsi
Dr. Louis G. Ortega
Dr. Eduardo Orti
Dr. Elliott F. Osserman
Dr. Elena I. R. Ottolenghi
Dr. Zoltan Ovary
Dr. M. D. Overholser*
Dr. Norbert I. A. Overweg
Dr. Irvine H. Page*
Dr. George Palade
Dr. Photini S. Papageorgiou
Dr. George D. Pappas
Dr. A. M. Pappenheimer, Jr.

Dr. John R. Pappenheimer*
Dr. Jean Papps*
Dr. Frank S. Parker
Dr. Raymond C. Parker*
Dr. Robert J. Parsons*
Dr. Pedro Pasik
Dr. Tauba Pasik
Dr. Mark W. Pasmantier
Dr. Gavril W. Pasternak
Dr. Jaygonda R. Patil
Dr. Pierluigi Patriarca
Dr. Philip Y. Patterson
Dr. Mary Ann Payne
Dr. O. H. Pearson
Dr. Edmund D. Pellegrino
Dr. Abraham Penner
Dr. James M. Perel
Dr. George A. Perera*
Dr. Eli Perlman
Dr. Gertrude Perlmann*
Dr. Benvenuto G. Pernis
Dr. James H. Pert
Dr. Demetrius Pertsemlidis
Dr. Barry W. Peterson
Dr. Malcolm L. Peterson
Dr. Rudolph Peterson
Dr. Mitchell L. Petusevsky
Dr. Frederick S. Philips
Dr. Robert A. Philips*
Dr. Sidney Pestka
Dr. Lennart Philipson
Dr. Emanuel T. Phillips
Dr. Mildred Phillips
Dr. Julia M. Phillips-Quagliata
Dr. John G. Pierce
Dr. Cynthia H. Pierce-Chase
Dr. Lou Ann Pilkington
Dr. Joseph B. Pincus
Dr. Matthew Pincus
Dr. Johanna Pindyck
Dr. Kermit L. Pines
Dr. Xavier Pi-Sunyer

*Life member.

Dr. Margaret Pittman*
Dr. Charles Plank
Dr. Calvin F. Plimpton
Dr. Charles M. Plotz
Dr. Fred Plum
Dr. Norman H. Plummer*
Dr. Beatriz G. T. Pogo
Dr. Alan Paul Poland
Dr. Roberta R. Pollock
Dr. William Pollack
Dr. Margaret J. Polley
Dr. Edwin A. Popenoe
Dr. J. W. Poppell
Dr. Laura Popper
Dr. Hans Popper
Dr. Keith R. Porter
Dr. Jerome G. Porush
Dr. Jerome B. Posner
Dr. Edward L. Pratt
Dr. Rudolf Preisig
Dr. John B. Price, Jr.
Dr. Richard W. Price
Dr. Marshall P. Primack
Dr. John W. Prineas
Dr. R. B. Pringle
Dr. Philip H. Prose
Dr. John F. Prudden
Dr. Lawrence Prutkin
Dr. Charles B. Pryles
Dr. Maynard E. Pullman
Dr. Dominick P. Purpura
Dr. Franco Quagliata
Dr. Paul G. Quie
Dr. James P. Quigley
Dr. Michel Rabinovitch
Dr. Julian Rachele*
Dr. Efraim Racker
Dr. Shalom Rackovsky
Dr. Bertha Radar
Dr. C. A. Ragan, Jr.
Dr. Kanti R. Rai

Dr. Ilene Raisfeld
Dr. Morris L. Rakieten*
Dr. Henry T. Randall
Dr. Helen M. Ranney
Dr. Felix T. Rapaport
Dr. Howard G. Rapaport
Dr. Richard H. Rapkin
Dr. Fred Rapp
Dr. Maurice M. Rapport
Dr. Sarah Ratner*
Dr. Aaron R. Rausen
Dr. Rulon W. Rawson
Dr. Lawrence W. Raymond
Dr. Stanley E. Read
Dr. George G. Reader
Dr. Kutumba K. Reddi
Dr. Walter Redisch
Dr. Colvin Manuel Redman
Dr. S. Frank Redo
Dr. George Reed
Dr. George N. Reeke, Jr.
Dr. Gabrielle H. Reem
Dr. Westley H. Reeves
Dr. Carl Reich
Dr. Edward Reich
Dr. Lee Reichman
Dr. Marcus M. Reidenberg
Dr. Maurice N. Richter*
Dr. Christine Reilly
Dr. Joseph F. Reilly
Dr. Leopold Reiner
Dr. Donald J. Reis
Dr. Paul Reznikoff*
Dr. Abby M. Rich
Dr. Goetz W. Richter
Dr. Ronald F. Rieder
Dr. Harold Rifkin
Dr. Richard A. Rifkind
Dr. Robert R. Riggio
Dr. Walter F. Riker, Jr.
Dr. Vernon Riley

*Life member.

Dr. David Allen Ringle
Dr. Harris Ripps
Dr. Marcos Rivelis
Dr. Richard S. Rivlin
Dr. Carleton W. Roberts
Dr. Jay Roberts
Dr. Kathleen E. Roberts
Dr. Richard B. Roberts
Dr. Alan G. Robinson
Dr. William G. Robinson
Dr. Dudley F. Rochester
Dr. Olga M. Rochovansky
Dr. Morris Rockstein
Dr. Robert G. Roeder
Dr. William M. Rogers*
Dr. Ida Pauline Rolf*
Dr. Marie C. Rosati
Dr. Harry M. Rose*
Dr. Herbert G. Rose
Dr. Gerald Rosen
Dr. John F. Rosen
Dr. Ora Rosen
Dr. Murray D. Rosenberg
Dr. Philip Rosenberg
Dr. Richard E. Rosenfeld
Dr. Isadore Rosenfeld
Dr. Herbert S. Rosenkranz
Dr. Arthur F. Rosenthal
Dr. William S. Rosenthal
Dr. Paul M. Rosman
Dr. William Rosner
Dr. Herbert Ross
Dr. Russell Ross
Dr. Pedro Rosso
Dr. Eugene F. Roth
Dr. Jesse Roth
Dr. Alan B. Rothballer
Dr. Sidney Rothbard*
Dr. Edmund O. Rothschild
Dr. M. A. Rothschild
Dr. Bruce Rowe
Dr. Lewis P. Rowland
Dr. Paul Royce

Dr. S. Jaime Rozovski
Dr. Albert L. Rubin
Dr. Benjamin A. Rubin
Dr. Meryl S. A. Rubin
Dr. Ronald P. Rubin
Dr. Walter Rubin
Dr. Daniel Rudman
Dr. Maria A. Rudzinska
Dr. Paul Ruegeseggar
Dr. George D. Ruggieri
Dr. Mark G. Rush
Dr. Henry I. Russek
Dr. Gregory Russell-Jones
Dr. Urs. S. Rutishauser
Dr. David D. Rutstein*
Dr. David Sabatini
Dr. Ruth Sager
Dr. David B. Sachar
Dr. Harold A. Sackeim
Dr. Robert Safirstfin
Dr. Stanley Walter Sajdera
Dr. Lester B. Salans
Dr. Gerald Salen
Dr. Letty G. M. Salentijn
Dr. Irving E. Salit
Dr. Lee Salk
Dr. Milton R. J. Salton
Dr. Abdol H. Samiy
Dr. Paul Samuel
Dr. Herbert Samuels
Dr. Stanley Samuels
Dr. John Sandson
Dr. B. J. Sanger*
Dr. Shigeru Sassa
Dr. Arthur Sawitsky
Dr. Philip N. Sawyer
Dr. Wilbur H. Sawyer
Dr. Brij Saxena
Dr. Robert G. Schacht
Dr. David Schachter
Dr. Russell W. Schaedler
Dr. Morris Schaeffer
Dr. Fenton Schaffner

*Life member.

Dr. Matthew D. Scharff
Dr. Joseph D. Schattner*
Dr. Frederick G. Schechter
Dr. Andreas S. Scheid
Dr. Margrit Scheid
Dr. Stephen S. Scheidt
Dr. Isaac Schenkein
Dr. Barbara M. Scher
Dr. William Scher
Dr. Donald Scherl
Dr. Lawrence Scherr
Dr. Peter B. Schiff
Dr. Gerald Schiffman
Dr. E. B. Schlesinger
Dr. R. W. Schlesinger*
Dr. Jeffrey Schlom
Dr. Detlef Schlondorff
Dr. Donald H. Schmidt
Dr. Willard C. Schmidt
Dr. Howard A. Schneider*
Dr. J. B. Schorr
Dr. Paul Schreibman
Dr. Steven Schutzer
Dr. Ernest Schwartz
Dr. Irving L. Schwartz
Dr. James H. Schwartz
Dr. Morton K. Schwartz
Dr. David Schwimmer
Dr. John J. Sciarra
Dr. James Sciubba
Dr. Morris J. Schoeneman
Dr. Ronald W. Schwizer
Dr. T. F. McNair Scott*
Dr. William Addison Scott
Dr. John C. Scott-Baker
Dr. Jean E. Sealey
Dr. Barry M. Segal
Dr. Sheldon J. Segal
Dr. George Seiden
Dr. Irving Seidman
Dr. Samuel Seifter

Dr. Stephen J. Seligman
Dr. Ewald Selkurt*
Dr. Indira Sen
Dr. Fabio Sereni
Dr. Aura E. Severinghaus*
Dr. David Schafritz
Dr. Robert E. Shank
Dr. James A. Shannon*
Dr. Harvey C. Shapiro
Dr. Herman S. Shapiro
Dr. L. L. Shapiro*
Dr. Lucille Shapiro
Dr. William R. Shapiro
Dr. Lewis Inman Sharp*
Dr. Aaron Shatkin
Dr. Elliott Shaw
Dr. Michael Shelanski
Dr. David Shemin*
Dr. Paul Sherlock
Dr. Raymond Lionel Sherman
Dr. Sol Sherry
Dr. Maurice E. Shils
Dr. Bong-Sop Shim
Dr. W. C. Shoemaker
Dr. Joyce E. Shriver
Dr. Charles D. Siegel
Dr. George Siegel
Dr. Morris Siegel*
Dr. Philip Siekevitz
Dr. Selma Silagi
Dr. Robert Silber
Dr. Maxmillian Silbermann*
Dr. Lawrence Silver
Dr. Richard T. Silver
Dr. Morris Silverman
Dr. Philip Silverman
Dr. William A. Silverman
Dr. Emanuel Silverstein
Dr. Martin E. Silverstein
Dr. Samuel C. Silverstein
Dr. Saul Silverstein

*Life member.

Dr. Michael Simberkoff
Dr. Eric J. Simon
Dr. Norman Simon
Dr. Joe L. Simpson
Dr. Melvin V. Simpson
Dr. Inder J. Singh
Dr. Gregory Siskind
Dr. William R. Sistrom
Dr. Anneliese L. Sitarz
Dr. Mark T. Skarstedt
Dr. Vladimir P. Skipski
Dr. Robert J. Slater
Dr. Daniel N. Slatkin
Dr. George K. Smelser*
Dr. Frank Rees Smith
Dr. James P. Smith
Dr. M. De Forest Smith*
Dr. Elizabeth M. Smithwick
Dr. Edna Sobel
Dr. Louis Soffer*
Dr. Richard Luber Soffer
Dr. John A. Sogn
Dr. Arthur Sohval
Dr. Leon Sokoloff
Dr. Samuel Solomon
Dr. Alex C. Solowey
Dr. Martin Sonenberg
Dr. Joseph A. Sonnabend
Dr. Hamilton Southworth*
Dr. Paul Spear
Dr. Abraham Spector
Dr. Francis Speer*
Dr. Robert Sisson Spiers
Dr. Frank C. Spencer
Dr. Gabriel Spergel
Dr. Morton Spivack
Dr. David Sprinson
Dr. Norton Spritz
Dr. Katherine Sprunt
Dr. Catherine L. Squires
Dr. P. R. Srinivasan
Dr. John M. Steele, Jr.

Dr. Neal H. Steigbigel
Dr. Richard M. Stein
Dr. William Stein*
Dr. Charles R. Steinman
Dr. Philip R. Steinmetz
Dr. Harry Steinberg
Dr. Herman Steinberg
Dr. Ralph M. Steinman
Dr. Kurt H. Stenzel
Dr. Kenneth Sterling
Dr. Joseph R. Stern
Dr. Marvin Stern
Dr. William Stern
Dr. Stephen Sternberg
Dr. Irmin Sternlieb
Dr. De Witt Stetten, Jr.*
Dr. Fred W. Stewart*
Dr. John M. Stewart
Dr. W. B. Stewart
Dr. Walter A. Stewart*
Dr. C. Chester Stock*
Dr. Richard J. Stockert
Dr. Walter Stoeckenius
Dr. Peter E. Stokes
Dr. Daniel J. Stone
Dr. Fritz Streuli
Dr. William T. Stubenbord
Dr. Jackson H. Stuckey
Dr. Horace W. Stunkard*
Dr. Osias Stutman
Dr. John Y. Sugg*
Dr. Barnet M. Sultzer
Dr. Martin I. Surks
Dr. Marcy Sussman
Dr. Joseph G. Sweeting

Dr. Roy C. Swingle
Dr. Margaret Prince Sykes
Dr. Wlodzimierz Szer
Dr. Milton Tabachnick
Dr. John Taggart*
Dr. Igor Tamm
Dr. Lilly S. Tang

*Life member.

Dr. Donald F. Tapley
Dr. Suresh S. Tate
Dr. Edward Lawrie Tatum
Dr. Harry Taube
Dr. Jurg Tauber
Dr. Sheldon B. Taubman
Dr. Howard Taylor, Jr.*
Dr. Alvin Teirstein
Dr. Constantin V. Teodoru
Dr. Robert D. Terry
Dr. Gail A. Theis
Dr. Henry M. Thomas
Dr. Lewis Thomas
Dr. David D. Thompson
Dr. Neils A. Thorn
Dr. David A. Tice
Dr. Edward Tolstoi*
Dr. Helene W. Toolan
Dr. William A. Triebel*
Dr. George L. Tritsch
Dr. Walter Troll
Dr. Jir Shiong Tsai
Dr. Orestes Tsolas
Dr. Gerard M. Turino
Dr. Gray H. Twombly*
Dr. Theodore Tyberg
Dr. Koji Uchizono
Dr. Sidney Udenfriend
Dr. Jonathan W. Uhr
Dr. John E. Ultmann
Dr. Harry E. Ungerleider*
Dr. Jay C. Unkeless
Dr. Arthur Canfield Upton
Dr. Morton Urivetzky
Dr. Virginia Utermohlen
Dr. Fred Valentine
Dr. Parker Vanamee
Dr. Ivo Van de Rijn
Dr. William G. Van der Kloot
Dr. Andre Varma
Dr. Mario Vassalle
Dr. Edward F. Vastola
Dr. Martha Vaughan

Dr. Frank Veith
Dr. Elliot S. Vesell
Dr. Carmine T. Vicale
Dr. Herman Villarreal, Jr.
Dr. F. Stephen Vogel
Dr. Mögens Volkert
Dr. William C. Von Glahn
Dr. Salome G. Waelsch
Dr. Bernard M. Wagner
Dr. Bonnie A. Wallace
Dr. Lila A. Wallis
Dr. Roderich Walter
Dr. John L. Wang
Dr. S. C. Wang
Dr. Lewis W. Wannamaker
Dr. George E. Wantz
Dr. Bettina Warburg*
Dr. Robert C. Warner
Dr. Louis R. Wasserman*
Dr. Norbert H. Wasserman
Dr. Alice M. Waterhouse*
Dr. Robert F. Watson*
Dr. Samuel Waxman
Dr. Annemarie Weber
Dr. Bruce Webster*
Dr. Richard P. Weeden
Dr. Rene Wegria
Dr. Richard Weil, III
Dr. Virginia L. Weimar
Dr. Leo Weiner
Dr. Herbert Weinfeld
Dr. I. Bernard Weinstein
Dr. Harel Weinstein
Dr. Stephen W. Weinstein
Dr. Irwin M. Weinstock
Dr. John M. Weir
Dr. Gerson Weiss
Dr. Harvey J. Weiss
Dr. Paul A. Weiss
Dr. Herbert Weissbach
Dr. Bernard Weissman
Dr. Charles Weissmann

*Life member.

270 ACTIVE MEMBERS

Dr. Gerald Weissmann
Dr. Babette Weksler
Dr. Francis M. Weld
Dr. Daniel Wellner
Dr. Gerhardt Werner
Dr. Sidney C. Werner*
Dr. W. Clarke Wescoe
Dr. C. D. West
Prof. Otto Westphal
Dr. Joseph P. Whalen
Dr. Abraham White
Dr. Abraham G. White
Dr. Ralph deVere White
Dr. John C. Whitsell, II
Dr. Edkhart Wiedeman
Dr. Stanley Wiener
Dr. Norman Wikler
Dr. Herbert B. Wilcox, Jr.*
Dr. David L. Williams
Dr. M. Henry Williams
Dr. John Wilson
Dr. Victor J. Wilson
Dr. Sidney J. Winawer
Dr. Erich E. Windhager
Dr. Myron Winick
Dr. Asher Winkelstein
Dr. Jonathan Winson
Dr. Robert M. Winters
Dr. Jonathan Wittenberg
Dr. Herbert Wohl
Dr. Abner Wolf*
Dr. David Wolf
Dr. George A. Wolf
Dr. Julius Wolf

Dr. Stewart G. Wolf, Jr.
Dr. James A. Wolff
Dr. Harvey Wolinsky
Dr. Sandra R. Wolman
Dr. Henry N. Wood
Dr. John A. Wood
Dr. John L. Wood*
Dr. James M. Woodruff
Dr. Kenneth R. Woods
Dr. Melvin H. Worth, Jr.
Dr. Walter D. Wosilait
Dr. Irving S. Wright*
Dr. Tze-Chein Wun
Dr. Melvin D. Yahr
Dr. Martin L. Yarmush
Dr. Sehchi Yasumura
Dr. Carol A. Yeadon
Dr. Chester L. Yntema*

Dr. Bruce Young
Dr. Stuart H. Young
Dr. Fuli Yu
Dr. Tasai-Fan Yu
Dr. Ralph Zalusky
Dr. Esmail D. Zanjani
Dr. Italo Zanzi
Dr. Charles G. Zaroulis
Dr. Vratislav Zbuzek
Dr. James E. Ziegler, Jr.*
Dr. Norton Zinder
Dr. Burton L. Zohman
Dr. Thomas R. Kozel
Dr. Joseph Zubin*
Dr. Marjorie B. Zucker
Dr. Dorothea Zucker-Franklin
Dr. Benjamin W. Zweifach

*Life member.

DATE DUE
